ENGLISH PROSE
NARRATIVE, DESCRIPTIVE
AND DRAMATIC

COMPILED BY
H. A. TREBLE

The World's Classics

Geoffrey Cumberlege
OXFORD UNIVERSITY PRESS
London   New York   Toronto

This Anthology of English Prose—Narrative, Descriptive, and Dramatic, was first published in 'The World's Classics' in 1916, and reprinted in 1917, 1921, 1925, 1928, 1941, 1946, and 1950.

PRINTED IN GREAT BRITAIN

PREFACE

The Editor wishes to acknowledge his indebtedness to several friends for much helpful advice, as well as to Mr. V. H. Collins, of the Oxford University Press, who suggested the idea of the Anthology in the first instance, and to Mr. J. C. Smith, to whom in great part is due the shape which the book has finally taken, and who throughout its preparation has placed at the service of Editor and Publisher the invaluable help of his taste and erudition.

Permission has been granted by Messrs. Constable & Co. for the extracts from George Meredith's *The Ordeal of Richard Feverel* and *Vittoria*.

H. A. T.

CONTENTS

CONTENTS

CONTENTS

SIR THOMAS MALORY

c. 1470

THE 'LAST WEIRD BATTLE IN THE WEST' AND THE PASSING OF ARTHUR

AND then the king let search all the towns for his knights that were slain, and interred them ; and salved them with soft salves that so sore were wounded. Then much people drew unto king Arthur. And then they said that Sir Mordred warred upon king Arthur with wrong. And then king Arthur drew him with his host down by the sea side, westward toward Salisbury, and there was a day assigned betwixt king Arthur and Sir Mordred, that they should meet upon a down beside Salisbury, and not far from the sea side, and this day was assigned on a Monday after Trinity Sunday, whereof king Arthur was passing glad, that he might be avenged upon Sir Mordred Then Sir Mordred araised much people about London, for they of Kent, Southsex, and Surrey, Estsex, and of Southfolk, and of Northfolk, held the most party with Sir Mordred, and many a' full noble knight drew unto Sir Mordred and to the king, but they loved Sir Launcelot drew unto Sir Mordred. So upon Trinity Sunday at night king Arthur dreamed a wonderful dream, and that was this, that him seemed he sat upon a chaflet in a chair, and the chair was fast to a wheel, and

B

thereupon sat king Arthur in the richest cloth of gold that might be made, and the king thought there was under him, far from him, an hideous deep black water, and therein were all manner of serpents, and worms, and wild beasts, foul and horrible, and suddenly the king thought the wheel turned up so down, and he fell among the serpents, and every beast took him by a limb, and then the king cried as he lay in his bed and slept, Help. And then knights, squires, and yeomen awaked the king; and then he was so amazed that he wist not where he was, and then he fell on slumbering again, not sleeping nor thoroughly waking. So the king seemed verily that there came Sir Gawaine unto him with a number of fair ladies with him.

And when king Arthur saw him, then he said, Welcome, my sister's son, I wend thou hadst been dead, and now I see thee on live, much am I beholding unto almighty Jesu. O fair nephew and my sister's son, what be these ladies that hither be come with you? Sir, said Sir Gawaine, all these be ladies for whom I have foughten when I was man living, and all these are those that I did battle for in righteous quarrel; and God hath given them that grace at their great prayer, by cause I did battle for them, that they should bring me hither unto you, thus much hath God given me leave, for to warn you of your death; for and ye fight as to-morn with Sir Mordred, as ye both have assigned, doubt ye not ye must be slain, and the most part of your people on both parties. And for the great grace and goodness that almighty Jesu hath unto you, and for pity of you, and many more other good men there shall be slain, God hath sent me to you of his special grace, to give you warning that in no wise ye do battle as to-morn, but that ye take a treaty for a month day ; and proffer you largely, so as to-morn to be put in a delay. For within a month shall come Sir Launcelot with all his noble knights, and rescue you worshipfully, and slay Sir Mordred and all that ever will hold with him. Then Sir Gawaine and all the ladies vanished. And anon the king called upon his knights, squires, and yeomen, and charged them wightly to fetch his noble lords and wise bishops unto him. And when they were come, the king told them his avision, what Sir Gawaine had told him, and warned him that if he fought on the morn he should be slain. Then the king commanded Sir Lucan de butlere, and his brother Sir Bedivere, with two bishops with them, and charged them in any wise, and they might take a treaty for a month day with Sir Mordred. And spare not, proffer him lands and goods as much as ye think best. So then they departed, and came to Sir Mordred, where he had a grim host of an hundred thousand men. And there they entreated Sir Mordred long time, and at the last Sir Mordred was agreed for to have Cornwall and Kent, by Arthur's days : after, all England, after the days of king Arthur.

Then were they condescended that king Arthur and Sir Mordred should meet betwixt both their hosts, and every each of them should bring fourteen persons. And they came with this word unto Arthur. Then said he, I am glad that this is done. And so he went into the field. And when Arthur should depart, he warned all his host that and they see any sword drawn, Look ye come on fiercely, and slay that traitor Sir Mordred, for I in no wise trust him. In like wise Sir Mordred warned his host that,—and ye see any sword drawn, look that ye come on fiercely, and so slay all that ever before you standeth, for in no wise I will not trust for this treaty. For I know well my father will be avenged on me. And so they met as their pointment was, and so they were agreed and accorded thoroughly. And wine was fetched, and they drank. Right so came an adder out of a little heath bush, and it stung a knight on the foot. And when the knight felt him stungen, he looked down and saw the adder, and then he drew his sword to slay the adder, and thought of none other harm. And when the host on both parties saw that sword drawn, then they blew beamous, trumpets, and horns, and shouted grimly. And so both hosts dressed them together. And king Arthur took his horse, and said, Alas this unhappy day, and so rode to his party. And Sir Mordred in like wise. And never was there seen a more dolefuller battle in no Christian land. For there was but rushing and riding, foining and striking, and many a grim word was there spoken either to other, and many a deadly stroke. But ever king Arthur rode throughout the battle of Sir Mordred many times, and did full nobly as a noble king should, and at all times he fainted never ; and Sir Mordred that day put him in devoir, and in great peril. And thus they fought all the long day, and never stinted till the noble knights were laid to the cold earth ; and ever they fought still till it was near night, and by that time was there an hundred thousand laid dead upon the down. Then was Arthur wood wroth

out of measure, when he saw his people so slain
from him. Then the king looked about him, and
then was he ware of all his host and of all his good
knights, were left no more on live but two knights,
that one was Sir Lucan de butlere, and his brother
Sir Bedivere, and they were full sore wounded
Jesu, mercy, said the king, where are all my noble
knights becomen? Alas that ever I should see
this doleful day. For now, said Arthur, I am
come to mine end. But would to God that I wist
where were that traitor Sir Mordred, that hath
caused all this mischief. Then was king Arthur
ware where Sir Mordred leaned upon his sword
among a great heap of dead men. Now give me
my spear, said Arthur unto Sir Lucan, for yonder
I have espied the traitor that all this woe hath
wrought. Sir, let him be, said Sir Lucan, for he is
unhappy. And if ye pass this unhappy day ye
shall be right well revenged upon him. Good lord,
remember ye of your night's dream, and what the
spirit of Sir Gawaine told you this night, yet God
of his great goodness hath preserved you hitherto.
Therefore, for God's sake, my lord, leave off by
this, for blessed be God ye have won the field.
For here we be three on live, and with Sir Mordred
is none on live. And if ye leave off now this
wicked day of destiny is past. Tide me death,
betide me life, saith the king, now I see him
yonder alone he shall never escape mine hands,
for at a better avail shall I never have him.
God speed you well, said Sir Bedivere. Then the
king gat his spear in both his hands, and ran
toward Sir Mordred, crying, Traitor, now is thy
death day come. And when Sir Mordred heard
Sir Arthur, he ran until him with his sword drawn

in his hand. And there king Arthur smote Sir
Mordred under the shield, with a foin of his spear,
throughout the body more than a fathom. And
when Sir Mordred felt that he had his death's
wound, he thrust himself, with the might that he
had up to the bur of king Arthur's spear. And
right so he smote his father Arthur with his
sword holden in both his hands, on the side of the
head, that the sword pierced the helmet and the
brain pan, and therewithal Sir Mordred fell stark
dead to the earth. And the noble Arthur fell in
a swoon to the earth, and there he swooned oft-
times. And Sir Lucan de butlere and Sir Bedivere
oft-times heave him up. And so weakly they led
him betwixt them both, to a little chapel not far
from the sea side. And when the king was there
he thought him well eased. Then heard they
people cry in the field. Now go thou, Sir Lucan,
said the king, and do me to wit what betokens that
noise in the field. So Sir Lucan departed, for he
was grievously wounded in many places. And so
as he yede, he saw and hearkened by the moonlight, how that pillers and robbers were come into
the field to pill and to rob many a full noble
knight of brooches and beads, of many a good
ring, and of many a rich jewel; and who that
were not dead all out, there they slew them for
their harness and their riches. When Sir Lucan
understood this work, he came to the king as soon
as he might, and told him all what he had heard
and seen. Therefore by my rede, said Sir Lucan,
it is best that we bring you to some town. I would
it were so, said the king. But I may not stand,
mine head works so. Ah Sir Launcelot, said
king Arthur, this day have I sore missed thee.

Alas, that ever I was against thee, for now have
I my death, whereof Sir Gawaine me warned in
my dream. Then Sir Lucan took up the king
the one part, and Sir Bedivere the other part,
and in the lifting the king swooned, and Sir Lucan
fell in a swoon with the lift, that the part of his
guts fell out of his body, and therewith the noble
knight's heart brast. And when the king awoke,
he beheld Sir Lucan, how he lay foaming at the
mouth, and part of his guts lay at his feet. Alas,
said the king, this is to me a full heavy sight,
to see this noble duke so die for my sake, for he
would have holpen me that had more need of help
than I. Alas, he would not complain him, his
heart was so set to help me. Now Jesu have
mercy upon his soul. Then Sir Bedivere wept for
the death of his brother. Leave this mourning
and weeping, said the king, for all this will not
avail me, for wit thou well and I might live
myself, the death of Sir Lucan would grieve me
evermore; but my time hieth fast, said the king.
Therefore, said Arthur unto Sir Bedivere, take
thou Excalibur, my good sword, and go with it to
yonder water side, and when thou comest there
I charge thee throw my sword in that water, and
come again and tell me what thou there seest.
My lord, said Bedivere, your commandment shall
be done, and lightly bring you word again. So
Sir Bedivere departed, and by the way he beheld
that noble sword, that the pommel and the haft
was all of precious stones; and then he said to
himself, If I throw this rich sword in the water,
thereof shall never come good, but harm and loss.
And then Sir Bedivere hid Excalibur under a tree.
And so, as soon as he might he came again unto

the king, and said he had been at the water,
and had thrown the sword in to the water. What
saw thou there ? said the king. Sir, he said, I saw
nothing but waves and winds. That is untruly
said of thee, said the king. Therefore go thou
lightly again, and do my commandment; as thou
art to me lief and dear, spare not, but throw it in.
Then Sir Bedivere returned again, and took the
sword in his hand ; and then him thought sin and
shame to throw away that noble sword, and so
efte he hid the sword, and returned again, and
told to the king that he had been at the water,
and done his commandment. What saw thou
there ? said the king. Sir, he said, I saw nothing
but the waters wappe and waves wanne. Ah,
traitor untrue, said king Arthur, now hast thou
betrayed me twice. Who would have wend that
thou, that hast been to me so lief and dear, and
thou art named a noble knight, and would betray
me for the richesse of the sword ? But now go
again lightly, for thy long tarrying putteth me in
great jeopardy of my life, for I have taken cold.
And but if thou do now as I bid thee, if ever I may
see thee, I shall slay thee with mine own hands ;
for thou wouldest for my rich sword see me dead.
Then Sir Bedivere departed, and went to the
sword, and lightly took it up, and went to the
water side, and there he bound the girdle about
the hilts, and then he threw the sword as far into
the water as he might, and there came an arm and
an hand above the water and met it, and caught
it, and so shook it thrice and brandished, and then
vanished away the hand with the sword in the
water. So Sir Bedivere came again to the king,
and told him what he saw. Alas, said the king,

help me hence, for I dread me I have tarried over long. Then Sir Bedivere took the king upon his back, and so went with him to that water side. And when they were at the water side, even fast by the bank hoved a little barge, with many fair ladies in it, and among them all was a queen, and all they had black hoods, and all they wept and shrieked when they saw king Arthur. Now put me into the barge, said the king : and so he did softly. And there received him three queens with great mourning ; and so they set them down, and in one of their laps king Arthur laid his head, and then that queen said : Ah, dear brother, why have ye tarried so long from me ? Alas, this wound on your head hath caught over-much cold. And so then they rowed from the land, and Sir Bedivere beheld all those ladies go from him. Then Sir Bedivere cried, Ah, my lord Arthur, what shall become of me now ye go from me, and leave me here alone among mine enemies. Comfort thyself, said the king, and do as well as thou mayest, for in me is no trust for to trust in. For I will into the vale of Avilion to heal me of my grievous wound. And if thou hear never more of me, pray for my soul. But ever the queens and ladies wept and shrieked, that it was pity to hear. And as soon as Sir Bedivere had lost the sight of the barge, he wept and wailed, and so took the forest, and so he went all that night, and in the morning he was ware betwixt two holts hoar of a chapel and an hermitage.

Morte d'Arthur. 1485.

JOHN LYLY

1553 ?–1606

THE WATCH

Gardens of the Palace

SAMIAS *and* DARES, EPITON

Enter the Watch

Samias. Shall we never see thy Master, Dares ?

Dares. Yes, let us go now, for to-morrow Cynthia will be there.

Epiton. I will go with you. But how shall we see for the Watch ?

Samias. Tush, let me alone ! I'll begin to them. Masters, God speed you.

1st Watch. Sir boy, we are all sped already.

Epiton (*aside*). So methinks, for they smell all of drink, like a beggar's beard.

Dares. But I pray, sirs, may we see Endymion ?

2nd Watch. No, we are commanded in Cynthia's name that no man shall see him.

Samias. No man ? Why, we are but boys.

1st Watch. Mass, neighbours, he says true ; for if I swear I will never drink my liquor by the quart, and yet call for two pints, I think with a safe conscience I may carouse both.

Dares. Pithily, and to the purpose.

2nd Watch. Tush, tush, neighbours, take me with you.

Samias. This will grow hot.

Dares. Let them alone

2nd Watch. If I say to my wife, Wife, I will have no raisins in my pudding, she puts in currants, small raisins are raisins, and boys are men. Even as my wife should have put no raisins in my pudding, so shall there no boys see Endymion.

Dares. Learnedly.

Epiton. Let Master Constable speak : I think he is the wisest among you.

Master Constable. You know, neighbours, 'tis an old saw, ' children and fools speak true.'

All say. True.

Master Constable. Well, there you see the men be the fools, because it is provided from the children.

Dares. Good.

Master Constable. Then say I, neighbours, that children must not see Endymion, because children and fools speak true.

Epiton. O wicked application !

Samias. Scurvily brought about !

1st Watch. Nay, he says true, and therefore till Cynthia have been here he shall not be uncovered. Therefore away !

Dares (*aside to* SAMIAS *and* EPITON). A watch, quoth you ? a man may watch seven years for a wise word, and yet go without it. Their wits are all as rusty as their bills.—But come on, Master Constable, shall we have a song before we go ?

Constable. With all my heart.

SONG

Watch.   Stand : who goes there ?
              We charge you, appear
              'Fore our Constable here.

(In the name of the Man in the Moon)
To us Billmen relate,
Why you stagger so late,
And how you come drunk so soon.

Pages. What are ye (scabs ?)

Watch. The Watch :
This the Constable.

Pages. A Patch.
Constable. Knock 'em down, unless they all stand.
If any run away,
'Tis the old Watchman's play,
To reach him a Bill of his hand.

Pages. O Gentlemen hold,
Your gowns freeze with cold,
And your rotten teeth dance in your
head ;

Epiton. Wine, nothing shall cost ye.
Samias. Nor huge fires to roast ye.
Dares. Then soberly let us be led.
Constable. Come, my brown Bills, we'll roar,
Bounce loud at Tavern door,
Omnes. And i'th' Morning steal all to bed.

[Exeunt.

Endymion. 1591.

FRANCIS BACON, VISCOUNT ST. ALBANS

1561-1626

NEW ATLANTIS

WE sailed from Peru (where we had continued by the space of one whole year), for China and Japan, by the South Sea, taking with us victuals for twelve months; and had good winds from the east, though soft and weak, for five months' space and more. But then the wind came about, and settled in the west for many days, so as we could make little or no way, and were sometimes in purpose to turn back. But then again there arose strong and great winds from the south, with a point east; which carried us up, for all that we could do, towards the north: by which time our victuals failed us, though we had made good spare of them. So that finding ourselves, in the midst of the greatest wilderness of waters in the world, without victual, we gave ourselves for lost men, and prepared for death. Yet we did lift up our hearts and voices to God above, who ' showeth His wonders in the deep '; beseeching Him of His mercy, that as in the beginning He discovered the face of the deep, and brought forth dry land, so He would now discover land to us, that we might not perish. And it came to pass that the next day about evening we saw within a kenning before us, towards the north, as it were thick clouds, which did put us in some hope of land; knowing how that part of the South Sea was utterly unknown; and might have islands or continents that hitherto were not come to light. Wherefore we bent our course thither, where we saw the appearance of land, all that night; and in the dawning of the next day, we might plainly discern that it was a land, flat to our sight, and full of boscage; which made it show the more dark. And after an hour and a half's sailing, we entered into a good haven, being the port of a fair city: not great, indeed, but well built, and that gave a pleasant view from the sea. And we thinking every minute long till we were on land, came close to the shore and offered to land. But straightways we saw divers of the people, with bastons in their hands, as it were, forbidding us to land: yet without any cries or fierceness, but only as warning us off, by signs that they made. Whereupon being not a little discomforted, we were advising with ourselves what we should do. During which time there made forth to us a small boat, with about eight persons in it, whereof one of them had in his hand a tipstaff of a yellow cane, tipped at both ends with blue, who came aboard our ship, without any show of distrust at all. And when he saw one of our number present himself somewhat afore the rest, he drew forth a little scroll of parchment (somewhat yellower than our parchment, and shining like the leaves of writing tables, but otherwise soft and flexible), and delivered it to our foremost man. In which scroll were written in ancient Hebrew, and in ancient Greek, and in good Latin of the school, and in Spanish, these words : Land ye not, none of you, and provide to be gone from this coast within sixteen days, except you have further time given you. Meanwhile, if you want fresh water, or victual, or help for your sick, or that your ship needeth repair, write down your wants, and you shall have that which belongeth to mercy.' This scroll was signed with a stamp of cherubin's wings, not spread, but hanging downwards ; and by them a cross. This being delivered, the officer returned, and left only a servant with us to receive our answer. Consulting hereupon amongst ourselves, we were much perplexed. The denial of landing, and hasty warning us away, troubled us much ; on the other side, to find that the people had languages, and were so full of humanity, did comfort us not a little. And above all, the sign of the Cross to that instrument, was to us a great rejoicing, and as it were a certain presage of good. Our answer was in the Spanish tongue, ' That for our ship, it was well ; for we had rather met with calms, and contrary winds, than any tempests. For our sick, they were many, and in very ill case ; so that if they were not permitted to land, they ran danger of their lives.' Our other wants we set down in particular ; adding, ' That we had some little store of merchandise, which, if it pleased them to deal for, it might supply our wants, without being chargeable unto them'. We offered some reward in pistolets unto the servant, and a piece of crimson velvet to be presented to the officer : but the servant took them not, nor would scarce look upon them ; and so left us, and went back in another little boat, which was sent for him.

About three hours after we had dispatched our
answer there came towards us a person (as it
seemed) of place. He had on him a gown with
wide sleeves, of a kind of water chamolet, of an
excellent azure colour, far more glossy than ours :
his under apparel was green, and so was his hat,
being in the form of a turban, daintily made, and
not so huge as the Turkish turbans ; and the
locks of his hair came down below the brims of it.
A reverend man was he to behold. He came in
a boat, gilt in some part of it, with four persons
more only in that boat ; and was followed by
another boat, wherein were some twenty. When
he was come within a flight-shot of our ship,
signs were made to us that we should send forth
some to meet him upon the water ; which we
presently did in our ship-boat, sending the principal man amongst us save one, and four of our
number with him. When we were come within
six yards of their boat, they called to us to stay,
and not to approach further, which we did. And
thereupon the man, whom I before described,
stood up, and with a loud voice, in Spanish, asked,
' Are ye Christians ? ' We answered, ' We were ' ;
fearing the less, because of the Cross we had seen
in the subscription. At which answer the said
person lift up his right hand towards Heaven, and
drew it softly to his mouth (which is the gesture
they use, when they thank God), and then said :
' If ye will swear, all of you, by the merits of the
Saviour, that ye are no pirates, nor have shed blood,
lawfully nor unlawfully, within forty days past,
you may have licence to come on land'. We said,
' We were all ready to take that oath'. Whereupon one of those that were with him, being (as it

seemed) a notary, made an entry of this act. Which done, another of the attendants of the great person, which was with him in the same boat, after his lord had spoken a little to him, said aloud: 'My lord would have you know, that it is not of pride, or greatness, that he cometh not aboard your ship: but for that, in your answer, you declare that you have many sick amongst you, he was warned by the Conservator of Health of the city that he should keep a distance'. We bowed ourselves towards him, and answered, 'We were his humble servants; and accounted for great honour and singular humanity towards us, that which was already done: but hoped well, that the nature of the sickness of our men was not infectious.' So he returned; and a while after came the notary to us aboard our ship, holding in his hand a fruit of that country, like an orange, but of colour between orange-tawny and scarlet; which cast a most excellent odour. He used it (as it seemeth) for a preservative against infection. He gave us our oath, 'By the name of Jesus, and His merits': and after told us, that the next day, by six of the clock in the morning, we should be sent to, and brought to the Strangers' House (so he called it), where we should be accommodated of things, both for our whole and for our sick. So he left us; and when we offered him some pistolets, he smiling said, 'He must not be twice paid for one labour'; meaning (as I take it), that he had salary sufficient of the State for his service. For (as I after learned) they call an officer that taketh rewards, twice-paid.

New Atlantis. 1627.

WILLIAM SHAKESPEARE

1564–1616

THE BAITING OF SHYLOCK

VENICE. A STREET.

Enter SALANIO *and* SALARINO.

Salanio. Now, what news on the Rialto ?

Salarino. Why, yet it lives there unchecked that Antonio hath a ship of rich lading wracked on the narrow seas ; the Goodwins, I think they call the place ; a very dangerous flat, and fatal, where the carcasses of many a tall ship lie buried, as they say, if my gossip Report be an honest woman of her word.

Salanio. I would she were as lying a gossip in that as ever knapped ginger, or made her neighbours believe she wept for the death of a third husband. But it is true,—without any slips of prolixity or crossing the plain highway of talk,— that the good Antonio, the honest Antonio,—O, that I had a title good enough to keep his name company !—

Salarino. Come, the full stop.

Salanio. Ha ! what sayst thou ? Why, the end is, he hath lost a ship.

Salarino. I would it might prove the end of his losses.

Salanio. Let me say ' amen ' betimes, lest the devil cross my prayer, for here he comes in the likeness of a Jew.

Enter SHYLOCK.

How now, Shylock! what news among the merchants?

Shylock. You knew, none so well, none so well as you, of my daughter's flight.

Salarino. That's certain: I, for my part, knew the tailor that made the wings she flew withal.

Salanio. And Shylock, for his own part, knew the bird was fledged; and then it is the complexion of them all to leave the dam.

Shylock. She is damned for it.

Salarino. That's certain, if the devil may be her judge.

Shylock. My own flesh and blood to rebel!

Salanio. Out upon it, old carrion! rebels it at these years?

Shylock. I say my daughter is my flesh and blood.

Salarino. There is more difference between thy flesh and hers than between jet and ivory; more between your bloods than there is between red wine and Rhenish. But tell us, do you hear whether Antonio have had any loss at sea or no?

Shylock. There I have another bad match: a bankrupt, a prodigal, who dare scarce show his head on the Rialto; a beggar, that used to come so smug upon the mart; let him look to his bond: he was wont to call me usurer; let him look to his bond: he was wont to lend money for a Christian courtesy; let him look to his bond.

Salarino. Why, I am sure, if he forfeit thou wilt not take his flesh: what's that good for?

Shylock. To bait fish withal: if it will feed

nothing else, it will feed my revenge. He hath disgraced me, and hindered me half a million, laughed at my losses, mocked at my gains, scorned my nation, thwarted my bargains, cooled my friends, heated mine enemies; and what's his reason? I am a Jew. Hath not a Jew eyes? hath not a Jew hands, organs, dimensions, senses, affections, passions? fed with the same food, hurt with the same weapons, subject to the same diseases, healed by the same means, warmed and cooled by the same winter and summer, as a Christian is? If you prick us, do we not bleed? if you tickle us, do we not laugh? if you poison us, do we not die? and if you wrong us, shall we not revenge? If we are like you in the rest, we will resemble you in that. If a Jew wrong a Christian, what is his humility? Revenge. If a Christian wrong a Jew, what should his sufferance be by Christian example? Why, revenge. The villany you teach me I will execute, and it shall go hard but I will better the instruction.

Enter a Servant.

Servant. Gentlemen, my master Antonio is at his house, and desires to speak with you both.

Salarino. We have been up and down to seek him.

Enter TUBAL.

Salanio. Here comes another of the tribe: a third cannot be matched, unless the devil himself turn Jew.

[*Exeunt* SALANIO, SALARINO *and* Servant.

Shylock. How now, Tubal! what news from Genoa? Hast thou found my daughter?

Tubal. I often came where I did hear of her, but cannot find her.

Shylock. Why there, there, there! a diamond gone, cost me two thousand ducats in Frankfort! The curse never fell upon our nation till now; I never felt it till now: two thousand ducats in that; and other precious, precious jewels. I would my daughter were dead at my foot, and the jewels in her ear! would she were hearsed at my foot, and the ducats in her coffin! No news of them? Why, so: and I know not what's spent in the search: Why thou—loss upon loss! the thief gone with so much, and so much to find the thief; and no satisfaction, no revenge: nor no ill luck stirring but what lights on my shoulders; no sighs but of my breathing; no tears but of my shedding.

Tubal. Yes, other men have ill luck too. Antonio, as I heard in Genoa,—

Shylock. What, what, what? ill luck, ill luck?

Tubal. —hath an argosy cast away, coming from Tripolis.

Shylock. I thank God! I thank God! Is it true? is it true?

Tubal. I spoke with some of the sailors that escaped the wrack.

Shylock. I thank thee, good Tubal. Good news, good news! ha, ha! Where? in Genoa?

Tubal. Your daughter spent in Genoa, as I heard, one night, fourscore ducats.

Shylock. Thou stick'st a dagger in me: I shall never see my gold again: fourscore ducats at a sitting! fourscore ducats!

Tubal. There came divers of Antonio's creditors

in my company to Venice, that swear he cannot choose but break.

Shylock. I am very glad of it : I'll plague him ; I'll torture him : I am glad of it.

Tubal. One of them showed me a ring that he had of your daughter for a monkey.

Shylock. Out upon her ! Thou torturest me, Tubal : it was my turquoise ; I had it of Leah when I was a bachelor : I would not have given it for a wilderness of monkeys.

Tubal. But Antonio is certainly undone.

Shylock. Nay, that 's true, that 's very true. Go, Tubal, fee me an officer ; bespeak him a fortnight before. I will have the heart of him, if he forfeit ; for, were he out of Venice, I can make what merchandise I will. Go, go, Tubal, and meet me at our synagogue ; go, good Tubal ; at our synagogue, Tubal. [*Exeunt.*

The Merchant of Venice. 1600.

THE WATCH

A STREET.

Enter DOGBERRY *and* VERGES, *with the* Watch.

Dogberry. Are you good men and true ?

Verges. Yea, or else it were pity but they should suffer salvation, body and soul.

Dogberry. Nay, that were a punishment too good for them, if they should have any allegiance in them, being chosen for the prince's watch.

Verges. Well, give them their charge, neighbour Dogberry.

Dogberry. First, who think you the most desartless man to be constable ?

1st Watch. Hugh Oatcake, sir, or George Seacoal; for they can write and read.

Dogberry. Come hither, neighbour Seacoal. God hath blessed you with a good name: to be a well-favoured man is the gift of fortune; but to write and read comes by nature.

2nd Watch. Both which, Master constable,—

Dogberry. You have: I knew it would be your answer. Well, for your favour, sir, why, give God thanks, and make no boast of it; and for your writing and reading, let that appear when there is no need of such vanity. You are thought here to be the most senseless and fit man for the constable of the watch; therefore bear you the lanthorn. This is your charge: you shall comprehend all vagrom men; you are to bid any man stand, in the prince's name.

Watch. How, if a' will not stand?

Dogberry. Why, then, take no note of him, but let him go; and presently call the rest of the watch together, and thank God you are rid of a knave.

Verges. If he will not stand when he is bidden, he is none of the prince's subjects.

Dogberry. True, and they are to meddle with none but the prince's subjects. You shall also make no noise in the streets: for, for the watch to babble and to talk is most tolerable and not to be endured.

2nd Watch. We will rather sleep than talk: we know what belongs to a watch.

Dogberry. Why, you speak like an ancient and most quiet watchman, for I cannot see how sleeping should offend; only have a care that your bills be not stolen. Well, you are to call at all the alehouses, and bid those that are drunk get them to bed.

Watch. How if they will not?

Dogberry. Why then, let them alone till they are sober : if they make you not then the better answer, you may say they are not the men you took them for.

Watch. Well, sir.

Dogberry. If you meet a thief, you may suspect him, by virtue of your office, to be no true man ; and, for such kind of men, the less you meddle or make with them, why, the more is for your honesty.

2nd Watch. If we know him to be a thief, shall we not lay hands on him ?

Dogberry. Truly, by your office, you may ; but I think they that touch pitch will be defiled. The most peaceable way for you, if you do take a thief, is, to let him show himself what he is and steal out of your company.

Verges. You have been always called a merciful man, partner.

Dogberry. Truly, I would not hang a dog by my will, much more a man who hath any honesty in him.

Verges. If you hear a child cry in the night, you must call to the nurse and bid her still it.

2nd Watch. How if the nurse be asleep and will not hear us ?

Dogberry. Why, then, depart in peace, and let the child wake her with crying ; for the ewe that will not hear her lamb when it baes, will never answer a calf when he bleats.

Verges. 'Tis very true.

Dogberry. This is the end of the charge. You

constable, are to present the prince's own person: if you meet the prince in the night, you may stay him.

Verges. Nay, by 'r lady, that I think, a' cannot.

Dogberry. Five shillings to one on 't, with any man that knows the statutes, he may stay him: marry, not without the prince be willing; for, indeed, the watch ought to offend no man, and it is an offence to stay a man against his will.

Verges. By 'r lady, I think it be so.

Dogberry. Ha, ah, ha! Well, masters, good night: an there be any matter of weight chances, call up me: keep your fellows' counsels and your own, and good night. Come, neighbour.

2nd Watch. Well, masters, we hear our charge: let us go sit here upon the church-bench till two, and then all go to bed.

Dogberry. One word more, honest neighbours. I pray you, watch about Signior Leonato's door; for the wedding being there to-morrow, there is a great coil to-night. Adieu; be vigitant, I beseech you.   [*Exeunt* DOGBERRY *and* VERGES.

Much Ado About Nothing. 1600.

THE PACES OF TIME

THE FOREST OF ARDEN.

ROSALIND (*in hiding*).

Enter ORLANDO *and* JAQUES.

Jaques. I thank you for your company; but, good faith, I had as lief have been myself alone.

Orlando. And so had I; but yet, for fashion' sake, I thank you too for your society.

Jaques. God be wi' you: let 's meet as little as we can.

Orlando. I do desire we may be better strangers.

Jaques. I pray you, mar no more trees with writing love-songs in their barks.

Orlando. I pray you mar no more of my verses with reading them ill-favouredly.

Jaques. Rosalind is your love's name ?

Orlando. Yes, just.

Jaques. I do not like her name.

Orlando. There was no thought of pleasing you when she was christened.

Jaques. What stature is she of ?

Orlando. Just as high as my heart.

Jaques. You are full of pretty answers. Have you not been acquainted with goldsmiths' wives, and conn'd them out of rings ?

Orlando. Not so ; but I answer you right painted cloth, from whence you have studied your questions.

Jaques. You have a nimble wit : I think 'twas made of Atalanta's heels. Will you sit down with me ? and we two will rail against our mistress the world, and all our misery.

Orlando. I will chide no breather in the world but myself, against whom I know most faults.

Jaques. The worst fault you have is to be in love.

Orlando. 'Tis a fault I will not change for your best virtue. I am weary of you.

Jaques. By my troth, I was seeking for a fool when I found you.

Orlando. He is drowned in the brook : look but in, and you shall see him.

Jaques. There I shall see mine own figure.

Orlando. Which I take to be either a fool or a cipher.

Jaques. I'll tarry no longer with you. Farewell, good Signior Love.

Orlando. I am glad of your departure. Adieu, good Monsieur Melancholy. [*Exit* JAQUES.

Rosalind. I will speak to him like a saucy lackey, and under that habit play the knave with him. Do you hear, forester?

Orlando. Very well: what would you?

Rosalind. I pray you, what is 't o'clock?

Orlando. You should ask me, what time o' day; there's no clock in the forest.

Rosalind. Then there is no true lover in the forest; else sighing every minute and groaning every hour would detect the lazy foot of Time as well as a clock.

Orlando. And why not the swift foot of Time? had not that been as proper?

Rosalind. By no means, sir. Time travels in divers paces with divers persons. I'll tell you who Time ambles withal, who Time trots withal, who Time gallops withal, and who he stands still withal.

Orlando. I prithee, who doth he trot withal?

Rosalind. Marry, he trots hard with a young maid between the contract of her marriage and the day it is solemnized; if the interim be but a se'nnight, Time's pace is so hard that it seems the length of seven year.

Orlando. Who ambles Time withal?

Rosalind. With a priest that lacks Latin, and a rich man that hath not the gout; for the one sleeps easily because he cannot study, and the other lives merrily because he feels no pain; the one lacking the burden of lean and wasteful learning, the other knowing no burden of heavy tedious penury. These Time ambles withal.

Orlando. Who doth he gallop withal?

Rosalind. With a thief to the gallows; for though he go as softly as foot can fall he thinks himself too soon there.

Orlando. Who stays it still withal?

Rosalind. With lawyers in the vacation; for they sleep between term and term, and then they perceive not how Time moves.

Orlando. Where dwell you, pretty youth?

Rosalind. With this shepherdess, my sister; here in the skirts of the forest, like fringe upon a petticoat.

Orlando. Are you native of this place?

Rosalind. As the cony, that you see dwell where she is kindled.

Orlando. Your accent is something finer than you could purchase in so removed a dwelling.

Rosalind. I have been told so of many: but indeed an old religious uncle of mine taught me to speak, who was in his youth an inland man; one that knew courtship too well, for there he fell in love. I have heard him read many lectures against it; and I thank God, I am not a woman, to be touched with so many giddy offences as he hath generally taxed their whole sex withal.

Orlando. Can you remember any of the principal evils that he laid to the charge of women?

Rosalind. There were none principal; they were all like one another as half-pence are; every one fault seeming monstrous till his fellow fault came to match it.

Orlando. I prithee, recount some of them.

Rosalind. No, I will not cast away my physic, but on those that are sick. There is a man haunts the forest, that abuses our young plants with carving 'Rosalind' on their barks; hangs odes upon hawthorns, and elegies on brambles; all, forsooth, deifying the name of Rosalind: if I could meet that fancy-monger, I would give him some good counsel, for he seems to have the quotidian of love upon him.

Orlando. I am he that is so love-shaked. I pray you, tell me your remedy.

Rosalind. There is none of my uncle's marks upon you: he taught me how to know a man in love; in which cage of rushes I am sure you are not prisoner.

Orlando. What were his marks?

Rosalind. A lean cheek, which you have not; a blue eye and sunken, which you have not; an unquestionable spirit, which you have not; a beard neglected, which you have not: but I pardon you for that, for, simply, your having in beard is a younger brother's revenue. Then, your hose should be ungartered, your bonnet unbanded, your sleeve unbuttoned, your shoe untied, and everything about you demonstrating a careless desolation. But you are no such man: you are rather point-device in your accoutrements; as loving yourself than seeming the lover of any other.

Orlando. Fair youth, I would I could make thee believe I love.

Rosalind. Me believe it! you may as soon make her that you love believe it; which, I warrant, she is apter to do than to confess she does; that is one of the points in the which women still give the lie to their consciences. But, in good sooth, are you he that hangs the verses on the trees, wherein Rosalind is so admired?

Orlando. I swear to thee, youth, by the white

hand of Rosalind, I am that he, that unfortunate he.

Rosalind. But are you so much in love as your rimes speak ?

Orlando. Neither rime nor reason can express how much.

Rosalind. Love is merely a madness, and, I tell you, deserves as well a dark house and a whip as madmen do ; and the reason why they are not so punished and cured is, that the lunacy is so ordinary that the whippers are in love too. Yet I profess curing it by counsel.

Orlando. Did you ever cure any so ?

Rosalind. Yes, one ; and in this manner. He was to imagine me his love, his mistress ; and I set him every day to woo me : at which time would I, being but a moonish youth, grieve, be effeminate, changeable, longing and liking ; proud, fantastical, apish, shallow, inconstant, full of tears, full of smiles, for every passion something, and for no passion truly anything, as boys and women are, for the most part, cattle of this colour ; would now like him, now loathe him ; then entertain him, then forswear him ; now weep for him, then spit at him ; that I drave my suitor from his mad humour of love to a living humour of madness, which was to forswear the full stream of the world. and to live in a nook merely monastic. And thus I cured him ; and this way will I take upon me to wash your liver as clean as a sound sheep's heart, that there shall not be one spot of love in 't.

Orlando. I would not be cured, youth.

Rosalind. I would cure you, if you would but call me Rosalind. and come every day to my cote and woo me.

Orlando. Now, by the faith of my love, I will: tell me where it is.

Rosalind. Go with me to it and I'll show it you ; and by the way you shall tell me where in the forest you live. Will you go ?

Orlando. With all my heart, good youth.

Rosalind. Nay, you must call me Rosalind. Come, sister, will you go ?   *[Exeunt.*

As You Like It. 1623.

INTERVIEW BETWEEN HAMLET AND ROSENCRANTZ AND GUILDENSTERN

ELSINORE. A ROOM IN THE CASTLE.

Guildenstern. Mine honoured lord !

Rosencrantz. My most dear lord !

Hamlet. My excellent good friends ! How dost thou, Guildenstern ? Ah, Rosencrantz ! Good lads, how do ye both ?

Rosencrantz. As the indifferent children of the earth.

Guildenstern. Happy in that we are not over happy ;
On Fortune's cap we are not the very button.

Hamlet. Nor the soles of her shoe ?

Rosencrantz. Neither, my lord. . . .

Hamlet. What news ?

Rosencrantz. None, my lord, but that the world's grown honest.

Hamlet. Then is doomsday near ; but your news is not true. Let me question more in particular : what have you, my good friends, deserved at the hands of Fortune, that she sends you to prison hither ?

Guildenstern. Prison, my lord !

Hamlet. Denmark's a prison.

Rosencrantz. Then is the world one.

Hamlet. A goodly one ; in which there are many confines, wards, and dungeons, Denmark being one o' the worst.

Rosencrantz. We think not so, my lord.

Hamlet. Why, then, 'tis none to you ; for there is nothing either good or bad, but thinking makes it so : to me it is a prison.

Rosencrantz. Why, then your ambition makes it one ; 'tis too narrow for your mind.

Hamlet. O God ! I could be bounded in a nutshell, and count myself a king of infinite space, were it not that I have bad dreams.

Guildenstern. Which dreams, indeed, are ambition, for the very substance of the ambitious is merely the shadow of a dream.

Hamlet. A dream itself is but a shadow.

Rosencrantz. Truly, and I hold ambition of so airy and light a quality that it is but a shadow's shadow.

Hamlet. Then are our beggars bodies, and our monarchs and outstretched heroes the beggars' shadows. Shall we to the court ? for, by my fay, I cannot reason.

Rosencrantz. }
Guildenstern. } We'll wait upon you.

Hamlet. No such matter ; I will not sort you with the rest of my servants, for, to speak to you like an honest man, I am most dreadfully attended. But, in the beaten way of friendship, what make you at Elsinore ?

Rosencrantz. To visit you, my lord; no other occasion.

Hamlet. Beggar that I am, I am even poor in thanks; but I thank you: and sure, dear friends, my thanks are too dear a halfpenny. Were you not sent for? Is it your own inclining? Is it a free visitation? Come, come, deal justly with me: come, come; nay, speak.

Guildenstern. What should we say, my lord?

Hamlet. Why anything, but to the purpose. You were sent for; and there is a kind of confession in your looks which your modesties have not craft enough to colour: I know the good king and queen have sent for you.

Rosencrantz. To what end, my lord?

Hamlet. That you must teach me. But let me conjure you, by the rights of our fellowship, by the consonancy of our youth, by the obligation of our ever-preserved love, and by what more dear a better proposer could charge you withal, be even and direct with me, whether you were sent for or no!

Rosencrantz. [*Aside to* GUILDENSTERN.] What say you?

Hamlet. [*Aside.*] Nay, then, I have an eye of you. If you love me, hold not off.

Guildenstern. My lord, we were sent for.

Hamlet. I will tell you why; so shall my anticipation prevent your discovery, and your secrecy to the king and queen moult no feather. I have of late,—but wherefore I know not,—lost all my mirth, forgone all custom of exercises; and indeed it goes so heavily with my disposition that this goodly frame, the earth, seems to me a sterile promontory; this most excellent canopy, the air,

look you, this brave o'erhanging firmament, this
majestical roof fretted with golden fire, why, it
appears no other thing to me but a foul and
pestilent congregation of vapours. What a piece
of work is a man ! How noble in reason ! how
infinite in faculty ! in form, in moving, how
express and admirable ! in action how like an
angel ! in apprehension how like a god ! the
beauty of the world ! the paragon of animals !
And yet, to me, what is this quintessence of dust ?
man delights not me ; no, nor woman neither,
though, by your smiling, you seem to say so.

Rosencrantz. My lord, there was no such stuff in
my thoughts.

Hamlet. Why did you laugh then, when I said,
' man delights not me ' ?

Rosencrantz. To think, my lord, if you delight
not in man, what lenten entertainment the players
shall receive from you : we coted them on the
way ; and hither are they coming, to offer you
service.

Hamlet. He that plays the king shall be
welcome ; his majesty shall have tribute of me ;
the adventurous knight shall use his foil and
target ; the lover shall not sigh gratis ; the
humorous man shall end his part in peace ; the
clown shall make those laugh whose lungs are
tickle o' the sere ; and the lady shall say her mind
freely, or the blank verse shall halt for 't. What
players are they ?

Rosencrantz. Even those you were wont to take
delight in, the tragedians of the city.

Hamlet. How chances it they travel ? their
residence, both in reputation and profit, was
better both ways.

Rosencrantz. I think their inhibition comes by the means of the late innovation.

Hamlet. Do they hold the same estimation they did when I was in the city? Are they so followed?

Rosencrantz. No, indeed they are not.

Hamlet. How comes it? Do they grow rusty?

Rosencrantz. Nay, their endeavour keeps in the wonted pace: but there is, sir, an aery of children, little eyases, that cry out on the top of question, and are most tyrannically clapped for 't: these are now the fashion, and so berattle the common stages,—so they call them,—that many wearing rapiers are afraid of goose-quills, and dare scarce come thither.

Hamlet. What! are they children? who maintains 'em? how are they escoted? Will they pursue the quality no longer than they can sing? will they not say afterwards, if they should grow themselves to common players,—as it is most like, if their means are no better,—their writers do them wrong, to make them exclaim against their own succession?

Rosencrantz. Faith, there has been much to-do on both sides: and the nation holds it no sin to tarre them to controversy: there was, for a while, no money bid for argument, unless the poet and the player went to cuffs in the question.

Hamlet. Is it possible?

Guildenstern. O! there has been much throwing about of brains.

Hamlet. Do the boys carry it away?

Rosencrantz. Ay, that they do, my lord; Hercules and his load too.

Hamlet. It is not very strange; for my uncle is King of Denmark, and those that would make

mows at him while my father lived, give twenty,
forty, fifty, a hundred ducats a-piece for his
picture in little. 'Sblood, there is something in
this more than natural, if philosophy could find
it out.   [*Flourish of trumpets within.*

Guildenstern. There are the players.

Hamlet. Gentlemen, you are welcome to
Elsinore. Your hands, come then; the appur-
tenance of welcome is fashion and ceremony:
let me comply with you in this garb, lest my
extent to the players—which, I tell you, must
show fairly outward—should more appear like
entertainment than yours. You are welcome;
but my uncle-father and aunt-mother are deceived.

Guildenstern. In what, my dear lord?

Hamlet. I am but mad north-north-west:
when the wind is southerly I know a hawk from
a handsaw

                                    Hamlet. 1603.

BEN JONSON

1573–1637

LONDON. MOORFIELDS

A BRAGGADOCIO

MATHEW, EDWARD KNOWELL, CAPTAIN BOBADILL, *and* STEPHEN.

Mathew. Sir, did your eyes ever taste the like clown of him where we were to-day, Mr. Wellbred's half-brother ? I think the whole earth cannot show his parallel, by this daylight.

E. Knowell. We were now speaking of him : Captain Bobadill tells me he is fallen foul o' you too.

Mathew. O, ay, sir, he threatened me with the bastinado.

Bobadill. Ay, but I think I taught you prevention this morning, for that : You shall kill him, beyond question ; if you be so generously minded.

Mathew. Indeed, it is a most excellent trick.
[*Fences.*

Bobadill. O, you do not give spirit enough to your motion, you are too tardy, too heavy ! O, it must be done like lightning, hay !
[*Practises at a post with his cudgel.*

Mathew. Rare, captain !

Bobadill. Tut ! 'tis nothing, an 't be not done in a —— punto.

E. Knowell. Captain, did you ever prove yourself upon any of our masters of defence here ?

Mathew. O, good sir ! yes, I hope he has.

Bobadill. I will tell you, sir. Upon my first coming to the city, after my long travel for knowledge, in that mystery only, there came three or four of 'em to me, at a gentleman's house, where it was my chance to be resident at that time, to intreat my presence at their schools : and withal so much importuned me, that I protest to you, as I am a gentleman, I was ashamed of their rude demeanour out of all measure : Well, I told 'em that to come to a public school, they should pardon me, it was opposite, in diameter, to my humour ; but if so be they would give their attendance at my lodging, I protested to do them what right or favour I could, as I was a gentleman, and so forth.

E. Knowell. So, sir ! then you tried their skill ?

Bobadill. Alas, soon tried : you shall hear, sir. Within two or three days after, they came ; and, by honesty, fair sir, believe me, I graced them exceedingly, showed them some two or three tricks of prevention have purchased 'em since a credit to admiration : they cannot deny this ; and yet now they hate me, and why ? because I am excellent ; and for no other vile reason on the earth.

E. Knowell. This is strange and barbarous, as ever I heard.

Bobadill. Nay, for a more instance of their preposterous natures ; but note, sir. They have assaulted me some three, four, five, six of them together, as I have walked alone in divers skirts i' the town, as Turnbull, Whitechapel, Shoreditch, which were then my quarters ; and since, upon the Exchange, at my lodging, and at my ordinary : where I have driven them afore me the whole

length of a street, in the open view of all our
gallants, pitying to hurt them, believe me. Yet,
all this lenity will not o'ercome their spleen;
they will be doing with the pismire, raising a hill
a man may spurn abroad with his foot at pleasure.
By myself, I could have slain them all, but I
delight not in murder. I am loth to bear any
other than this bastinado for 'em: yet I hold it
good polity not to go disarmed, for though I be
skilful, I may be oppressed with multitudes.

E. Knowell. Ay, believe me, may you, sir: and
in my conceit, our whole nation should sustain
the loss by it, if it were so.

Bobadill. Alas, no! what's a peculiar man to
a nation? not seen.

E. Knowell. O, but your skill, sir.

Bobadill. Indeed, that might be some loss;
but who respects it? I will tell you, sir, by the
way of private, and under seal; I am a gentleman, and live here obscure, and to myself; but
were I known to her majesty and the lords,—
observe me,—I would undertake, upon this poor
head and life, for the public benefit of the state,
not only to spare the entire lives of her subjects
in general; but to save the one half, nay, three
parts of her yearly charge in holding war, and
against what enemy soever. And how would
I do it, think you?

E. Knowell. Nay, I know not, nor can I
conceive.

Bobadill. Why thus, sir. I would select nineteen more, to myself, throughout the land;
gentlemen they should be of good spirit, strong and
able constitution; I would choose them by an
instinct, a character that I have: and I would

teach these nineteen the special rules, as your
punto, your reverso, your stoccata, your imbroc-
cata, your passada, your montanto ; till they
could all play very near, or altogether as well as
myself. This done, say the enemy were forty
thousand strong, we twenty would come into the
field the tenth of March, or thereabouts ; and we
would challenge twenty of the enemy ; they
could not in their honour refuse us : Well, we
would kill them ; challenge twenty more, kill
them ; twenty more, kill them ; twenty more,
kill them too ; and thus would we kill, every man,
his twenty a day, that's twenty score ; twenty
score, that's two hundred ; two hundred a day,
five days a thousand : forty thousand ; forty
times five, five times forty, two hundred days
kills them all up, by computation. And this will
I venture my poor gentleman-like carcase to perform, provided there be no treason practised upon
us, by fair and discreet manhood ; that is, civilly
by the sword.

E. Knowell. Why, are you so sure of your
hand, captain, at all times ?

Bobadill. Tut ! never miss thrust, upon my
reputation with you.

E. Knowell. I would not stand in Downright's
state then, an you meet him, for the wealth of any
one street in London.

Bobadill. Why, sir, you mistake me : if he
were here now, by this welkin, I would not draw
my weapon on him. Let this gentleman do his
mind : but I will bastinado him, by the bright sun,
wherever I meet him.

Mathew. Faith and I'll have a fling at him, at
my distance.

E. Knowell. God's, so, look where he is! yonder he goes. [DOWNRIGHT *crosses the stage.*

Downright. What peevish luck have I, I cannot meet with these bragging rascals!

Bobadill. It's not he, is it?

E. Knowell. Yes, faith, it is he.

Mathew. I'll be hang'd then if that were he.

E. Knowell. Sir, keep your hanging good for some greater matter, for I assure you that was he.

Stephen. Upon my reputation, it was he.

Bobadill. Had I thought it had been he, he must not have gone so: but I can hardly be induced to believe it was he yet.

E. Knowell. That I think, sir.

Re-enter DOWNRIGHT.

But see, he is come again.

Downright. O, Pharaoh's foot, have I found you? Come, draw, to your tools; draw, gipsy, or I'll thresh you.

Bobadill. Gentleman of valour, I do believe in thee; hear me——

Downright. Draw your weapon, then.

Bobadill. Tall man, I never thought on it till now—Body of me, I had a warrant of the peace served on me, even now as I came along, by a water-bearer; this gentleman saw it, Mr. Mathew.

Downright. 'Sdeath! you will not draw, then?

[*Disarms and beats him.* MATHEW *runs away.*

Bobadill. Hold, hold! under thy favour, forbear!

Downright. Prate again, as you like this, you whoreson foist, you! You'll control the point, you? Your consort is gone? had he stayed, he had shared with you, sir. [*Exit.*

Bobadill. Well, gentlemen, bear witness. I was
bound to the peace, by this good day.

E. Knowell. No, faith, it's an ill day, captain,
never reckon it other : but, say you were bound
to the peace, the law allows you to defend yourself : that 'll prove but a poor excuse.

Bobadill. I cannot tell, sir. I desire good
construction, in fair sort. I never sustain'd the
like disgrace, by heaven ! sure I was struck with
a planet thence, for I had no power to touch my
weapon.

E. Knowell. Ay, like enough ; I have heard of
many that have been beaten under a planet :
go, get you to a surgeon ! 'Slid ! an these be your
tricks, your passadas, and your mountantos, I'll
none of them. [*Exit Bobadill.*] O, manners !
that this age should bring forth such creatures !
that nature should be at leisure to make them !
Come, coz.   [*Exeunt.*

Every Man in His Humour. 1616.

OVERDO IN THE STOCKS

The back of URSULA'S *Booth.*

OVERDO in the stocks, People, &c.

Enter QUARLOUS *with the licence, and* EDGWORTH.

Quarlous. Well, sir, you are now discharged ;
beware of being spied hereafter.

Edgworth. Sir, will it please you, enter in here
at Ursla's, and take part of a silken gown, a velvet
petticoat, or a wrought smock ; I am promised
such, and I can spare any gentleman a moiety.

Quarlous. Keep it for your companions in beastliness, I am none of 'em, sir. If I had not already forgiven you a greater trespass, or thought you yet worth my beating, I would instruct your manners, to whom you made your offers. But go your ways, talk not to me, the hangman is only fit to discourse with you; the hand of beadle is too merciful a punishment for your trade of life. [*Exit* EDGWORTH.]—I am sorry I employ'd this fellow, for he thinks me such; *facinus quos inquinat, æquat.* But it was for sport; and would I make it serious, the getting of this license is nothing to me, without other circumstances concur. I do think how impertinently I labour, if the word be not mine that the ragged fellow mark'd: and what advantage I have given Ned Winwife in this time now of working her, though it be mine He'll go near to form to her what a debauched rascal I am, and fright her out of all good conceit of me: I should do so by him, I am sure, if I had the opportunity. But my hope is in her temper yet; and it must needs be next to despair, that is grounded on any part of a woman's discretion. I would give, by my troth now, all I could spare, to my clothes and my sword, to meet my tatter'd soothsayer again, who was my judge i' the question, to know certainly whose word he has damn'd or saved; for till then I live but under a reprieve. I must seek him. Who be these?

Enter BRISTLE *and some of the* Watch, *with* WASPE.

Waspe. Sir, you are a Welsh cuckold, and a prating runt, and no constable.

Bristle. You say very well.—Come, put in his

leg in the middle roundel, and let him hole
there.

                      [They put him in the stocks.

Waspe. You stink of leeks, metheglin, and
cheese, you rogue.

Bristle. Why, what is that to you, if you sit
sweetly in the stocks in the mean time ? if you
have a mind to stink too, your breeches sit close
enough to your bum. Sit you merry, sir.

Quarlous. How now, Numps ?

Waspe. It is no matter how ; pray you look off.

Quarlous. Nay, I'll not offend you, Numps ;
I thought you had sat there to be seen.

Waspe. And to be sold, did you not ? pray you
mind your business, an you have any.

Quarlous. Cry you mercy, Numps ; does your
leg lie high enough ?

Enter HAGGISE.

Bristle. How now, neighbour Haggise, what
says justice Overdo's worship to the other
offenders ?

Haggise. Why, he says just nothing ; what
should he say, or where should he say ? He is not
to be found, man; he ha' not been seen i' the
Fair here all this live-long day, never since seven
a clock i' the morning. His clerks know not what
to think on 't. There is no court of Pie-poulders
yet. Here they be return'd.

Enter others of the Watch *with* BUSY.

Bristle. What shall be done with 'em, then,
in your discretion ?

Haggise. I think we were best put 'em in the
stocks in discretion (there they will be safe in

discretion) for the valour of an hour, or such a
thing, till his worship come.

Bristle. It is but a hole matter if we do, neighbour Haggise; come, sir, [*to* WASPE.] here is
company for you; heave up the stocks.

[*As they open the stocks,* WASPE *puts his shoe
on his hand, and slips it in for his leg.*

Waspe. I shall put a trick upon your Welsh
diligence perhaps.   [*Aside.*

Bristle. Put in your leg, sir.   [*To* BUSY.

Quarlous. What, Rabbi Busy! is he come?

Busy. I do obey thee; the lion may roar, but
he cannot bite. I am glad to be thus separated
from the heathen of the land, and put apart in the
stocks, for the holy cause.

Waspe. What are you, sir?

Busy. One that rejoiceth in his affliction, and
sitteth here to prophesy the destruction of fairs
and May-games, wakes and Whitson-ales, and
doth sigh and groan for the reformation of these
abuses.

Waspe. [*to* OVERDO.] And do you sigh and groan
too, or rejoice in your affliction?

Overdo. I do not feel it, I do not think of it,
it is a thing without me: Adam, thou art above
these batteries, these contumelies. *In te manca
ruit fortuna*, as thy friend Horace says; thou art
one, *Quem neque pauperies, neque mors, neque
vincula, terrent.* And therefore, as another friend
of thine says, I think it be thy friend Persius,
Non te quæsiveris ̃xtra.

Quarlous. What's here! a stoic i' the stocks?
the fool is turn'd philosopher.

Busy. Friend, I will leave to communicate my
spirit with you, if I hear any more of those super-

stitious relics, those lists of Latin, the very rags of Rome, and patches of popery.

Waspe. Nay, an' you begin to quarrel, gentlemen, I'll leave you. I ha' paid for quarrelling too lately: look you, a device, but shifting in a hand for a foot. God b' w' you. [*Slips out his hand.*

Busy. Wilt thou then leave thy brethren in tribulation?

Waspe. For this once, sir. [*Exit, running.*

Busy. Thou art a halting neutral; stay him there, stop him, that will not endure the heat of persecution.

Bristle. How now, what's the matter?

Busy. He is fled, he is fled, and dares not sit it out.

Bristle. What, has he made an escape! which way? follow, neighbour Haggise.

[*Exeunt* HAGGISE *and* Watch.

Enter Dame PURECRAFT.

Purecraft. O me, in the stocks! have the wicked prevail'd?

Busy. Peace, religious sister, it is my calling, comfort yourself; an extraordinary calling, and done for my better standing, my surer standing, hereafter.

Enter TROUBLEALL, *with a can.*

Troubleall. By whose warrant, by whose warrant, this?

Quarlous. O, here's my man dropt in, I look'd for.

Overdo. Ha!

Purecraft. O, good sir, they have set the faithful here to be wonder'd at; and provided holes for the holy of the land.

Troubleall. Had they warrant for it ? shew'd they justice Overdo's hand ? if they had no warrant, they shall answer it.

Re-enter HAGGISE.

Bristle. Sure you did not lock the stocks sufficiently, neighbour Toby.

Haggise. No! see if you can lock 'em better.

Bristle. They are very sufficiently lock'd, and truly ; yet something is in the matter.

Troubleall. True, your warrant is the matter that is in question ; by what warrant ?

Bristle. Madman, hold your peace, I will put you in his room else in the very same hole, do you see ?

Quarlous. How, is he a madman ?

Troubleall. Shew me justice Overdo's warrant, I obey you.

Haggise. You are a mad fool, hold your tongue.
                    [*Exeunt* HAGGISE *and* BRISTLE.

Troubleall. In justice Overdo's name, I drink to you, and here's my warrant.   [*Shews his can.*

Overdo. Alas, poor wretch ! how it yearns my heart for him !   [*Aside.*

Quarlous. If he be mad, it is in vain to question him. I'll try him though.—Friend, there was a gentlewoman shew'd you two names some hours since, Argalus and Palemon, to mark in a book ; which of 'em was it you mark'd ?

Troubleall. I mark no name but Adam Overdo, that is the name of names, he only is the sufficient magistrate ; and that name I reverence, shew it me.

Quarlous. This fellow's mad indeed : I am further off now than afore.

Overdo. I shall not breathe in peace till I have made him some amends. [*Aside.*

Quarlous. Well, I will make another use of him is come in my head : I have a nest of beards in my trunk, one something like his.

Re-enter BRISTLE *and* HAGGISE.

Bristle. This mad fool has made me that I know not whether I have lock'd the stocks or no ; I think I lock'd 'em. [*Tries the locks.*

Troubleall. Take Adam Overdo in your mind, and fear nothing.

Bristle. 'Slid, madness itself ! hold thy peace, and take that. [*Strikes him.*

Troubleall. Strikest thou without a warrant ? take thou that.

[*They fight, and leave open the stocks in the scuffle.*

Busy. We are delivered by miracle ; fellow in fetters, let us not refuse the means ; this madness was of the spirit : the malice of the enemy hath mock'd itself. [*Exeunt* BUSY *and* OVERDO.

Purecraft. Mad do they call him ! the world is mad in error, but he is mad in truth : I love him o' the sudden (the cunning man said all true) and shall love him more and more. How well it becomes a man to be mad in truth ! O, that I might be his yoke-fellow, and be mad with him, what a many should we draw to madness in truth with us !

Bristle. How now, all 'scaped ! where 's the woman ? it is witchcraft ! her velvet hat is a witch, o' my conscience, or my key ! t' one.—The madman was a devil, and I am an ass ; so bless me, my place, and mine office ! [*Exeunt, affrighted.*

Bartholomew Fair. 1614.

BEN JONSON (1573–1635) with GEORGE CHAPMAN (1559 ?–1634) and JOHN MARSTON (1575 ?–1634)

ON THAMES' SIDE

Enter PETRONEL, *and* SEAGUL, *bareheaded.*

Petronel. Zounds! Captain, I tell thee we are cast up o' the coast of France. 'Sfoot! I am not drunke still, I hope. Dost remember where we were last night?

Seagul. No, by my troth, knight, not I; but methinks we have been a horrible while upon the water and in the water.

Petronel. Aye me! we are undone for ever! Hast any money about thee?

Seagul. Not a penny, by Heaven!

Petronel. Not a penny betwixt us, and cast ashore in France!

Seagul. Faith, I cannot tell that; my brains nor mine eyes are not mine own yet.

Enter Two Gentlemen.

Petronel. 'Sfoot! wilt not believe me? I know 't by th' elevation of the pole, and by the altitude and latitude of the climate. See, here comes a couple of French gentlemen; I knew we were in France; dost thou think our Englishmen are so Frenchified, that a man knows not whether he be in France or in England, when he sees 'em? What shall we do? We must e'en to 'em, and intreat some relief of 'em. Life is sweet, and we have no other means to relieve our lives now but their charities.

Seagul. Pray you, do you beg on 'em then; you can speak French.

Petronel. Monsieur, plaît-il d'avoir pitié de notre grande infortune. Je suis un pauvre chevalier d'Angleterre qui a souffert l'infortune de naufrage.

1st Gent. Un pauvre chevalier d'Angleterre?

[Petronel]. Oui, monsieur, il est trop vrai; mais vous savez bien, nous sommes tous sujets à fortune.

2nd Gent. A poor knight of England?—a poor knight of Windsor, are you not? Why speake you this broken French, when y'are a whole Englishman? On what coast are you, think you?

1st Gent. On the coast of Dogs, sir; y'are i' th' Ile a Dogs, I tell you. I see y'ave been washed in the Thames here, and I believe ye were drowned in a tavern before, or else you would never have took boat in such a dawning as this was. Farewell, farewell; we will not know you for shaming of you. I ken the man weel; he's one of my thirty pound knights.

2nd Gent. Now this is he that stole his knighthood o' the grand day for four pound given to a page; all the money in 's purse, I wot well.

[Exeunt.

Seagul. Death! Colonel, I knew you were over shot.

Petronel. Sure I think now, indeed, Captain Seagul, we were something overshot.

Eastward Hoe! 1605.

JOHN MILTON

1608-1674

HE ANNOUNCES HIS INTENTION OF
WRITING AN EPIC

For although a poet, soaring in the high region
of his fancies, with his garland and singing robes
about him, might, without apology, speak more
of himself than I mean to do ; yet for me sitting
here below in the cool element of prose, a mortal
thing among many readers of no empyreal conceit,
to venture and divulge unusual things of myself,
I shall petition to the gentler sort, it may not be
envy to me. I must say, therefore, that after
I had from my first years, by the ceaseless diligence
and care of my father, whom God recompense,
been exercised to the tongues, and some sciences,
as my age would suffer, by sundry masters and
teachers, both at home and at the schools, it was
found that whether aught was imposed me by them
that had the overlooking, or betaken to of mine
own choice in English, or other tongue, prosing or
versing, but chiefly this latter, the style, by certain
vital signs it had, was likely to live. But much
latelier in the private academies of Italy, whither
I was favoured to resort, perceiving that some
trifles which I had in memory, composed at under
twenty or thereabout (for the manner is, that every
one must give some proof of his wit and reading
there), met with acceptance above what was

looked for ; and other things, which I had shifted
in scarcity of books and conveniences to patch up
amongst them, were received with written encomiums, which the Italian is not forward to
bestow on men of this side the Alps ; I began thus
far to assent both to them and divers of my friends
here at home, and not less to an inward prompting
which now grew daily upon me, that by labour and
intent study (which I take to be my portion in this
life), joined with the strong propensity of nature,
I might perhaps leave something so written to
aftertimes, as they should not willingly let it die.
These thoughts at once possessed me, and these
other ; that if I were certain to write as men buy
leases, for three lives and downward, there ought
no regard be sooner had, than to God's glory, by
the honour and instruction of my country. For
which cause, and not only for that I knew it would
be hard to arrive at the second rank among the
Latins, I applied myself to that resolution, which
Aristo followed against the persuasions of Bembo,
to fix all the industry and art I could unite to the
adorning of my native tongue ; not to make verbal
curiosities the end (that were a toilsome vanity),
but to be an interpreter and relater of the best and
sagest things among mine own citizens throughout
this island in the mother dialect. That what the
greatest and choicest wits of Athens, Rome, or
modern Italy, and those Hebrews of old did for
their country, I, in my proportion, with this over
and above, of being a Christian, might do for
mine : not caring to be once named abroad, though
perhaps I could attain to that, but content with
these British islands as my world ; whose fortune
hath hitherto been, that if the Athenians, as some

say, made their small deeds great and renowned by their eloquent writers, England hath had her noble achievements made small by the unskilful handling of monks and mechanics.

Time serves not now, and perhaps I might seem too profuse to give any certain account of what the mind at home, in the spacious circuits of her musing, hath liberty to propose to her self, though of highest hope and hardest attempting; whether that epic form whereof the two poems of Homer, and those other two of Virgil and Tasso, are a diffuse, and the book of Job a brief model : or whether the rules of Aristotle herein are strictly to be kept, or nature to be followed, which in them that know art, and use judgement, is no transgression, but an enriching of art : and lastly, what king or knight, before the conquest, might be chosen in whom to lay the pattern of a Christian hero. And as Tasso gave to a prince of Italy his choice whether he would command him to write of Godfrey's expedition against the Infidels, or Belisarius against the Goths, or Charlemain against the Lombards ; if to the instinct of nature and the emboldening of art aught may be trusted, and that there be nothing adverse in our climate, or the fate of this age, it haply would be no rashness, from an equal diligence and inclination, to present the like offer in our own ancient stories. Or whether those dramatic constitutions, wherein Sophocles and Euripides reign, shall be found more doctrinal and exemplary to a nation. The Scripture also affords us a divine pastoral drama in the Song of Salomon, consisting of two persons, and a double chorus, as Origen rightly judges. And the Apocalypse of Saint John is the majestic image of a high and stately tragedy

shutting up and intermingling her solemn scenes
and acts with a sevenfold chorus of hallelujahs and
harping symphonies : and this my opinion the
grave authority of Pareus, commenting that book,
is sufficient to confirm. Or if occasion shall lead,
to imitate those magnific odes and hymns, wherein
Pindarus and Callimachus are in most things
worthy, some others in their frame judicious, in
their matter most an end faulty. But those
frequent songs throughout the law and prophets
beyond all these, not in their divine argument
alone, but in the very critical art of composition,
may be easily made appear over all the kinds of
lyric poesy to be incomparable. These abilities,
wheresoever they be found, are the inspired gift of
God, rarely bestowed, but yet to some (though
most abuse) in every nation : and are of power,
beside the office of a pulpit, to inbreed and cherish
in a great people the seeds of virtue and public
civility, to allay the perturbations of the mind,
and set the affections in right tune ; to celebrate
in glorious and lofty hymns the throne and equipage
of God's almightiness, and what He works, and
what He suffers to be wrought with high providence
in His Church ; to sing the victorious agonies of
martyrs and saints, the deeds and triumphs of just
and pious nations, doing valiantly through faith
against the enemies of Christ ; to deplore the
general relapses of kingdoms and states from
justice and God's true worship. Lastly, whatsoever in religion is holy and sublime, in virtue
amiable or grave, whatsoever hath passion or
admiration in all the changes of that which is
called fortune from without, or the wily subtleties
and refluxes of man's thoughts from within ; all

these things with a solid and treatable smoothness to paint out and describe. Teaching over the whole book of sanctity and virtue, through all the instances of example, with such delight to those especially of soft and delicious temper, who will not so much as look upon Truth herself, unless they see her elegantly dressed; that whereas the paths of honesty and good life appear now rugged and difficult, though they be indeed easy and pleasant, they would then appear to all men both easy and pleasant, though they were rugged and difficult indeed. And what a benefit this would be to our youth and gentry, may be soon guessed by what we know of the corruption and bane which they suck in daily from the writings and interludes of libidinous and ignorant poetasters, who having scarce ever heard of that which is the main consistence of a true poem, the choice of such persons as they ought to introduce, and what is moral and decent to each one; do for the most part lay up vicious principles in sweet pills to be swallowed down, and make the taste of virtuous documents harsh and sour.

The Reason of Church Government. **1642.**

JOHN BUNYAN

1628-1688

CHRISTIAN AND APOLLYON IN THE VALLEY OF HUMILIATION

BUT now in this Valley of *Humiliation* poor *Christian* was hard put to it, for he had gone but a little way before he espied a foul *Fiend* coming over the field to meet him; his name is *Apollyon*. Then did *Christian* begin to be afraid, and to cast in his mind whether to go back, or to stand his ground. But he considered again, that he had no Armor for his back, and therefore thought that to turn the back to him might give him greater advantage with ease to pierce him with his Darts; therefore he resolved to venture, and stand his ground. For thought he, had I no more in mine eye than the saving of my life, 'twould be the best way to stand.

So he went on, and *Apollyon* met him. Now the Monster was hideous to behold, he was cloathed with scales like a Fish (and they are his pride) he had Wings like a Dragon, feet like a Bear, and out of his belly came Fire and Smoke, and his mouth was as the mouth of a Lion. When he was come up to *Christian*, he beheld him with a disdainful countenance, and thus began to question with him.

Apollyon. Whence come you, and whither are you bound?

Christian. I am come from the City of *Destruction*, which is the place of all evil, and am going to the City of *Zion.*

Apollyon. *By this I perceive thou art one of my Subjects, for all that Country is mine ; and I am the Prince and God of it. How is it then that thou hast ran away from thy King ? Were it not that I hope thou mayest do me more service, I would strike thee now at one blow to the ground.*

Christian. I was born indeed in your Dominions, but your service was hard, and your wages such as a man could not live on, *for the wages of Sin is death ;* therefore when I was come to years, I did as other considerate persons do, look out if perhaps I might mend my self.

Apollyon. *There is no Prince that will thus lightly lose his Subjects, neither will I as yet lose thee. But since thou complainest of thy service and wages be content to go back ; what our Country will afford, I do here promise to give thee.*

Christian. But I have let myself to another, even to the King of Princes, and how can I with fairness go back with thee ?

Apollyon. *Thou hast done in this, according to the Proverb, changed a bad for a worse : but it is ordinary for those that have professed themselves his Servants, after a while to give him the slip, and return again to me : do thou so too, and all shall be well.*

Christian. I have given him my faith, and sworn my Allegiance to him ; how then can I go back from this, and not be hanged as a Traitor ?

Apollyon. *Thou didst the same to me, and yet I am willing to pass by all, if now thou wilt yet turn again, and go back.*

Christian. What I promised thee was in my nonage; and besides, I count that the Prince under whose Banner now I stand, is able to absolve me; yea, and to pardon also what I did as to my compliance with thee: and besides, (O thou destroying *Apollyon*) to speak truth, I like his Service, his Wages, his Servants, his Government, his Company, and Country better than thine: and therefore leave off to perswade me further, I am his Servant, and I will follow him.

Apollyon. Consider again when thou art in cool blood, what thou art like to meet with in the way that thou goest. Thou knowest that for the most part, his Servants come to an ill end, because they are transgressors against me, and my ways. How many of them have been put to shameful deaths! and besides, thou countest his service better than mine, whereas he never came yet from the place where he is, to deliver any that served him out of our hands; but as for me, how many times, as all the World very well knows, have I delivered, either by power or fraud, those that have faithfully served me, from him and his, though taken by them, and so I will deliver thee.

Christian. His forbearing at present to deliver them, is on purpose to try their love, whether they will cleave to him to the end: and as for the ill end thou sayest they come to, that is most glorious in their account. For for present deliverance, they do not much expect it; for they stay for their Glory, and then they shall have it, when their Prince comes in his, and the Glory of the Angels.

Apollyon. Thou hast already been unfaithful in thy service to him, and how doest thou think to receive wages of him?

Christian. Wherein, O *Apollyon*, have I been unfaithful to him?

Apollyon. *Thou didst faint at first setting out, when thou wast almost choked in the Gulf of Dispond; thou didst attempt wrong ways to be rid of thy burden, whereas thou shouldest have stayed till thy Prince had taken it off: thou didst sinfully sleep and lose thy choice thing: thou wast also almost perswaded to go back, at the sight of the Lions; and when thou talkest of thy Journey, and of what thou hast heard, and seen, thou art inwardly desirous of vain-glory in all that thou sayest or doest.*

Christian. All this is true, and much more, which thou hast left out; but the Prince whom I serve and honour, is merciful, and ready to forgive: but besides, these infirmities possessed me in thy Country, for there I suckt them in, and I have groaned under them, been sorry for them, and have obtained pardon of my Prince.

Apollyon. Then *Apollyon* broke out into a grievous rage, saying, *I am an Enemy to this Prince: I hate his Person, his Laws, and People: I am come out on purpose to withstand thee.*

Christian. *Apollyon,* beware what you do, for I am in the King's Highway, the way of Holiness, therefore take heed to your self.

Apollyon. Then *Apollyon* straddled quite over the whole breadth of the way, and said, I am void of fear in this matter, prepare thy self to die, for I swear by my Infernal Den, that thou shalt go no further, here will I spill thy soul; and with that, he threw a flaming Dart at his Breast, but *Christian* had a Shield in his hand, with which he caught it, and so prevented the danger of that. Then did *Christian* draw, for he saw 'twas time to bestir him;

and *Apollyon* as fast made at him, throwing Darts
as thick as Hail; by the which, notwithstanding
all that *Christian* could do to avoid it, *Apollyon*
wounded him in his head, his hand and foot; this
made *Christian* give a little back: *Apollyon* therefore followed his work amain, and *Christian* again
took courage, and resisted as manfully as he could.
This sore combat lasted for above half a day, even
till *Christian* was almost quite spent. For you
must know that *Christian* by reason of his wounds,
must needs grow weaker and weaker.

Then *Apollyon* espying his opportunity, began
to gather up close to *Christian*, and wrestling with
him, gave him a dreadful fall; and with that,
Christian's Sword flew out of his hand. Then said
Apollyon, I am sure of thee now; and with that, he
had almost prest him to death, so that *Christian*
began to despair of life. But as God would have it,
while *Apollyon* was fetching of his last blow, thereby to make a full end of this good Man, *Christian*
nimbly reached out his hand for his Sword, and
caught it, saying, *Rejoice not against me, O mine
Enemy! when I fall, I shall arise;* and with that,
gave him a deadly thrust, which made him give
back, as one that had received his mortal wound:
Christian perceiving that, made at him again, saying,
*Nay, in all these things we are more than Conquerors,
through him that loved us.* And with that, *Apollyon*
spread forth his Dragon's wings, and sped him
away, that *Christian* saw him no more.

In this Combat no man can imagine, unless he
had seen and heard as I did, what yelling, and
hideous roaring *Apollyon* made all the time of the
fight, he spake like a Dragon: and on the other
side, what sighs and groans brast from *Christian's*

heart. I never saw him all the while give so much as one pleasant look, till he perceived he had wounded *Apollyon* with his two-edged Sword, then indeed he did smile, and look upward : but 'twas the dreadfullest sight that ever I saw.

So when the Battle was over, *Christian* said, I will here give thanks to him that hath delivered me out of the mouth of the Lion; to him that did help me against *Apollyon* : and so he did, saying,

> *Great* Beelzebub, *the Captain of this Fiend,*
> *Design'd my ruin ; therefore to this end*
> *He sent him harnest out, and he with rage*
> *That Hellish was, did fiercely me engage :*
> *But blessed Michael helped me, and I*
> *By dint of Sword, did quickly make him fly :*
> *Therefore to him let me give lasting praise,*
> *And thank and bless his holy name always.*

Then there came to him an hand, with some of the leaves of the Tree of Life, the which *Christian* took, and applied to the wounds that he had received in the Battle, and was healed immediately. He also sat down in that place to eat Bread, and to drink of the Bottle that was given him a little before ; so being refreshed, he addressed himself to his Journey, with his Sword drawn in his hand, for he said, I know not but some other Enemy may be at hand. But he met with no other affront from *Apollyon*, quite through this Valley.

The Pilgrim's Progress. 1678.

THE MEETING WITH MR. VALIANT-FOR-
TRUTH

THEN they went on, and just at the place where
Little-faith formerly was Robbed, there stood
a man with his Sword drawn, and his Face all
bloody. Then said Mr. *Great-heart* What art thou ?
The man made Answer, saying, I am one whose
Name is *Valiant-for-Truth*. I am a Pilgrim, and
am going to the Coelestial City. Now as I was in my
way, there was three men did beset me, and pro-
pounded unto me these three things. 1. Whether
I would become one of them ? 2. Or go back
from whence I came ? 3. Or die upon the place ?
To the first I answered, I had been a true Man
a long Season, and therefore, it could not be
expected that I now should cast in my Lot with
Thieves. Then they demanded what I would say
to the second. So I told them that the Place from
whence I came, had I not found Incommodity
there, I had not forsaken it at all, but finding it
altogether unsuitable to me, and very unprofitable
for me, I forsook it for this Way. Then they
asked me what I said to the third. And I told
them, my Life cost more dear far, than that I
should lightly give it away. Besides, you have
nothing to do thus to put things to my Choice ;
wherefore at your Peril be it, if you meddle. Then
these three, to wit, *Wildhead*, *Inconsiderate*, and
Pragmatick, drew upon me, and I also drew upon
them.

So we fell to it, one against three, for the space
of above three Hours. They have left upon me,

as you see, some of the Marks of their Valour, and
have also carried away with them some of mine.
They are but just now gone. I suppose they might,
as the saying is, hear your Horse dash, and so they
betook them to flight.

Great-heart. But here was great Odds, three
against one.

Valiant-for-truth. 'Tis true, but *little* and *more,*
are nothing to him that has the Truth on his side.
*Though an Host should encamp against me, said one,
my Heart shall not fear. Tho' War should rise
against me, in this will I be Confident,* &c. Besides,
said he, I have read in some Records, that one man
has fought an army ; and how many did *Sampson*
slay with the Jaw-Bone of an Ass ?

Great-heart. Then said the Guide, *Why did you
not cry out, that some might a come in for your
Succour ?*

Valiant-for-truth. So I did, to my King, who
I knew could hear, and afford invisible Help, and
that was sufficient for me.

Great-heart. Then said Great-heart *to Mr.*
Valiant-for-truth, *Thou hast worthily behaved
thyself ; let me see thy Sword.* So he shewed it
him.

When he had taken it in his Hand, and looked
thereon a while, he said, Ha ! *It is a right* Jerusalem
Blade.

Valiant-for-truth. It is so. Let a man have one
of *these Blades,* with a Hand to wield it, and skill
to use it, and he may venture upon an Angel with
it. He need not fear its holding, if he can but tell
how to lay on. Its Edges will never blunt. It
will cut *Flesh,* and *Bones,* and *Soul,* and *Spirit,* and
all.

Great-heart. But you fought a great while, *I wonder you was not weary?*

Valiant-for-truth. I fought till my Sword did cleave to my Hand; and when they were joined together, as if a Sword grew out of my Arm, and when the Blood run thorow my Fingers, then I fought with most Courage.

Great-heart. Thou hast done well. Thou hast resisted unto Blood, striving against Sin. Thou shalt abide by us, come in, and go out with us; for we are thy Companions.

Then they took him and washed his Wounds, and gave him of what they had, to refresh him, and so they went on together. Now as they went on, because Mr. *Great-heart* was delighted in him (for he loved one greatly that he found to be a man of his Hands) and because there was with his Company them that was feeble and weak, therefore he questioned with him about many things; as first, *what Country-man he was?*

Valiant-for-truth. I am of *Dark-land*, for there I was born, and there my Father and Mother are still.

Great-heart. Dark-land, said the Guide, *Doth not that lye upon the same Coast with the City of* Destruction?

Valiant-for-truth. Yes it doth. Now that which caused me to come on Pilgrimage, was this. We had one Mr. *Tell-true* came into our parts, and he told it about what *Christian* had done, that went from the City of *Destruction.* Namely, how he had forsaken his *Wife* and *Children*, and had betaken himself to a *Pilgrim's* Life. It was also confidently reported how he had killed a *Serpent* that did come out to resist him in his Journey, and how he got thorow to whither he intended. It was also told what Welcome he had at all his Lord's Lodgings; specially when he came to the Gates of the Celestial City. For there, said the man, He was received with sound of Trumpet by a company of shining ones. He told it also, how all the Bells in the City did ring for Joy at his Reception, and what Golden Garments he was cloathed with; with many other things that now I shall forbear to relate. In a word, that man so told the Story of *Christian* and his Travels, that my Heart fell into a burning haste to be gone after him, nor could Father or Mother stay me, so I got from them, and am come thus far on my Way.

Great-heart. *You came in at the Gate, did you not ?*

Valiant-for-truth. Yes, yes. For the same man also told us, that all would be nothing, if we did not begin to enter this way at the Gate.

Great-heart. *Look you,* said the Guide, *to* Christiana, *The Pilgrimage of your Husband, and what he has gotten thereby, is spread abroad far and near.*

Valiant-for-truth. Why, is this *Christian's* Wife?

Great-heart. *Yes, that it is ; and these are also her four Sons.*

Valiant. What ! and going on Pilgrimage too ?

Great-heart. *Yes verily, they are following after.*

Valiant. It glads me at Heart ! Good man ! How joyful will he be, when he shall see them that would not go with him, yet to enter after him in at the Gates into the City ?

Great-heart. *Without doubt it will be a Comfort to him. For next to the Joy of seeing himself there, it will be a Joy to meet there his Wife and his Children.*

Valiant. But now you are upon that, pray let me hear your Opinion about it. Some make a Question whether we shall know one another when we are there ?

Great-heart. *Do they think they shall know themselves then ? Or that they shall rejoyce to see themselves in that Bliss ? And if they think they shall know and do these, why not know others, and rejoyce in their Welfare also ?*

Again, since Relations are our second self, tho' that State will be dissolved there, yet why may it not be rationally concluded that we shall be more glad to see them there, than to see they are wanting ?

Valiant. Well, I perceive whereabouts you are as to this. Have you any more things to ask me about my beginning to come on Pilgrimage ?

Great-heart. *Yes. Was your Father and Mother willing that you should become a Pilgrim ?*

Valiant. Oh, no. They used all means imaginable to perswade me to stay at Home.

Great-heart. *Why, what could they say against it ?*

Valiant. They said it was an idle Life, and if I myself were not inclined to Sloth and Laziness, I would never countenance a Pilgrim's Condition

Great-heart. *And what did they say else ?*

Valiant. Why, They told me, That it was a dangerous Way ; yea the most dangerous Way in the World, said they, is that which the Pilgrims go.

Great-heart. *Did they show wherein this way is so dangerous ?*

Valiant. Yes, and that in many Particulars.

Great-heart. *Name some of them.*

Valiant. They told me of the Slough of *Dispond,* where *Christian* was well-nigh smothered. They told me that there were Archers standing ready in

Beelzebub-Castle, to shoot them that should knock at the *Wicket*-Gate for Entrance. They told me also of the Wood and dark Mountains, of the Hill *Difficulty*, of the Lions, and also of the three Giants, *Bloody-Man*, *Maul*, and *Slay-good*. They said moreover, that there was a foul *Fiend* haunted the Valley of *Humiliation*, and that *Christian* was, by him, almost bereft of Life. Besides, said they, you must go over the *Valley of the Shadow of Death*, where the *Hobgoblins* are, where the Light is Darkness, where the way is full of Snares, Pits, Traps, and Gins. They told me also of *Giant-Despair*, of *Doubting-Castle*, and of the *Ruins* that the Pilgrims met with there. Further, they said, I must go over the enchanted Ground, which was dangerous. And that after all this, I should find a River, over which I should find no Bridge, and that that River did lie betwixt me and the Coelestial Country.

Great-heart. And was this all?

Valiant. No, they also told me that this way was full of *Deceivers*, and of Persons that laid await there, to turn good men out of the Path.

Great-heart. But how did they make that out?

Valiant. They told me that Mr. *Worldly-wise-Man* did there lie in wait to deceive. They also said that there was *Formality* and *Hypocrisy* continually on the Road. They said also that *By-ends*, *Talkative*, or *Demas*, would go near to gather me up; that the Flatterer would catch me in his Net; or that with green-headed *Ignorance* I would presume to go on to the Gate, from whence he always was sent back to the Hole that was in the side of the Hill, and made to go the By-way to Hell.

Great-heart. *I promise you, this was enough to discourage. But did they make an end here?*

Valiant. No, stay. They told me also of many that had tried that way of old, and that had gone a great way therein, to see if they could find something of the Glory there that so many had so much talked of from time to time; and how they came back again, and befooled themselves for setting a foot out of Doors in that Path, to the Satisfaction of all the Country. And they named several that did so, as *Obstinate* and *Pliable*, *Mistrust*, and *Timorous*, *Turn-away*, and old *Atheist*, with several more; who, they said, had, some of them, gone far to see if they could find, but not one of them found so much Advantage by going as amounted *to the weight of a Feather*.

Great-heart. *Said they any thing more to discourage you?*

Valiant. Yes, they told me of one Mr. *Fearing*, who was a Pilgrim, and how *he* found this way so solitary, that he never had comfortable Hour therein; also that Mr. *Dispondency* had like to been starved therein; yea, and also, which I had almost forgot, that *Christian* himself, about whom there has been such a Noise, after all his Ventures for a Coelestial Crown, was certainly drowned in the black River, and never went foot further, however it was smothered up.

Great-heart. *And did none of these things discourage you?*

Valiant. No. They seemed but as so many Nothings to me.

Great-heart. *How came that about?*

Valiant. Why, I still believed what Mr. *Telltrue* had said; and that carried me beyond them all.

Great-heart. Then this was your Victory, even your Faith.

Valiant. It was so. I believed and therefore came out, got into the Way, fought all that set themselves against me, and by believing am come to this Place.

The Pilgrim's Progress, Part II.   1678.

DANIEL DEFOE

1661 ?–1731

SIEGE OF THE OLD TREE

THEY observed also, that this noise of the
Indians went farther and farther off, so that they
were satisfied the Indians fled away, except on one
side, where they heard a doleful groaning and
howling, and where it continued a good while,
which they supposed was from some or other of
them being wounded, and howling by reason of
their wounds ; or killed, and others howling over
them ; but our men had enough of making dis-
coveries ; so they did not trouble themselves to
look farther, but resolved to take this opportunity
to retreat. But the worst of their adventure was
to come ; for as they came back they passed by
a prodigious great trunk of an old tree ; what tree
it was they said they did not know, but it stood
like an old decayed oak in a park, where the keepers
in England take a *stand*, as they call it, to shoot
a deer ; and it stood just under the steep side of
a great rock or hill, that our people could not see
what was beyond it.

As they came by this tree, they were of a sudden
shot at from the top of the tree, with seven arrows
and three lances, which, to our great grief, killed
two of our men, and wounded three more. This
was the more surprising, because, being without
any defence, and so near the trees, they expected

more lances and arrows every moment; nor would
flying do them any service, the Indians being, as
appeared, very good marksmen. In this extremity
they had happily this presence of mind, viz. to run
close to the tree, and stand, as it were, under it;
so that those above could not come at, or see them,
to throw their lances at them. This succeeded,
and gave them time to consider what to do: they
knew their enemies and murtherers were above,
for they heard them talk, and those above knew
those were below; but they below were obliged to
keep close for fear of their lances from above. At
length, one of our men looking a little more strictly
than the rest, thought he saw the head of one of the
Indians, just over a dead limb of the tree, which, it
seems, the creature sat upon. One man immediately fired, and levelled his piece so true, that the
shot went through the fellow's head, and down he
fell out of the tree immediately, and came upon
the ground with such force, with the height of his
fall, that if he had not been killed with the shot, he
would certainly have been killed with dashing his
body against the ground.

This so frightened themselves, that besides the
howling noise they made in the tree, our men
heard a strange clutter of them in the body of the
tree, from whence they concluded they had made
the tree hollow, and were got to hide themselves
there. Now, had this been the case, they were
secure enough from our men, for it was impossible
any of our men could get up the tree on the outside,
there being no branches to climb by; and, to
shoot at the tree, that they tried several times to
no purpose, for the tree was so thick that no shot
would enter it. They made no doubt however,

but that they had their enemies in a trap, and that a small siege would either bring them down tree and all, or starve them out; so they resolved to keep their post, and send to us for help. Accordingly two of them came away to us for more hands, and particularly desired, that some of our carpenters might come with tools, to help to cut down the tree, or at least to cut down other wood, and set fire to it; and that, they concluded, would not fail to bring them out.

Accordingly our men went like a little army, and with mighty preparations for an enterprise, the like of which has scarce been ever heard, to form the siege of a great tree. However, when they came there, they found the task difficult enough, for the old trunk was indeed a very great one, and very tall, being at least two-and-twenty foot high, with seven old limbs standing out every way on the top, but decayed, and very few leaves, if any, left on it.

William the Quaker, whose curiosity led him to go among the rest, proposed, that they should make a ladder, and get up upon the top, and then throw wildfire into the tree, and smoke them out. Others proposed going back, and getting a great gun out of the ship, which should split the tree in pieces with the iron bullets; others, that they should cut down a great deal of wood and pile it up round the tree, and set it on fire, and to burn the tree, and the Indians in it.

These consultations took up our people no less than two or three days, in all which time they heard nothing of the supposed garrison within this wooden castle, nor any noise within. William's project was first gone about, and a large strong

ladder was made, to scale this wooden tower; and
in two or three hours' time, it would have been
ready to mount; when, on a sudden, they heard
the noise of the Indians in the body of the tree
again, and a little after, several of them appeared
in the top of the tree, and threw some lances down
at our men; one of which struck one of our seamen
a-top of the shoulder, and gave him such a desperate
wound, that the surgeons not only had a great deal
of difficulty to cure him, but the poor man endured
such horrible tortures, that we all said they had
better have killed him outright. However, he
was cured at last, though he never recovered the
perfect use of his arm, the lance having cut some
of the tendons on the top of the arm, near the
shoulder, which, as I suppose, performed the office
of motion to the limb before; so that the poor man
was a cripple all the days of his life. But to return
to the desperate rogues in the tree: our men shot
at them, but did not find they had hit them, or any
of them; but as soon as ever they shot at them,
they could hear them huddle down into the trunk
of the tree again, and there to be sure they were safe.

Well, however, it was this which put by the
project of William's ladder; for when it was done,
who would venture up among such a troop of bold
creatures as were there, and who, they supposed,
were desperate by their circumstances? And as
but one man at a time could go up, they began to
think that it would not do; and indeed I was of
the opinion (for about this time I was come to
their assistance) that the going up the ladder would
not do, unless it was thus, that a man should, as it
were, run just up to the top, and throw some fireworks into the tree, and so come down again; and

this we did two or three times, but found no effect
of it. At last, one of our gunners made a stinkpot, as we called it, being a composition which only
smokes, but does not flame or burn ; but withal the
smoke of it is so thick, and the smell of it so intoler-
ably nauseous, that it is not to be suffered. This
he threw into the tree himself, and we waited for
the effect of it, but heard or saw nothing all that
night, or the next day ; so we concluded the men
within were all smothered : when, on a sudden,
the next night, we heard them upon the top of the
tree again, shouting and hallooing like madmen.

We concluded, as anybody would, that this was
to call for help, and we resolved to continue our
siege ; for we were all enraged to see ourselves so
baulked by a few wild people whom we thought we
had safe in our clutches ; and indeed never was
there so many concurring circumstances to delude
men, in any case we had met with. We resolved
however to try another stinkpot the next night, and
our engineer and gunner had got it ready, when
hearing a noise of the enemy, on the top of the tree,
and in the body of the tree, I was not willing to let
the gunner go up the ladder, which, I said, would
be but to be certain of being murthered. However,
he found a medium for it, and that was to go up
a few steps, and with a long pole in his hand, to
throw it in upon the top of the tree, the ladder
being standing all this while against the top of the
tree ; but when the gunner, with his machine at
the top of his pole, came to the tree with three
other men to help him, behold the ladder was
gone.

This perfectly confounded us, and we now concluded the Indians in the tree had by this piece of

negligence taken the opportunity, and come all down the ladder, made their escape, and had carried away the ladder with them. I laughed most heartily at my friend William, who, as I said, had the direction of the siege, and had set up a ladder, for the garrison, as we called them, to get down upon, and run away. But when daylight came, we were all set to rights again; for there stood our ladder, hauled up on the top of the tree, with about half of it in the hollow of the tree, and the other half upright in the air. Then we began to laugh at the Indians for fools, that they could not as well have found their way down by the ladder, and have made their escape, as to have pulled it up by main strength into the tree.

We then resolved upon fire, and so to put an end to the work at once, and burn the tree and its inhabitants together; and accordingly we went to work to cut wood, and in a few hours' time we got enough, as we thought, together; and piling it up round the bottom of the tree, we set it on fire: so waiting at a distance, to see when the gentlemen's quarters being too hot for them would come flying out at the top. But we were quite confounded, when, on a sudden, we found the fire all put out by a great quantity of water thrown upon it. We then thought the devil must be in them, to be sure. Says William, This is certainly the cunningest piece of Indian engineering that ever was heard of, and there can be but one thing more to guess at, besides witchcraft and dealing with the devil, which I believe not one word of, says he; and that must be, that this is an artificial tree, or a natural tree artificially made hollow down into the earth, through root and all; and that these creatures

have an artificial cavity underneath it, quite into
the hill, or a way to go through, and under the hill,
to some other place ; and where that other place is,
we know not ; but if it be not our own fault, I'll
find the place, and follow them into it, before I am
two days older. He then called the carpenters to
know of them, if they had any large saws that
would cut through the body, and they told him
they had not any saws that were long enough, nor
could men work into such a monstrous old stump
in a great while ; but that they would go to work
with it with their axes, and undertake to cut it
down in two days, and stock up the root of it in
two more. But William was for another way,
which proved much better than all this ; for he
was for silent work, that, if possible, he might catch
some of the fellows in it ; so he sets twelve men to
it with large augers, to bore great holes into the side
of the tree, to go almost through, but not quite
through ; which holes were bored without noise,
and when they were done, he filled them all with
gunpowder, stopping strong plugs bolted crossways into the holes, and then boring a slanting hole
of a less size down into the greater hole all which
were filled with powder, and at once blown up.
When they took fire, they made such a noise, and
tore and split the tree in so many places, and in
such a manner, that we could see plainly another
another blast would demolish it, and so it did.
Thus at the second time we could at two or three
places put our hands into them, and discovered
the cheat, namely, that there was a cave or hole
dug into the earth, from or through the bottom of
the hollow, and that it had communication with
another cave further in, where we heard the voices

of several of the wild folks calling and talking to one another.

When we came thus far we had a great mind to get at them, and William desired, that three men might be given him with hand-grenadoes, and he promised to go down first, and boldly he did so; for William, give him his due, had the heart of a lion.

They had pistols in their hands, and swords by their sides; but, as they had taught the Indians before, by their stinkpots, the Indians returned them in their own kind, for they made such a smoke come up out of the entrance into the cave or hollow, that William and his three men, were glad to come running out of the cave, and out of the tree too, for mere want of breath, and indeed they were almost stifled.

Never was a fortification so well defended, or assailants so many ways defeated; we were now for giving it over, and particularly I called William, and told him, I could not but laugh to see us spinning out our time here for nothing; that I could not imagine what we were doing, that it was certain the rogues that were in it were cunning to the last degree, and it would vex anybody to be so baulked by a few naked ignorant fellows; but still it was not worth our while to push it any further, nor was there anything that I knew of to be got by the conquest when it was made, so that I thought it high time to give it over.

William acknowledged that what I said was just, and that there was nothing but our curiosity to be gratified in this attempt; and though, as he said, he was very desirous to have searched into the thing, yet he would not insist upon it, so we resolved to quit it, and come away, which we did

However, William said, before we went, he would
have this satisfaction of them, viz. that he burnt
down the tree and stopped up the entrance into
the cave. While he was doing this, the gunner
told him he would have one satisfaction of the
rogues, and this was, that he would make a mine
of it, and see which way it had vent. Upon this
he fetches two barrels of powder out of the ships,
and placed them in the inside of the hollow cave,
as far in as he durst go to carry them, and then
filling up the mouth of the cave where the tree
stood, and ramming it sufficiently hard, leaving
only a pipe or touchhole, he gave fire to it, and
stood at a distance, to see which way it would
operate, when, on the sudden, he found the force
of the powder burst its way out among some bushes
on the other side the little hill I mentioned, and
that it came roaring out there as out of the mouth
of a cannon ; immediately running thither we saw
the effects of the powder.

First, we saw that there was the other mouth of
the cave, which the powder had so torn and opened,
that the loose earth was so fallen in again, that
nothing of shape could be discerned ; but there we
saw what was become of the garrison of Indians too,
who had given us all this trouble ; for some of
them had no arms, some no legs, some no head,
some lay half buried in the rubbish of the mine, that
is to say, in the loose earth that fell in ; and, in
short, there was a miserable havoc made of them
all, for we had good reason to believe, not one of
them that were in the inside could escape, but
rather were shot out of the mouth of the cave
like a bullet out of a gun.

Captain Singleton. 1720.

DURING THE GREAT PLAGUE

MUCH about the same time I walked out into the fields towards Bow; for I had a great mind to see how things were managed in the river and among the ships; and as I had some concern in shipping, I had a notion that it had been one of the best ways of securing one's self from the infection to have retired into a ship; and musing how to satisfy my curiosity in that point, I turned away over the fields from Bow to Bromley, and down to Black-wall to the stairs, which are there for landing or taking water.

Here I saw a poor man walking on the bank, or sea-wall, as they call it, by himself. I walked a while also about, seeing the houses all shut up; at last I fell into some talk, at a distance, with this poor man; first I asked him how people did thereabouts. 'Alas, sir!' says he, 'almost all desolate; all dead or sick. Here are very few families in this part, or in that village,' pointing at Poplar, 'where half of them are not dead already, and the rest sick.' Then he pointed to one house. 'There they are all dead,' said he, 'and the house stands open; nobody dares go into it. A poor thief', says he, 'ventured in to steal something, but he paid dear for his theft, for he was carried to the churchyard too last night.' Then he pointed to several other houses. 'There', says he, 'they are all dead, the man and his wife, and five children. There', says he, 'they are shut up; you see a watchman at the door'; and so of other houses. 'Why,' says I, 'what do you here all alone?' 'Why,' says he, 'I am a poor, desolate man; it has pleased God I am not yet visited, though my family is, and one of my children dead.' ' How do you mean, then,' said I, ' that you are not visited ?' 'Why,' says he, ' that's my house,' pointing to a very little, low-boarded house, ' and there my poor wife and two children live,' said he, ' if they may be said to live, for my wife and one of the children are visited, but I do not come at them.' And with that word I saw the tears run very plentifully down his face ; and so they did down mine too, I assure you.

But said I, 'Why do you not come at them ? How can you abandon your own flesh and blood ?' ' Oh, sir,' says he, ' the Lord forbid ! I do not abandon them ; I work for them as much as I am able ; and, blessed be the Lord, I keep them from want ;' and with that I observed he lifted up his eyes to heaven, with a countenance that presently told me I had happened on a man that was no hypocrite, but a serious, religious, good man, and his ejaculation was an expression of thankfulness that, in such a condition as he was in, he should be able to say his family did not want. ' Well,' says I, ' honest man, that is a great mercy as things go now with the poor. But how do you live, then, and how are you kept from the dreadful calamity that is now upon us all ?' ' Why, sir,' says he, ' I am a waterman, and there's my boat,' says he, ' and the boat serves me for a house. I work in it in the day, and I sleep in it in the night ; and what I get I lay down upon that stone,' says he, showing me a broad stone on the other side of the street, a good way from his house ; 'and then', says he, ' I halloo, and call to them till I make them hear ; and they come and fetch it.'

' Well, friend,' says I, ' but how can you get any money as a waterman ? Does anybody go by water these times ? ' ' Yes, sir,' says he, ' in the way I am employed there does. Do you see there,' says he, ' five ships lie at anchor,' pointing down the river a good way below the town, ' and do you see,' says he, ' eight or ten ships lie at the chain there, and at anchor yonder,' pointing above the town. ' All those ships have families on board, of their merchants and owners, and such-like, who have locked themselves up and live on board, close shut in, for fear of the infection ; and I tend on them to fetch things for them, carry letters, and do what is absolutely necessary, that they may not be obliged to come on shore ; and every night I fasten my boat on board one of the ship's boats, and there I sleep by myself, and, blessed be God, I am preserved hitherto.'

' Well,' said I, ' friend, but will they let you come on board after you have been on shore here, when this is such a terrible place, and so infected as it is ? '

' Why, as to that,' said he, ' I very seldom go up the ship-side, but deliver what I bring to their boat, or lie by the side, and they hoist it on board. If I did, I think they are in no danger from me, for I never go into any house on shore, or touch anybody, no, not of my own family ; but I fetch provisions for them.'

' Nay,' says I, ' but that may be worse, for you must have those provisions of somebody or other ; and since all this part of the town is so infected, it is dangerous so much as to speak with anybody, for this village,' said I, ' is, as it were, the beginning of London, though it be at some distance from it.'

'That is true,' added he; 'but you do not understand me right; I do not buy provisions for them here. I row up to Greenwich and buy fresh meat there, and sometimes I row down the river to Woolwich and buy there; then I go to single farm-houses on the Kentish side, where I am known, and buy fowls and eggs and butter, and bring to the ships, as they direct me, sometimes one, sometimes the other. I seldom come on shore here, and I came now only to call to my wife and hear how my little family do, and give them a little money, which I received last night.'

'Poor man!' said I; 'and how much hast thou gotten for them?'

'I have gotten four shillings,' said he, 'which is a great sum, as things go now with poor men; but they have given me a bag of bread too, and a salt fish and some flesh; so all helps out.'

'Well,' said I, 'and have you given it them yet?'

'No,' said he; 'but I have called, and my wife has answered that she cannot come out yet, but in half-an-hour she hopes to come, and I am waiting for her. Poor woman!' says he, 'she is brought sadly down. She has a swelling, and it is broke, and I hope she will recover; but I fear the child will die, but it is the Lord——'

Here he stopped, and wept very much.

'Well, honest friend,' said I, 'thou hast a sure Comforter, if thou hast brought thyself to be resigned to the will of God; He is dealing with us all in judgement.'

'Oh, sir!' says he, 'it is infinite mercy if any of us are spared, and who am I to repine!'

'Sayest thou so?' said I, 'and how much less is

my faith than thine ? '   And here my heart smote
me, suggesting how much better this poor man's
foundation was on which he stayed in the danger
than mine ; that he had nowhere to fly ; that he
had a family to bind him to attendance, which
I had not ; and mine was mere presumption, his
a true dependence, and a courage resting on God ;
and yet that he used all possible caution for his
safety.

I turned a little way from the man while these
thoughts engaged me, for, indeed, I could no more
refrain from tears than he.

At length, after some further talk, the poor
woman opened the door and called, ' Robert,
Robert.' He answered, and bid her stay a few
moments and he would come ; so he ran down the
common stairs to his boat and fetched up a sack,
in which was the provisions he had brought from
the ships ; and when he returned he hallooed again.
Then he went to the great stone which he showed
me and emptied the sack, and laid all out, everything by themselves, and then retired ; and his
wife came with a little boy to fetch them away,
and he called and said such a captain had sent such
a thing, and such a captain such a thing, and at the
end adds, ' God has sent it all ; give thanks to Him.'
When the poor woman had taken up all, she was so
weak she could not carry it at once in, though the
weight was not much neither ; so she left the biscuit,
which was in a little bag, and left a little boy to
watch it till she came again.

Well, but ', says I to him, ' did you leave her
the four shillings too, which you said was your
week's pay ? '

' Yes, yes,' says he ; ' you shall hear her own it '

So he calls again, ' Rachel, Rachel,' which, it seems, was her name, ' did you take up the money ?' ' Yes,' said she. ' How much was it ?' said he. ' Four shillings and a groat,' said she. ' Well, well,' says he, ' the Lord keep you all ; ' and so he turned to go away.

As I could not refrain contributing tears to this man's story, so neither could I refrain my charity for his assistance ; so I called him, ' Hark thee, friend,' said I, ' come hither, for I believe thou art in health, that I may venture thee ; ' so I pulled out my hand, which was in my pocket before, ' Here,' says I, ' go and call thy Rachel once more, and give her a little more comfort from me. God will never forsake a family that trust in Him as thou dost.' So I gave him four other shillings, and bade him go lay them on the stone and call his wife.

I have not words to express the poor man's thankfulness, neither could he express it himself but by tears running down his face. He called his wife, and told her God had moved the heart of a stranger, upon hearing their condition, to give them all that money, and a great deal more such as that he said to her. The woman, too, made signs of the like thankfulness, as well to Heaven as to me, and joyfully picked it up ; and I parted with no money all that year that I thought better bestowed.

A Journal of the Plague Year. 1722.

SIR JOHN VANBRUGH

1664–1726

WHITEHALL

YOUNG FASHION, LORY, *and* WATERMAN.

Young Fashion. Come, pay the waterman, and take the portmantle.

Lory. Faith, sir, I think the waterman had as good take the portmantle, and pay himself.

Young Fashion. Why, sure there's something left in't.

Lory. But a solitary old waistcoat, upon my honour, sir.

Young Fashion. Why, what's become of the blue coat, sirrah?

Lory. Sir, 'twas eaten at Gravesend; the reckoning came to thirty shillings, and your privy purse was worth but two half-crowns.

Young Fashion. 'Tis very well.

Waterman. Pray, master, will you please to dispatch me?

Young Fashion. Ay, here, a—Canst thou change me a guinea?

Lory [*aside*]. Good.

Waterman. Change a guinea, master! Ha, ha, your honour's pleas'd to compliment.

Young Fashion. I'gad I don't know how I shall pay thee then, for I have nothing but gold about me.

Lory [*aside*]. Hum, hum.

Young Fashion. What dost thou expect, friend ?

Waterman. Why, master, so far against wind and tide, is richly worth half a piece.

Young Fashion. Why, faith, I think thou art a good consciable fellow. I'gad, I begin to have so good an opinion of thy honesty, I care not if I leave my portmantle with thee, till I send thee thy money.

Waterman. Ha! God bless your honour; I should be as willing to trust you, master, but that you are, as a man may say, a stranger to me, and these are nimble times; there are a great many sharpers stirring. [*Taking up the portmantle.*] Well, master, when your worship sends the money, your portmantle shall be forthcoming; my name's Tugg, my wife keeps a brandy-shop in Drab-Alley at Wapping.

Young Fashion. Very well; I'll send for 't to-morrow. [*Exit* Waterman.

Lory. So——Now, sir, I hope you'll own yourself a happy man, you have outliv'd all your cares.

Young Fashion. How so, sir ?

Lory. Why, you have nothing left to take care of.

Young Fashion. Yes, sirrah, I have myself and you to take care of still.

Lory. Sir, if you could but prevail with somebody else to do that for you, I fancy we might both fare the better for 't.

Young Fashion. Why, if thou canst tell me where to apply myself, I have at present so little money, and so much humility about me, I don't know but I may follow a fool's advice.

Lory. Why then, sir, your fool advises you to

lay aside all animosity, and apply to Sir Novelty, your elder brother.

Young Fashion. Damn my elder brother.

Lory. With all my heart; but get him to redeem your annuity, however.

Young Fashion. My annuity! 'Sdeath, he's such a dog, he would not give his powder-puff to redeem my soul.

Lory. Look you, sir, you must wheedle him, or you must starve.

Young Fashion. Look you, sir, I will neither wheedle him, nor starve.

Lory. Why? what will you do then?

Young Fashion. I'll go into the army.

Lory. You can't take the oaths; you are a Jacobite.

Young Fashion. Thou may'st as well say I can't take orders because I'm an atheist.

Lory. Sir, I ask your pardon; I find I did not know the strength of your conscience, so well as I did the weakness of your purse.

Young Fashion. Methinks, sir, a person of your experience should have known, that the strength of the conscience proceeds from the weakness of the purse.

Lory. Sir, I am very glad to find you have a conscience able to take care of us, let it proceed from what it will; but I desire you'll please to consider, that the army alone will be but a scanty maintenance for a person of your generosity (at least as rents now are paid); I shall see you stand in damnable need of some auxiliary guineas for your *menus plaisirs;* I will therefore turn fool once more for your service, and advise you to go directly to your brother.

Young Fashion. Art thou then so impregnable a blockhead, to believe he'll help me with a farthing?

Lory. Not if you treat him *de haut en bas*, as you use to do.

Young Fashion. Why, how would'st have me treat him?

Lory. Like a trout, tickle him.

Young Fashion. I can't flatter——

Lory. Can you starve?

Young Fashion. Yes——

Lory. I can't; Goodbye t'ye, sir—— [*Going.*

Young Fashion. Stay, thou wilt distract me. What would'st thou have me to say to him?

Lory. Say nothing to him, apply yourself to his favourites; speak to his periwig, his cravat, his feather, his snuff-box, and when you are well with them——desire him to lend you a thousand pounds. I'll engage you prosper.

Young Fashion. 'Sdeath and Furies! Why was that coxcomb thrust into the world before me? O Fortune—Fortune—thou art a bitch, by Gad——   [*Exeunt.*

                                    The Relapse. 1696.

JONATHAN SWIFT

1667–1745

THE SPIDER AND THE BEE

THINGS were at this crisis, when a material accident fell out. For, upon the highest corner of a large window, there dwelt a certain spider, swollen up to the first magnitude by the destruction of infinite numbers of flies, whose spoils lay scattered before the gates of his palace, like human bones before the cave of some giant. The avenues to his castle were guarded with turnpikes and palisadoes, all after the modern way of fortification. After you had passed several courts, you came to the centre, wherein you might behold the constable himself in his own lodgings, which had windows fronting to each avenue, and ports to sally out, upon all occasions of prey or defence. In this mansion he had for some time dwelt in peace and plenty, without danger to his person, by swallows from above, or to his palace, by brooms from below : when it was the pleasure of fortune to conduct thither a wandering bee, to whose curiosity a broken pane in the glass had discovered itself, and in he went ; where, expatiating a while, he at last happened to alight upon one of the outward walls of the spider's citadel ; which, yielding to the unequal weight, sunk down to the very foundation. Thrice he endeavoured to force his passage, and thrice the centre shook. The spider within, feeling the terrible convulsion, supposed at first that nature was approaching to her final dissolution ; or else, that Beelzebub, with all his legions, was come to revenge the death of many thousands of his subjects, whom this enemy had slain and devoured. However, he at length valiantly resolved to issue forth, and meet his fate. Meanwhile the bee had acquitted himself of his toils, and, posted securely at some distance, was employed in cleansing his wings, and disengaging them from the ragged remnants of the cobweb. By this time the spider was adventured out, when, beholding the chasms, the ruins, and dilapidations of his fortress, he was very near at his wit's end ; he stormed and swore like a madman, and swelled till he was ready to burst. At length, casting his eye upon the bee, and wisely gathering causes from events (for they knew each other by sight) A plague split you, said he ; is it you, with a vengeance, that have made this litter here ? could not you look before you, and be d—d ? do you think I have nothing else to do (in the devil's name) but to mend and repair after you ?—Good words, friend, said the bee, (having now pruned himself, and being disposed to droll), I'll give you my hand and word to come near your kennel no more ; I was never in such a confounded pickle since I was born.—Sirrah, replied the spider, if it were not for breaking an old custom in our family, never to stir abroad against an enemy, I should come and teach you better manners.—I pray, have patience, said the bee, or you will spend your substance, and, for aught I see, you may stand in need of it all towards the repair of your house.— Rogue, rogue, replied the spider, yet, methinks you should have more respect to a person, whom all the world allows to be so much your betters.—

By my troth, said the bee, the comparison will amount to a very good jest; and you will do me a favour to let me know the reasons that all the world is pleased to use in so hopeful a dispute. At this the spider, having swelled himself into the size and posture of a disputant, began his argument in the true spirit of controversy, with a resolution to be heartily scurrilous and angry, to urge on his own reasons, without the least regard to the answers or objections of his opposite; and fully predetermined in his mind against all conviction.

Not to disparage myself, said he, by the comparison with such a rascal, what art thou but a vagabond without house or home, without stock or inheritance, born to no possession of your own, but a pair of wings and a drone-pipe? Your livelihood is an universal plunder upon nature; a freebooter over fields and gardens; and, for the sake of stealing, will rob a nettle as readily as a violet. Whereas I am a domestic animal, furnished with a native stock within myself. This large castle (to show my improvements in the mathematics) is all built with my own hands, and the materials extracted altogether out of my own person.

I am glad, answered the bee, to hear you grant at least that I am come honestly by my wings and my voice; for then, it seems, I am obliged to Heaven alone for my flights and my music; and Providence would never have bestowed on me two such gifts, without designing them for the noblest ends. I visit indeed all the flowers and blossoms of the field and the garden; but whatever I collect from thence, enriches myself, without the least injury to their beauty, their smell, or their taste. Now, for you and your skill in architecture, and other mathematics, I have little to say : in that building of yours there might, for aught I know, have been labour and method enough ; but, by woful experience for us both, 'tis too plain, the materials are naught ; and I hope you will henceforth take warning, and consider duration and matter, as well as method and art. You boast, indeed, of being obliged to no other creature, but of drawing and spinning out all from yourself ; that is to say, if we may judge of the liquor in the vessel, by what issues out, you possess a good plentiful store of dirt and poison in your breast ; and, though I would by no means lessen or disparage your genuine stock of either, yet, I doubt you are somewhat obliged, for an increase of both, to a little foreign assistance. Your inherent portion of dirt does not fail of acquisitions, by sweepings exhaled from below ; and one insect furnishes you with a share of poison to destroy another. So that, in short, the question comes all to this ; whether is the nobler being of the two, that which, by a lazy contemplation of four inches round, by an overweening pride, which, feeding and engendering on itself, turns all into venom, producing nothing at all, but flybane and a cobweb ; or that which, by a universal range, with long search, much study, true judgement, and distinction of things, brings home honey and wax ?

This dispute was managed with such eagerness, clamour, and warmth, that the two parties of books, in arms below, stood silent a while, waiting in suspense what would be the issue ; which was not long undetermined : for the bee, grown impatient at so much loss of time, fled straight away to a bed of roses, without looking for a reply ; and left the spider, like an orator, collected in himself, and just prepared to burst out.

It happened upon this emergency, that Aesop broke silence first. He had been of late most barbarously treated by a strange effect of the regent's humanity, who had tore off his title-page, sorely defaced one-half of his leaves, and chained him fast among a shelf of moderns. Where, soon discovering how high the quarrel was likely to proceed, he tried all his arts, and turned himself to a thousand forms. At length, in the borrowed shape of an ass, the regent mistook him for a modern ; by which means he had time and opportunity to escape to the ancients, just when the spider and the bee were entering into their contest ; to which he gave his attention with a world of pleasure ; and when it was ended, swore in the loudest key, that in all his life he had never known two cases so parallel and adapt to each other, as that in the window, and this upon the shelves. The disputants, said he, have admirably managed the dispute between them, have taken in the full strength of all that is to be said on both sides, and exhausted the substance of every argument *pro* and *con*. It is but to adjust the reasonings of both to the present quarrel, then to compare and apply the labours and fruits of each, as the bee hath learnedly deduced them, and we shall find the conclusion fall plain and close upon the moderns and us. For, pray, gentlemen, was ever anything so modern as the spider in his air, his turns, and his paradoxes ? He argues in the behalf of you his brethren, and himself, with many boastings of his native stock

and great genius; that he spins and spits wholly
from himself, and scorns to own any obligation
or assistance from without. Then he displays to
you his great skill in architecture, and improvement
in the mathematics. To all this the bee, as an
advocate, retained by us the ancients, thinks fit
to answer; that, if one may judge of the great
genius or inventions of the moderns by what they
have produced, you will hardly have countenance
to bear you out, in boasting of either. Erect your
schemes with as much method and skill as you
please; yet if the materials be nothing but dirt,
spun out of your own entrails (the guts of modern
brains) the edifice will conclude at last in a cobweb;
the duration of which, like that of other spiders'
webs, may be imputed to their being forgotten, or
neglected, or hid in a corner. For anything else
of genuine that the moderns may pretend to,
I cannot recollect; unless it be a large vein of
wrangling and satire, much of a nature and
substance with the spider's poison; which, however they pretend to spit wholly out of themselves,
is improved by the same arts, by feeding upon
the insects and vermin of the age. As for us the
ancients, we are content, with the bee, to pretend
to nothing of our own, beyond our wings and our
voice: that is to say, our flights and our language.
For the rest, whatever we have got, has been by
infinite labour and search, and ranging through
every corner of nature; the difference is, that,
instead of dirt and poison, we have rather chose
to fill our hives with honey and wax; thus
furnishing mankind with the two noblest of
things, which are sweetness and light.

The Battle of the Books. 1704.

GULLIVER AND THE LILLIPUTIANS

I LAY down on the grass, which was very short and soft, where I slept sounder than ever I remember to have done in my life, and, as I reckoned, above nine hours; for when I awaked it was just daylight. I attempted to rise, but was not able to stir; for as I happened to lie on my back, I found my arms and legs were strongly fastened on each side to the ground, and my hair, which was long and thick, tied down in the same manner. I likewise felt several slender ligatures across my body, from my arm-pits to my thighs. I could only look upwards; the sun began to grow hot, and the light offended mine eyes. I heard a confused noise about me, but, in the posture I lay, could see nothing except the sky. In a little time I felt something alive moving on my left leg, which, advancing gently forward over my breast, came almost up to my chin, when, bending mine eyes downwards as much as I could, I perceived it to be a human creature not six inches high, with a bow and arrow in his hands, and a quiver at his back. In the meantime, I felt at least forty more of the same kind (as I conjectured) following the first. I was in the utmost astonishment, and roared so loud, that they all ran back in a fright; and some of them, as I was afterwards told, were hurt with the falls they got by leaping from my sides upon the ground. However, they soon returned; and one of them, who ventured so far as to get a full sight of my face, lifting up his hands and eyes by way of admiration, cried out, in a shrill but distinct voice, *Hekinah degul!* the

others repeated the same words several times;
but I then knew not what they meant. I lay all
this while, as the reader may believe, in great
uneasiness; at length, struggling to get loose,
I had the fortune to break the strings, and wrench
out the pegs that fastened my left arm to the
ground; for, by lifting it up to my face, I discovered
the methods they had taken to bind me, and, at
the same time, with a violent pull, which gave me
excessive pain, I a little loosened the strings that
tied down my hair on the left side, so that I was
just able to turn my head about two inches.
But the creatures ran off a second time before
I could seize them; whereupon there was a great
shout in a very shrill accent, and after it ceased,
I heard one of them cry aloud, *Tolgo phonac*;
when in an instant I felt above an hundred arrows
discharged on my left hand, which pricked me
like so many needles; and, besides, they shot
another flight into the air, as we do bombs in
Europe, whereof many, I suppose, fell on my
body (though I felt them not) and some on my
face, which I immediately covered with my left
hand. When this shower of arrows was over,
I fell a-groaning with grief and pain; and then,
striving again to get loose, they discharged another
volley larger than the first, and some of them
attempted with spears to stick me in the sides,
but, by good luck, I had on me a buff jerkin, which
they could not pierce. I thought it the most
prudent method to lie still; and my design was
to continue so till night, when, my left hand being
already loose, I could easily free myself : and as
for the inhabitants, I had reason to believe I might
be a match for the greatest armies they could bring

against me, if they were all of the same size with
him that I saw. But fortune disposed otherwise
of me. When the people observed I was quiet,
they discharged no more arrows ; but by the noise
I heard, I knew their numbers increased ; and
about four yards from me, over against my right
ear, I heard a knocking for above an hour, like
that of people at work, when, turning my head
that way, as well as the pegs and strings would
permit me, I saw a stage erected about a foot and
a half from the ground, capable of holding four
of the inhabitants, with two or three ladders to
mount it : from whence one of them, who seemed
to be a person of quality, made me a long speech,
whereof I understood not one syllable. But I
should have mentioned, that before the principal
person began his oration, he cried out three times,
Langro dehul san (these words and the former
were afterwards repeated and explained to me).
Whereupon immediately about fifty of the inhabitants came and cut the strings that fastened the
left side of my head, which gave me the liberty of
turning it to the right, and of observing the person
and gesture of him that was to speak. He appeared
to be of a middle age, and taller than any of the
other three who attended him, whereof one was
a page that held up his train, and seemed to be
somewhat longer than my middle finger ; the other
two stood one on each side to support him. He
acted every part of an orator, and I could observe
many periods of threatenings, and others of
promises, pity, and kindness. I answered in
a few words, but in the most submissive manner,
lifting up my left hand and both mine eyes to the
sun, as calling him for a witness ; and, being almost

famished with hunger, having not eaten a morsel for some hours before I left the ship, I found the demands of nature so strong upon me, that I could not forbear showing my impatience (perhaps against the strict rules of decency) by putting my finger frequently on my mouth, to signify that I wanted food. The *Hurgo* (for so they call a great lord, as I afterwards learnt) understood me very well. He descended from the stage, and commanded that several ladders should be applied to my sides, on which above an hundred of the inhabitants mounted, and walked towards my mouth, laden with baskets full of meat, which had been provided and sent thither by the King's orders, upon the first intelligence he received of me. I observed there was the flesh of several animals, but could not distinguish them by the taste. There were shoulders, legs, and loins, shaped like those of mutton, and very well dressed, but smaller than the wings of a lark. I ate them by two or three at a mouthful, and took three loaves at a time, about the bigness of musket bullets. They supplied me as they could, showing a thousand marks of wonder and astonishment at my bulk and appetite. I then made another sign that I wanted drink. They found by my eating that a small quantity would not suffice me ; and, being a most ingenious people, they slung up with great dexterity one of their largest hogsheads, then rolled it towards my hand, and beat out the top ; I drank it off at a draught, which I might well do, for it did not hold half a pint, and tasted like a small wine of Burgundy, but much more delicious. They brought me a second hogshead, which I drank in the same manner, and made signs for more ; but they had none to give me. When I had performed these wonders, they shouted for joy, and danced upon my breast, repeating several times, as they did at first, *Hekinah degul*. They made me a sign that I should throw down the two hogsheads, but first warning the people below to stand out of the way, crying aloud, *Borach mivola*; and when they saw the vessels in the air, there was a universal shout of *Hekinah degul*. I confess, I was often tempted, while they were passing backwards and forwards on my body, to seize forty or fifty of the first that came in my reach, and dash them against the ground. But the remembrance of what I had felt, which probably might not be the worst they could do, and the promise of honour I made them, for so I interpreted my submissive behaviour, soon drove out these imaginations. Besides, I now considered myself as bound by the laws of hospitality to a people who had treated me with so much expense and magnificence. However, in my thoughts I could not sufficiently wonder at the intrepidity of these diminutive mortals, who durst venture to mount and walk upon my body, while one of my hands was at liberty, without trembling at the very sight of so prodigious a creature as I must appear to them. After some time, when they observed that I made no more demands for meat, there appeared before me a person of high rank from his Imperial Majesty. His Excellency, having mounted on the small of my right leg, advanced forwards up to my face, with about a dozen of his retinue And producing his credentials under the signet royal, which he applied close to mine eyes, spoke about ten minutes without any signs of anger, but with a kind of determinate resolution, often pointing forwards, which, as I afterwards found, was towards the capital city, about half a mile distant, whither it was agreed by his Majesty in Council that I must be conveyed. I answered in few words, but to no purpose, and made a sign with my hand that was loose, putting it to the other (but over his Excellency's head, for fear of hurting him or his train) and then to my own head and body, to signify that I desired my liberty. It appeared that he understood me well enough, for he shook his head by way of disapprobation, and held his hand in a posture to show that I must be carried as a prisoner. However, he made other signs to let me understand that I should have meat and drink enough, and very good treatment. Whereupon I once more thought of attempting to break my bonds ; but again, when I felt the smart of their arrows upon my face and hands, which were all in blisters, and many of the darts still sticking in them, and observing likewise that the number of my enemies increased, I gave tokens to let them know that they might do with me what they pleased. Upon this the *Hurgo* and his train withdrew with much civility and cheerful countenances. Soon after I heard a general shout, with frequent repetitions of the words, *Peplom selan,* and I felt great numbers of the people on my left side, relaxing the cords to such a degree, that I was able to turn upon my right. They had daubed my face and both my hands with a sort of ointment very pleasant to the smell, which in a few minutes removed all the smart of their arrows. These circumstances, added to the refreshment I had received by their victuals and drink, which were very nourishing, disposed me to sleep. I slept about eight hours, as I was afterwards assured, and it was no wonder, for the physicians, by the Emperor's order, had mingled a sleepy potion in the hogsheads of wine.

It seems that, upon the first moment I was discovered sleeping on the ground after my landing, the Emperor had early notice of it by an express; and determined in council that I should be tied in the manner I have related, (which was done in the night while I slept) that plenty of meat and drink should be sent to me, and a machine prepared to carry me to the capital city. . . .

These people are most excellent mathematicians, and arrived to a great perfection in mechanics, by the countenance and encouragement of the Emperor, who is a renowned patron of learning. This Prince hath several machines fixed on wheels, for the carriage of trees and other great weights. He often builds his largest men-of-war, whereof some are nine foot long, in the woods where the timber grows, and has them carried on these engines three or four hundred yards to the sea. Five hundred carpenters and engineers were immediately set at work to prepare the greatest engine they had. It was a frame of wood raised three inches from the ground, about seven feet long and four wide, moving upon twenty-two wheels. The shout I heard was upon the arrival of this engine, which, it seems, set out in four hours after my landing. It was brought parallel to me as I lay. But the principal difficulty was to raise and place me in this vehicle. Eighty poles, each of one foot high, were erected for this purpose, and very strong cords of the bigness of pack-thread were fastened by hooks to many bandages, which the workmen had girt round my neck, my hands, my body, and my legs. Nine hundred of the strongest men were employed to draw up these cords by many pulleys fastened on the poles, and thus, in less than three hours I was raised and slung into the engine, and there tied fast. All this I was told, for, while the whole operation was performing, I lay in a profound sleep, by the force of that soporiferous medicine infused into my liquor. Fifteen hundred of the Emperor's largest horses, each about four inches and an half high, were employed to draw me towards the metropolis, which, as I said, was half a mile distant.

Gulliver's Travels. 1726

WILLIAM CONGREVE

1670–1729

BOUDOIR BILLINGSGATE

A Room in Lady WISHFORT'S *House.*
Lady WISHFORT *at her toilet*, PEG *waiting.*

Lady. Merciful, no news of Foible yet?

Peg. No, madam.

Lady. I have no more patience—if I have not fretted myself 'till I am pale again, there's no veracity in me. Fetch me the red—the red, do you hear, sweetheart? An errant ash colour, as I'm a person. Look you how this wench stirs! Why dost thou not fetch me a little red? Didst thou not hear me, mopus?

Peg. The red ratafia does your ladyship mean, or the cherry-brandy?

Lady. Ratafia, fool? No, fool. Not the ratafia, fool—grant me patience! I mean the Spanish paper, idiot, complexion darling. Paint, paint, paint, dost thou understand that, changeling, dangling thy hands like bobbins before thee? Why dost thou not stir, puppet? thou wooden thing upon wires.

Peg. Lord, madam, your ladyship is so impatient —I cannot come at the paint, madam, Mrs. Foible has locked it up, and carried the key with her.

Lady. Pox take you both—fetch me the cherry-brandy then. [*Exit* PEG.

I'm as pale and as faint, I look like Mrs. Qualm-

sick the curate's wife, that's always breeding—
Wench, come, come, wench, what art thou doing,
sipping? tasting? Save thee, dost thou not
know the bottle?

Re-enter PEG *with a bottle and china cup.*

Peg. Madam, I was looking for a cup.

Lady. A cup, save thee, and what a cup hast
thou brought! Dost thou take me for a fairy, to
drink out of an acorn? Why didst thou not
bring thy thimble? Hast thou ne'er a brass
thimble clinking in thy pocket with a bit of
nutmeg? I warrant thee. Come, fill, fill.—So
—again. See who that is.—[*One knocks.*] Set
down the bottle first. Here, here, under the
table—What, wouldst thou go with the bottle in
thy hand like a tapster? As I'm a person, this
wench has lived in an inn upon the road, before
she came to me, like Maritornes the Asturian in
Don Quixote. No Foible yet?

Peg. No, madam, Mrs. Marwood.

Lady. O Marwood, let her come in. Come in,
good Marwood.

Enter Mrs. MARWOOD.

Mrs. Marwood. I'm surprised to find your
ladyship in *déshabillé* at this time of day.

Lady. Foible's a lost thing; has been abroad
since morning, and never heard of since.

Mrs. Marwood. I saw her but now, as I came
masked through the Park, in conference with
Mirabell.

Lady. With Mirabell! You call my blood
into my face, with mentioning that traitor. She
durst not have the confidence. I sent her to

negotiate an affair, in which if I'm detected I'm undone. If that wheedling villain has wrought upon Foible to detect me, I'm ruined. Oh my dear friend, I'm a wretch of wretches if I'm detected.

Mrs. Marwood. O madam, you cannot suspect Mrs. Foible's integrity.

Lady. O, he carries poison in his tongue that would corrupt integrity itself. If she has given him an opportunity, she has as good as put her integrity into his hands. Ah, dear Marwood, what's integrity to an opportunity?—Hark! I hear her.—Dear friend, retire into my closet, that I may examine her with more freedom—You'll pardon me, dear friend, I can make bold with you—There are books over the chimney—Quarles and Prynne, and the *Short View of the Stage*, with Bunyan's works to entertain you. [*To* PEG.]— Go, you thing, and send her in.

[*Exeunt* Mrs. MARWOOD *and* PEG.

Enter FOIBLE.

Lady. O Foible, where hast thou been? what hast thou been doing?

Foible. Madam, I have seen the party.

Lady. But what hast thou done?

Foible. Nay, 'tis your ladyship has done, and are to do; I have only promised. But a man so enamoured—so transported! Well, if worshipping of pictures be a sin—poor Sir Rowland, I say.

Lady. The miniature has been counted like— But hast thou not betrayed me, Foible? Hast thou not detected me to that faithless Mirabell? —What hadst thou to do with him in the Park? Answer me, has he got nothing out of thee?

Foible. So, the devil has been beforehand with me, what shall I say?—Alas, madam, could I help it, if I met that confident thing? Was I in fault? If you had heard how he used me, and all upon your ladyship's account, I'm sure you would not suspect my fidelity. Nay, if that had been the worst I could have borne: but he had a fling at your ladyship too; and then I could not hold: but i' faith I gave him his own.

Lady. Me? What did the filthy fellow say?

Foible. O madam; 'tis a shame to say what he said—with his taunts and his fleers, tossing up his nose. Humph (says he), what! you are a hatching some plot (says he), you are so early abroad, or catering (says he), ferreting for some disbanded officer, I warrant—half pay is but thin subsistence (says he)—Well, what pension does your lady propose? Let me see (says he), what! she must come down pretty deep now, she's superannuated (says he) and——

Lady. Ods my life, I'll have him, I'll have him murdered. I'll have him poisoned. Where does he eat? I'll marry a drawer to have him poisoned in his wine. I'll send for Robin from Locket's— immediately.

Foible. Poison him? Poisoning's too good for him. Starve him, madam, starve him; marry Sir Rowland, and get him disinherited. O you would bless yourself, to hear what he said.

Lady. A villain! superannuated!

Foible. Humph (says he), I hear you are laying designs against me too (says he), and Mrs. Milla-mant is to marry my uncle; (he does not suspect a word of your ladyship;) but (says he) I'll fit you for that, I warrant you (says he), I'll hamper

you for that (says he), you and your old frippery
too (says he), I'll handle you——

Lady. Audacious villain! handle me, would
he durst—Frippery? old frippery! Was there
ever such a foul-mouthed fellow? I'll be married
to-morrow, I'll be contracted to-night.

Foible. The sooner the better, madam.

Lady. Will Sir Rowland be here, say'st thou?
when, Foible?

Foible. Incontinently, madam. No new sheriff's
wife expects the return of her husband after knighthood, with that impatience in which Sir Rowland
burns for the dear hour of kissing your ladyship's
hand after dinner.

Lady. Frippery! superannuated frippery! I'll
frippery the villain; I'll reduce him to frippery
and rags: a tatterdemalion—I hope to see him
hung with tatters, like a Long-Lane penthouse,
or a gibbet-thief. A slander-mouthed railer: I
warrant the spendthrift prodigal's in debt as much
as the million lottery, or the whole court upon
a birthday. I'll spoil his credit with his tailor. Yes,
he shall have my niece with her fortune, he shall.

Foible. He! I hope to see him lodge in Ludgate
first, and angle into Black-Friars for brass farthings,
with an old mitten.

Lady. Ay, dear Foible; thank thee for that,
dear Foible. He has put me out of all patience.
I shall never recompose my features, to receive
Sir Rowland with any economy of face. This
wretch has fretted me that I am absolutely decayed.
Look, Foible.

Foible. Your ladyship has frowned a little too
rashly, indeed, madam. There are some cracks
discernible in the white varnish.

Lady. Let me see the glass—Cracks, say'st thou ? Why, I am arrantly flea'd—I look like an old peeled wall. Thou must repair me, Foible, before Sir Rowland comes; or I shall never keep up to my picture.

Foible. I warrant you, madam; a little art once made your picture like you ; and now a little of the same art must make you like your picture. Your picture must sit for you, madam.

Lady. But art thou sure Sir Rowland will not fail to come ? Or will he not fail when he does come ? Will he be importunate, Foible, and push ? For if he should not be importunate—I shall never break decorums—I shall die with confusion, if I am forced to advance—Oh no, I can never advance—I shall swoon if he should expect advances. No, I hope Sir Rowland is better bred, than to put a lady to the necessity of breaking her forms. I won't be too coy neither.— I won't give him despair—but a little disdain is not amiss ; a little scorn is alluring.

Foible. A little scorn becomes your ladyship.

Lady. Yes, but tenderness becomes me best— a sort of a dyingness—You see that picture has a sort of a—Ha, Foible ? A swimmingness in the eyes—Yes, I'll look so—my niece affects it ; but she wants features. Is Sir Rowland handsome ? Let my toilet be removed—I'll dress above. I'll receive Sir Rowland here. Is he handsome ? Don't answer me. I won't knew : I'll be surprised. I'll be taken by surprise

Foible. By storm, madam. Sir Rowland's a brisk man.

Lady. Is he ! O then he'll importune, if he's a brisk man. I shall save decorums if Sir Rowland

importunes. I have a mortal terror at the apprehension of offending against decorums. O I'm
glad he's a brisk man. Let my things be removed,
good Foible.   [*Exit.*

The Way of the World. 1700.

MIRABELL AND MRS. MILLAMANT

A Room in Lady WISHFORT'S *House.*

MRS. MILLAMANT, MIRABELL.

Mirabell. 'Like Daphne she, as lovely and as
coy.' Do you lock yourself up from me, to make
my search more curious ? Or is this pretty artifice
contrived, to signify that here the chase must end,
and my pursuit be crowned, for you can fly no
further ?

Mrs. Millamant. Vanity ! No—I'll fly and be
followed to the last moment, though I am upon
the very verge of matrimony, I expect you should
solicit me as much as if I were wavering at
the grate of a monastery, with one foot over the
threshold. I'll be solicited to the very last, nay
and afterwards.

Mirabell. What, after the last ?

Mrs. Millamant. O, I should think I was poor
and had nothing to bestow, if I were reduced to
an inglorious ease, and freed from the agreeable
fatigues of solicitation.

Mirabell. But do not you know, that when
favours are conferred upon instant and tedious
solicitation, that they diminish in their value, and
that both the giver loses the grace, and the receiver
lessens his pleasure ?

Mrs. Millamant. It may be in things of

common application; but never sure in love.
O, I hate a lover that can dare to think he draws
a moment's air, independent on the bounty of his
mistress. There is not so impudent a thing in
nature, as the saucy look of an assured man,
confident of success. The pedantic arrogance of
a very husband has not so pragmatical an air.
Ah! I'll never marry, unless I am first made
sure of my will and pleasure.

Mirabell. Would you have 'em both before
marriage? Or will you be contented with the
first now, and stay for the other 'till after grace?

Mrs. Millamant. Ah, don't be impertinent—
My dear liberty, shall I leave thee? My faithful
solitude, my darling contemplation, must I bid
you then adieu? Ay-h, adieu—my morning
thoughts, agreeable wakings, indolent slumbers,
all ye *douceurs*, ye *sommeils du matin*, adieu—I
can't do't, 'tis more than impossible—Positively,
Mirabell, I'll lie abed in a morning as long as I
please.

Mirabell. Then I'll get up in a morning as
early as I please.

Mrs. Millamant. Ah! Idle creature, get up
when you will—And d'ye hear, I won't be called
names after I'm married; positively I won't be
called names.

Mirabell. Names!

Mrs. Millamant. Ay, as wife, spouse, my dear,
joy, jewel, love, sweetheart, and the rest of that
nauseous cant, in which men and their wives are
so fulsomely familiar—I shall never bear that—
Good Mirabell, don't let us be familiar or fond, nor kiss
before folks, like my Lady Fadler and Sir Francis:
nor go to Hyde Park together the first Sunday in

a new chariot, to provoke eyes and whispers; and then never be seen there together again; as if we were proud of one another the first week, and ashamed of one another ever after. Let us never visit together, nor go to a play together, but let us be very strange and well bred: let us be as strange as if we had been married a great while; and as well bred as if we were not married at all.

Mirabell. Have you any more conditions to offer? Hitherto your demands are pretty reasonable.

Mrs. Millamant. Trifles,—as liberty to pay and receive visits to and from whom I please; to write and receive letters, without interrogatories or wry faces on your part; to wear what I please; and choose conversation with regard only to my own taste; to have no obligation upon me to converse with wits that I don't like, because they are your acquaintance; or to be intimate with fools, because they may be your relations. Come to dinner when I please, dine in my dressing-room when I'm out of humour, without giving a reason. To have my closet inviolate; to be sole empress of my tea-table, which you must never presume to approach without first asking leave. And lastly, wherever I am, you shall always knock at the door before you come in. These articles subscribed, if I continue to endure you a little longer, I may by degrees dwindle into a wife.

Mirabell. Your bill of fare is something advanced in this latter account. Well, have I liberty to offer conditions—that when you are dwindled into a wife, I may not be beyond measure enlarged into a husband?

Mrs. Millamant. You have free leave, propose your utmost, speak and spare not.

Mirabell. I thank you. *Imprimis* then, I covenant that your acquaintance be general; that you admit no sworn confident, or intimate of your own sex; no she-friend to screen her affairs under your countenance, and tempt you to make trial of a mutual secrecy. No decoy-duck to wheedle you a fop-scrambling to the play in a mask—then bring you home in a pretended fright, when you think you shall be found out—and rail at me for missing the play, and disappointing the frolic which you had to pick me up and prove my constancy.

Mrs. Millamant. Detestable *imprimis!* I go to the play in a mask!

Mirabell. *Item,* I article, that you continue to like your own face as long as I shall: and while it passes current with me, that you endeavour not to new coin it. To which end, together with all vizards for the day, I prohibit all masks for the night, made of oiled-skins and I know not what—hog's bones, hare's gall, pig water, and the marrow of a roasted cat. In short, I forbid all commerce with the gentlewoman in what-d'ye-call-it Court. *Item,* I shut my doors against all bawds with baskets, and pennyworths of muslin, china, fans, atlasses, &c.—Lastly, to the dominion of the tea-table I submit.—But with *proviso*, that you exceed not in your province; but restrain yourself to native and simple tea-table drinks, as tea, chocolate, and coffee. As likewise to genuine and authorized tea-table talk—such as mending of fashions, spoiling reputations, railing at absent friends, and so forth—but that on no account you encroach upon the men's prerogative, and presume to drink healths, or toast fellows : for prevention of which, I banish all foreign forces, all auxiliaries to the tea-table, as orange-brandy, and aniseed, cinnamon, citron and Barbado's-waters, together with ratafia and the most noble spirit of clary.—But for cowslip-wine, poppy-water, and all dormitives, those I allow.— These provisos admitted, in other things I may prove a tractable and complying husband.

Mrs. Millamant. O horrid provisos ! filthy strong waters ! I toast fellows, odious men ! I hate your odious provisos.

Mirabell. Then we're agreed. Shall I kiss your hand upon the contract ?

The Way of the World. 1700.

JOSEPH ADDISON

1672-1719

THE TALE OF MARRATON

Felices errore suo.—Lucan i. 454.

There is a tradition among the Americans, that one of their countrymen descended in a vision to the great repository of souls, or, as we call it here, to the other world ; and that upon his return he gave his friends a distinct account of everything he saw among those regions of the dead. A friend of mine, whom I have formerly mentioned, prevailed upon one of the interpreters of the Indian kings, to inquire of them, if possible, what tradition they have among them of this matter : which, as well as he could learn by those many questions which he asked them at several times, was in substance as follows.

The visionary, whose name was Marraton, after having travelled for a long space under an hollow mountain, arrived at length on the confines of this world of spirits, but could not enter it by reason of a thick forest made up of bushes, brambles, and pointed thorns, so perplexed and interwoven with one another, that it was impossible to find a passage through it. Whilst he was looking about for some track or pathway that might be worn in any part of it, he saw an huge lion couched under the side of it, who kept his eye upon him in the same

posture as when he watches for his prey. The
Indian immediately started back, whilst the lion
rose with a spring, and leaped towards him.
Being wholly destitute of all other weapons, he
stooped down to take up a huge stone in his hand,
but to his infinite surprise grasped nothing, and
found the supposed stone to be only the apparition
of one. If he was disappointed on this side, he
was as much pleased on the other, when he found
the lion, which had seized on his left shoulder, had
no power to hurt him, and was only the ghost of
that ravenous creature which it appeared to be.
He no sooner got rid of his impotent enemy, but
he marched up to the wood, and after having
surveyed it for some time, endeavoured to press into
one part of it that was a little thinner than the rest ;
when again, to his great surprise, he found that the
bushes made no resistance, but that he walked
through briers and brambles with the same ease as
through the open air, and, in short, that the whole
wood was nothing else but a wood of shades. He
immediately concluded that this huge thicket of
thorns and brakes was designed as a kind of fence
or quick-set hedge to the ghosts it enclosed ; and
that probably their soft substances might be torn
by these subtle points and prickles, which were too
weak to make any impressions in flesh and blood.
With this he resolved to travel through this intricate wood ; when by degrees he felt a gale of
perfumes breathing upon him, that grew stronger
and sweeter in proportion as he advanced. He had
not proceeded much further when he observed the
thorns and briers to end, and give place to a thousand beautiful green trees covered with blossoms
of the finest scents and colours, that formed

a wilderness of sweets, and were a kind of lining to those ragged scenes which he had before passed through. As he was coming out of this delightful part of the wood, and entering upon the plains it enclosed, he saw several horsemen rushing by him, and a little while after heard the cry of a pack of dogs. He had not listened long before he saw the apparition of a milk-white steed, with a young man on the back of it, advancing upon full stretch after the souls of about an hundred beagles that were hunting down the ghost of an hare, which ran away before them with an unspeakable swiftness. As the man on the milk-white steed came by him, he looked upon him very attentively, and found him to be the young prince Nicharagua, who died about half a year before, and, by reason of his great virtues, was at that time lamented over all the western parts of America.

He had no sooner got out of the wood, but he was entertained with such a landscape of flowery plains, green meadows, running streams, sunny hills, and shady vales, as were not to be represented by his own expressions, nor, as he said, by the conceptions of others   This happy region was peopled with innumerable swarms of spirits, who applied themselves to exercises and diversions according as their fancies led them. Some of them were tossing the figure of a quoit ; others were pitching the shadow of a bar ; others were breaking the apparition of a horse ; and multitudes employing themselves upon ingenious handicrafts with the souls of *departed utensils*, for that is the name which in the Indian language they give their tools when they are burnt or broken. As he travelled through this delightful scene, he was very often

tempted to pluck the flowers that rose everywhere
about him in the greatest variety and profusion,
having never seen several of them in his own
country; but he quickly found that, though they
were objects of his sight, they were not liable to his
touch. He at length came to the side of a great
river, and being a good fisherman himself, stood
upon the banks of it some time to look upon an
angler that had taken a great many shapes of
fishes, which lay flouncing up and down by him.

I should have told my reader, that this Indian
had formerly been married to one of the greatest
beauties of his country, by whom he had several
children. This couple were so famous for their
love and constancy to one another, that the
Indians to this day, when they give a married man
joy of his wife, wish that they may live together
like Marraton and Yaratilda. Marraton had not
stood long by the fisherman when he saw the
shadow of his beloved Yaratilda, who had for some
time fixed her eye upon him, before he discovered
her. Her arms were stretched out towards him;
floods of tears ran down her eyes; her looks, her
hands, her voice called him over to her; and at the
same time seemed to tell him that the river was
unpassable. Who can describe the passion, made
up of joy, sorrow, love, desire, astonishment, that
rose in the Indian upon the sight of his dear
Yaratilda? He could express it by nothing but
his tears, which ran like a river down his cheeks as
he looked upon her. He had not stood in this
posture long before he plunged into the stream that
lay before him; and finding it to be nothing but
the phantom of a river, walked on the bottom of it
till he arose on the other side. At his approach

Yaratilda flew into his arms, whilst Marraton wished himself disencumbered of that body, which kept her from his embraces. After many questions and endearments on both sides, she conducted him to a bower which she had dressed with her own hands, with all the ornaments that could be met with in those blooming regions. She had made it gay beyond imagination, and was every day adding something new to it. As Marraton stood astonished at the unspeakable beauty of her habitation, and ravished with the fragrancy that came from every part of it, Yaratilda told him that she was preparing this bower for his reception, as well knowing that his piety to his god, and his faithful dealing towards men, would certainly bring him to that happy place whenever his life should be at an end. She then brought two of her children to him, who died some years before, and resided with her in the same delightful bower; advising him to breed up those others which were still with him in such a manner, that they might hereafter all of them meet together in this happy place.

The tradition tells us further, that he had afterwards a sight of those dismal habitations which are the portion of ill men after death; and mentions several molten seas of gold, in which were plunged the souls of barbarous Europeans, who put to the sword so many thousands of poor Indians for the sake of that precious metal; but having already touched upon the chief points of this tradition, and exceeded the measure of my paper, I shall not give any further account of it.—C.

The Spectator No. 56.

ANOTHER VISIT TO WESTMINSTER ABBEY

Ire tamen restat, Numa quo devenit, et Ancus.
Hor. Ep. vi. l. 1. ver. 27.

With *Ancus,* and with *Numa,* kings of *Rome,*
We must descend into the silent tomb.

My friend Sir Roger de Coverley told me t' other
night, that he had been reading my paper upon
Westminster Abbey, in which, says he, there are
a great many ingenious fancies. He told me at
the same time, that he observed I had promised
another paper upon the tombs, and that he should
be glad to go and see them with me, not having
visited them since he had read history. I could
not at first imagine how this came into the knight's
head, till I recollected that he had been very busy
all last summer upon Baker's Chronicle, which he
has quoted several times in his disputes with Sir
Andrew Freeport since his last coming to town.
Accordingly I promised to call upon him the next
morning, that we might go together to the Abbey.

I found the knight under his butler's hand, who
always shaves him. He was no sooner dressed
than he called for a glass of the widow Trueby's
water, which he told me he always drank before
he went abroad. He recommended to me a dram
of it at the same time, with so much heartiness,
that I could not forbear drinking it. As soon as
I had got it down, I found it very unpalatable;
upon which the knight, observing that I had made
several wry faces, told me that he knew I should
not like it at first, but that it was the best thing
in the world against the stone or gravel.

I could have wished indeed that he had

acquainted me with the virtues of it sooner ; but it was too late to complain, and I knew what he had done was out of goodwill. Sir Roger told me further, that he looked upon it to be very good for a man whilst he stayed in town, to keep off infection, and that he got together a quantity of it upon the first news of the sickness being at Dantzick : when of a sudden turning short to one of his servants who stood behind him, he bid him call a hackney-coach, and take care it was an elderly man that drove it.

He then resumed his discourse upon Mrs. Trueby's water, telling me that the widow Trueby was one who did more good than all the doctors and apothecaries in the country ; that she distilled every poppy that grew within five miles of her ; that she distributed her water gratis among all sorts of people : to which the knight added, that she had a very great jointure, and that the whole country would fain have it a match between him and her ; ' and truly,' says Sir Roger, ' if I had not been engaged, perhaps I could not have done better.'

His discourse was broken off by his man's telling him he had called a coach. Upon our going to it, after having cast his eye upon the wheels, he asked the coachman if his axle-tree was good ; upon the fellow's telling him he would warrant it, the knight turned to me, told me he looked like an honest man, and went in without further ceremony.

We had not gone far, when Sir Roger, popping out his head, called the coachman down from his box, and, upon his presenting himself at the window, asked him if he smoked ; as I was considering what this would end in, he bid him stop by the way at any good tobacconist's, and take in a roll of their best Virginia. Nothing material happened in the remaining part of our journey, till we were set down at the west end of the Abbey.

As we went up the body of the church, the knight pointed at the trophies upon one of the new monuments, and cried out, 'A brave man, I warrant him!' Passing afterwards by Sir Cloudsly Shovel, he flung his hand that way, and cried, 'Sir Cloudsly Shovel, a very gallant man!' As we stood before Busby's tomb, the knight uttered himself again after the same manner. 'Dr. Busby, a great man! he whipped my grandfather; a very great man! I should have gone to him myself, if I had not been a blockhead; a very great man!'

We were immediately conducted into the little chapel on the right hand. Sir Roger planting himself at our historian's elbow, was very attentive to everything he said, particularly to the account he gave us of the lord who cut off the king of Morocco's head. Among several other figures, he was very well pleased to see the statesman Cecil upon his knees; and concluding them all to be great men, was conducted to the figure which represents that martyr to good housewifery, who died by the prick of a needle. Upon our interpreter's telling us that she was a maid of honour to Queen Elizabeth, the knight was very inquisitive into her name and family; and after having regarded her finger for some time, 'I wonder', says he, 'that Sir Richard Baker has said nothing of her in his Chronicle.'

We were then conveyed to the two coronation chairs, where my old friend, after having heard that the stone underneath the most ancient of them, which was brought from Scotland, was called Jacob's pillar, sat himself down in the chair; and looking like the figure of an old Gothic king, asked our interpreter, what authority they had to say that Jacob had ever been in Scotland? The fellow, instead of returning him an answer, told him, that he hoped his honour would pay his forfeit. I could observe Sir Roger a little ruffled upon being thus trepanned; but our guide not insisting upon his demand, the knight soon recovered his good humour, and whispered in my ear, that if Will Wimble were with us, and saw those two chairs, it would go hard but he would get a tobacco-stopper out of one or t' other of them.

Sir Roger, in the next place, laid his hand upon Edward the Third's sword, and leaning upon the pommel of it, gave us the whole history of the Black Prince; concluding, that, in Sir Richard Baker's opinion, Edward the Third was one of the greatest princes that ever sat upon the English throne.

We were then shown Edward the Confessor's tomb; upon which Sir Roger acquainted us, that he was the first who touched for the evil; and afterwards Henry the Fourth's, upon which he shook his head, and told us there was fine reading in the casualties of that reign.

Our conductor then pointed to that monument where there is the figure of one of our English kings without an head: and upon giving us to know, that the head, which was of beaten silver, had been stolen away several years since: 'Some Whig, I'll warrant you,' says Sir Roger; 'you ought to lock up your kings better; they will carry off the body too, if you don't take care.'

The glorious names of Henry the Fifth and Queen Elizabeth gave the knight great opportu-

nities of shining, and of doing justice to Sir Richard
Baker, who, as our knight observed with some
surprise, had a great many kings in him, whose
monuments he had not seen in the abbey.

For my own part, I could not but be pleased to
see the knight show such an honest passion for the
glory of his country, and such a respectful gratitude
to the memory of its princes.

I must not omit, that the benevolence of my
good old friend, which flows out towards every one
he converses with, made him very kind to our
interpreter, whom he looked upon as an extraordinary man ; for which reason he shook him by
the hand at parting, telling him, that he should
be very glad to see him at his lodgings in Norfolk
Buildings, and talk over these matters with him
more at leisure.   *Spectator*.   No. 329.

SIR ROGER AT THE THEATRE

*Respicere exemplar vitae morumque iubebo
Doctum imitatorem, et veras hinc ducere voces.*
                          HOR. Ars Poet. ver. 317.

Those are the likest copies, which are drawn
From the original of human life.   ROSCOMMON.

MY friend Sir Roger de Coverley, when we last
met together at the club, told me that he had
a great mind to see the new tragedy with me,
assuring me at the same time, that he had not been
at a play these twenty years.   ' The last I saw ',
said Sir Roger, ' was *The Committee,* which I should
not have gone to neither, had not I been told
beforehand that it was a good Church of England
comedy.'   He then proceeded to inquire of me

who this *Distressed Mother* was; and upon hearing
that she was Hector's widow, he told me that her
husband was a brave man, and that when he was
a school-boy he had read his life at the end of the
dictionary. My friend asked me, in the next
place, if there would not be some danger in coming
home late, in case the Mohocks should be abroad.
'I assure you,' says he, 'I thought I had fallen
into their hands last night; for I observed two or
three lusty black men that followed me half-way
up Fleet Street, and mended their pace behind me
in proportion as I put on to get away from them.
You must know,' continued the knight, with
a smile, 'I fancied they had a mind to *hunt* me;
for I remember an honest gentleman in my
neighbourhood, who was served such a trick in
King Charles II's time, for which reason he has not
ventured himself in town ever since. I might have
shown them very good sport, had this been their
design; for as I am an old fox-hunter, I should
have turned and dodged, and have played them
a thousand tricks they had never seen in their lives
before.' Sir Roger added, that if these gentlemen
had any such intention, they did not succeed very
well in it; 'for I threw them out', says he, 'at
the end of Norfolk Street, where I doubled the
corner, and got shelter in my lodgings before they
could imagine what was become of me. However,'
says the knight, 'if Captain Sentry will make one
with us to-morrow night, and if you will both of
you call upon me about four o'clock, that we may
be at the house before it is full, I will have my
own coach in readiness to attend you, for John tells
me he has got the fore-wheels mended.'

The Captain, who did not fail to meet me there

at the appointed hour, bid Sir Roger fear nothing, for that he had put on the same sword which he made use of at the battle of Steenkirk. Sir Roger's servants, and among the rest my old friend the butler, had, I found, provided themselves with good oaken plants, to attend their master upon this occasion. When we had placed him in his coach, with myself at his left hand, the Captain before him, and his butler at the head of his footmen in the rear, we convoyed him in safety to the playhouse, where, after having marched up the entry in good order, the Captain and I went in with him, and seated him betwixt us in the pit. As soon as the house was full, and the candles lighted, my old friend stood up and looked about him with that pleasure, which a mind seasoned with humanity naturally feels in itself, at the sight of a multitude of people who seem pleased with one another, and partake of the same common entertainment. I could not but fancy myself, as the old man stood up in the middle of the pit, that he made a very proper centre to a tragic audience. Upon the entering of Pyrrhus, the knight told me that he did not believe the king of France himself had a better strut. I was indeed very attentive to my old friend's remarks, because I looked upon them as a piece of natural criticism ; and was well pleased to hear him, at the conclusion of almost every scene, telling me that he could not imagine how the play would end. One while he appeared much concerned for Andromache, and a little while after as much for Hermione ; and was extremely puzzled to think what would become of Pyrrhus.

When Sir Roger saw Andromache's obstinate refusal to her lover's importunities, he whispered

me in the ear, that he was sure she would never
have him; to which he added, with a more than
ordinary vehemence, 'You can't imagine, sir,
what it is to have to do with a widow.' Upon
Pyrrhus his threatening afterwards to leave her,
the knight shook his head and muttered to himself,
'Ay, do if you can.' This part dwelt so much
upon my friend's imagination, that at the close
of the third act, as I was thinking of something
else, he whispered in my ear, 'These widows,
sir, are the most perverse creatures in the world.
But pray,' says he, 'you that are a critic, is this
play according to your dramatic rules, as you call
them? Should your people in tragedy always talk to
be understood? Why, there is not a single sentence
in this play that I do not know the meaning of.'

The fourth act very unluckily began before I had
time to give the old gentleman an answer: 'Well,'
says the knight, sitting down with great satisfaction,
'I suppose we are now to see Hector's ghost.' He
then renewed his attention, and, from time to time,
fell a-praising the widow. He made, indeed, a
little mistake as to one of her pages, whom at his
first entering he took for Astyanax: but he quickly
set himself right in that particular, though, at the
same time, he owned he should have been very
glad to have seen the little boy, 'Who', said he,
'must needs be a very fine child by the account
that is given of him.' Upon Hermione's going
off with a menace to Pyrrhus, the audience gave
a loud clap; to which Sir Roger added, 'On my
word, a notable young baggage!'

As there was a very remarkable silence and stillness in the audience during the whole action, it
was natural for them to take the opportunity of

these intervals between the acts, to express their opinion of the players, and of their respective parts. Sir Roger hearing a cluster of them praise Orestes, struck in with them, and told them that he thought his friend Pylades was a very sensible man; as they were afterwards applauding Pyrrhus, Sir Roger put in a second time, 'And let me tell you,' says he, 'though he speaks but little, I like the old fellow in whiskers as well as any of them.'   Captain Sentry seeing two or three wags who sat near us, lean with an attentive ear towards Sir Roger, and fearing lest they should smoke the knight, plucked him by the elbow, and whispered something in his ear, that lasted till the opening of the fifth act. The knight was wonderfully attentive to the account which Orestes gives of Pyrrhus his death, and at the conclusion of it told me, it was such a bloody piece of work, that he was glad it was not done upon the stage.   Seeing afterwards Orestes in his raving fit, he grew more than ordinary serious, and took occasion to moralize (in his way) upon an evil conscience, adding, that Orestes, in his madness, looked as if he saw something.

As we were the first that came into the house, so we were the last that went out of it; being resolved to have a clear passage for our old friend, whom we did not care to venture among the justling of the crowd.   Sir Roger went out fully satisfied with his entertainment, and we guarded him to his lodgings in the same manner that we brought him to the playhouse; being highly pleased, for my own part, not only with the performance of the excellent piece which had been presented, but with the satisfaction which it had given to the good old man.

Spectator.   No. 335.

SIR RICHARD STEELE

1672–1729

A SCENE IN NEWGATE

YOUNG BOOKWIT, LATINE, SIMON, STORM,
with the crowd of Gaol-birds.

Storm. I apprehend, sir, by Mr. Turnkey, the
gentleman there with a broken nose, that you're
brought in for murther. I honour you, sir;—
I don't question but 'twas done like a gentleman.

Y. Bookwit. I hope it will appear so.

Storm. I come, I fear, sir, to your acquaintance
with some prejudice, because you see me thus in
irons,—but affliction is the portion of the virtuous
and the gallant.

Y. Bookwit. It does not depress, sir, but manifest the brave.

Storm. Right, sir, I find you're noble. You
may, perhaps, have heard of me—My name is
Storm. This person, my friend, who is called
Faggot, and myself, being exposed by an ungrateful
world to feel its cruelty and contempt of ragged
virtue, made war upon it, and in open day infested
their high road.

Y. Bookwit. Your humble servant, gentlemen,
I do conceive you. Your spirits could not stoop
to barter on the change, to sneer in courts, to lie,
to flatter, or to creep for bread. You therefore
chose rather to prey like lions, than betray like
crocodiles, or fawn like dogs. You took upon

you to interrupt the commerce of a cheating world, to unload the usurer of his anxious pelf, and save the thoughtless landed boy he travelled to undo, —with a thousand such good actions; by which means you two are infamous, for what two millions of you had been glorious.

Storm. Right, sir; I see you're knowing, sir, and learned in man. This gentleman, Mr. Charcoal the chemist, was our secret correspondent, and as we never robbed a poor man, so he never cheated a fool, but still imposed on your most sprightly wits and genius—fellows of fire and metal, whose quick fancies and eager wishes formed reasons for their undoing. He is a follower of the great Raimundus Lullius; the public think to frighten him into their own purposes. But he'll leave the ungrateful world without the secret.

Charcoal. You know, sir, he that first asserted the Antipodes died for that knowledge; and I, sir, having found out the melioration of metals, the ignorant will needs call it coining; and I am to be hanged for 't, would you think it?

Y. Bookwit. When, pray sir, are you to be immortal?

Charcoal. On Friday next. I'm very unhappy our acquaintance is to be short. I'm very sorry your business is not over, sir, that, if it must be, we might go together.

Y. Bookwit. I'm highly obliged to you, sir.

Charcoal. Yet let me tell you, sir, because by secret sympathy I'm yours, I must acquaint you, if you can obtain the favour of an opportunity and a crucible, I can show projection—directly Sol, sir, Sol, sir, more bright than that high luminary the Latins called so—wealth shall be yours; we'll turn each bar about us into golden ingots. Sir, can you lend me half-a-crown?

Y. Bookwit. Oh, sir, a trifle between such old acquaintance.

Storm. You'll be indicted, sir, to-morrow. I would advise you, when your indictment's read, to one thing: that is, don't cavil at false Latin; but if by chance there should be a word of good, except to that, and puzzle the whole court.

Y. Bookwit. Sir, I'm obliged——

Storm. I defy the world to say I ever did an ill thing. I love my friend—but there is always some little trifle given to prisoners they call garnish; we of the road are above it, but o' t' other side of the house, silly rascals that came voluntarily hither——Such as are in for fools, signed their own mittimus, in being bound for others, may perhaps want it: I'll be your faithful almoner.

Y. Bookwit. O, by all means, sir.

[*Gives him money.*

Storm. Pray, sir, is that your footman?

Y. Bookwit. He is my friend, sir.

Storm. Look you, sir, the only time to make use of a friend is in extremity; do you think you could not hang him, and save yourself? Sir, my service to you; your own health.

1st Prisoner. Captain, your health.

[*Gives it to the next prisoner.*

2nd Prisoner. Captain, your health.

Storm. But perhaps the captain likes brandy better. So-ho! brandy there. [*Drinks.*] But you don't, perhaps, like these strong liquors. Cider, ho! Drink to him in it. Gentlemen all! But, captain, I see you don't love cider neither. You and I will be for claret then. Aye, marry!

I knew this would please [*Drinks*] you. [*Drinks again.*] Faith, we'll make an end on't ; I'm glad you like it.

Turnkey. I'm sorry, Captain Storm, to see you impose upon a gentleman, and put him to charge in his misfortune. If a petty larceny fellow had done this—but one of the road !

Storm. I beg your pardon, sir, I don't question but the captain understands there is a fee to you for going to the keeper's side.

[BOOKWIT *and* LATINE *give him money.*
Exeunt with Turnkey, SIMON *following.*]

Nay, nay, you must stay here.

Simon. Why, I am Simon, Madam Penelope's man.

Storm. Then Madam Penelope's man must strip for garnish ; indeed, Master Simon, you must.

Simon. Thieves ! Thieves ! Thieves !

Storm. Thieves ! Thieves ! Why, you senseless dog, do you think there's thieves in Newgate ? Away with him to the tap-house. [*Pushes him off.*] We'll drink his coat off. Come, my little chemist, thou shalt transmute this jacket into liquor ; liquor that will make us forget the evil day. And while day is ours, let us be merry.

For little villains must submit to fate,
That great ones may enjoy the world in state.

[*Exeunt.*

The Lying Lover. 1704.

THE STORY OF ALEXANDER SELKIRK

Talia monstrabat, relegens errata retrorsum.
                              —VIRGIL, *Aen.* iii. 690.

UNDER the title of this paper, I do not think it
foreign to my design, to speak of a man born in
Her Majesty's dominions, and relate an adventure
in his life so uncommon, that it is doubtful whether
the like has happened to any other of human race.
The person I speak of is Alexander Selkirk, whose
name is familiar to men of curiosity, from the fame
of his having lived four years and four months
alone in the island of Juan Fernandez. I had the
pleasure frequently to converse with the man soon
after his arrival in England, in the year 1711. It
was matter of great curiosity to hear him, as he is
a man of good sense, give an account of the different
revolutions in his own mind in that long solitude.
When we consider how painful absence from
company for the space of but one evening is to
the generality of mankind, we may have a sense
how painful this necessary and constant solitude
was to a man bred a sailor, and ever accustomed
to enjoy and suffer, eat, drink, and sleep, and perform all offices of life, in fellowship and company.
He was put ashore from a leaky vessel, with the
captain of which he had had an irreconcilable difference ; and he chose rather to take his fate in this
place, than in a crazy vessel, under a disagreeable
commander. His portion were a sea-chest, his
wearing clothes and bedding, a firelock, a pound of
gunpowder, a large quantity of bullets, a flint and
steel, a few pounds of tobacco, a hatchet, a knife,

a kettle, a bible, and other books of devotion, together with pieces that concerned navigation, and his mathematical instruments. Resentment against his officer, who had ill-used him, made him look forward on this change of life, as the more eligible one, till the instant in which he saw the vessel put off ; at which moment, his heart yearned within him, and melted at the parting with his comrades and all human society at once. He had in provisions for the sustenance of life but the quantity of two meals, the island abounding only with wild goats, cats and rats. He judged it most probable that he should find more immediate and easy relief, by finding shell-fish on the shore, than seeking game with his gun. He accordingly found great quantities of turtles, whose flesh is extremely delicious, and of which he frequently ate very plentifully on his first arrival, till it grew disagreeable to his stomach, except in jellies. The necessities of hunger and thirst, were his greatest diversions from the reflection on his lonely condition. When those appetites were satisfied, the desire of society was as strong a call upon him, and he appeared to himself least necessitous when he wanted everything ; for the supports of his body were easily attained, but the eager longings for seeing again the face of man during the interval of craving bodily appetites, were hardly supportable. He grew dejected, languid, and melancholy, scarce able to refrain from doing himself violence, till by degrees, by the force of reason, and frequent reading of the Scriptures, and turning his thoughts upon the study of navigation, after the space of eighteen months, he grew thoroughly reconciled to his condition. When he had made this conquest,

the vigour of his health, disengagement from the
world, a constant, cheerful, serene sky, and a temperate air, made his life one continual feast, and
his being much more joyful than it had before
been irksome. He now taking delight in everything, made the hut in which he lay, by ornaments
which he cut down from a spacious wood, on the
side of which it was situated, the most delicious
bower, fanned with continual breezes, and gentle
aspirations of wind, that made his repose after the
chase equal to the most sensual pleasures.

I forgot to observe, that during the time of his
dissatisfaction, monsters of the deep, which frequently lay on the shore, added to the terrors of
his solitude ; the dreadful howlings and voices
seemed too terrible to be made for human ears ;
but upon the recovery of his temper, he could with
pleasure not only hear their voices, but approach
the monsters themselves with great intrepidity.
He speaks of sea-lions, whose jaws and tails were
capable of seizing or breaking the limbs of a man,
if he approached them : but at that time his
spirits and life were so high, that he could act so
regularly and unconcerned, that merely from being
unruffled in himself, he killed them with the
greatest ease imaginable : for observing, that
though their jaws and tails were so terrible, yet
the animals being mighty slow in working themselves round, he had nothing to do but place himself exactly opposite to their middle, and as close
to them as possible, he dispatched them with his
hatchet at will.

The precautions which he took against want, in
case of sickness, was to lame kids when very young,
so as that they might recover their health, but

never be capable of speed. These he had in great numbers about his hut; and when he was himself in full vigour, he could take at full speed the swiftest goat running up a promontory, and never failed of catching them but on a descent.

His habitation was extremely pestered with rats, which gnawed his clothes and feet when sleeping. To defend him against them, he fed and tamed numbers of young kitlings, who lay about his bed, and preserved him from the enemy. When his clothes were quite worn out, he dried and tacked together the skins of goats, with which he clothed himself, and was inured to pass through woods, bushes, and brambles with as much carelessness and precipitance as any other animal. It happened once to him, that running on the summit of a hill, he made a stretch to seize a goat, with which under him, he fell down a precipice, and lay senseless for the space of three days, the length of which time he measured by the moon's growth since his last observation. This manner of life grew so exquisitely pleasant, that he never had a moment heavy upon his hands; his nights were untroubled, and his days joyous, from the practice of temperance and exercise. It was his manner to use stated hours and places for exercises of devotion, which he performed aloud, in order to keep up the faculties of speech and to utter himself with greater energy.

When I first saw him, I thought, if I had not been let into his character and story, I could have discerned that he had been much separated from company, from his aspect and gesture; there was a strong but cheerful seriousness in his look, and a certain disregard to the ordinary things about him, as if he had been sunk in thought. When the ship which brought him off the island came in, he received them with the greatest indifference, with relation to the prospect of going off with them, but with great satisfaction in an opportunity to refresh and help them. The man frequently bewailed his return to the world, which could not, he said, with all its enjoyments, restore him to the tranquillity of his solitude. Though I had frequently conversed with him, after a few months' absence he met me in the street, and though he spoke to me, I could not recollect that I had seen him; familiar converse in this town had taken off the loneliness of his aspect, and quite altered the air of his face.

This plain man's story is a memorable example, that he is happiest who confines his wants to natural necessities; and he that goes further in his desires, increases his wants in proportion to his acquisitions; or to use his own expression, ' I am now worth £800, but shall never be so happy, as when I was not worth a farthing.'

Englishman. No. 26. 1713.

GEORGE FARQUHAR

1678–1707

A RECRUITING SCENE

The Street

Enter KITE, *leading* COSTAR PEARMAIN *in one hand, and* THOMAS APPLETREE *in the other, both drunk.*

KITE *sings.*

Our prentice Tom may now refuse
To wipe his scoundrel master's shoes ;
For now he 's free to sing and play,
Over the hills and far away,
Over the hills, &c.   [*The Mob sing the Chorus.*

We all shall lead more happy lives,
By getting rid of brats and wives,
That scold and brawl both night and day ;
Over the hills and far away.
Over the hills, &c.

Hey, boys ! thus we soldiers live, drink, sing, dance, play ; we live, as one should say—we live— 'tis impossible to tell how we live. We're all princes. Why—why, you're a king, you're an emperor, and I'm a prince. Now, ain't we—

Appletree. No, sergeant, I'll be no emperor.

Kite. No !

Appletree. No, I'll be a justice of peace.

Kite. A justice of peace, man !

Appletree. Aye, wauns will I; for since this Pressing Act, they are greater than any emperor under the sun.

Kite. Done! you're a justice of peace, and you're a king, and I'm a duke; and a rum duke, an't I?

Pearmain. No, but I'll be no king.

Kite. What then?

Pearmain. I'll be a queen.

Kite. A queen!

Pearmain. Aye, Queen of England; that's greater than any king of 'em all.

Kite. Bravely said, faith! Huzza for the Queen!—[*All huzza.*] But heark'ee, you Mr. Justice, and you Mr. Queen, did you ever see the Queen's picture.

Both. No, no.

Kite. I wonder at that, I have two of 'em set in gold, and as like her Majesty, God bless the mark! [*He takes two broad pieces out of his pocket.*] See here, they're set in gold. [*Gives one to each.*]

Appletree. The wonderful works of Nature!
                              [*Looking at it.*

Pearmain. What's this written about? Here's a posy, I believe,—*Ca-ro-lus.*—What's that, sergeant?

Kite. Oh, Carolus!—Why, Carolus is Latin for Queen Anne, that's all.

Pearmain. 'Tis a fine thing to be a scollard! Sergeant, will you part with this? I'll buy it on you, if it come within the compass of a crawn.

Kite. A crown! Never talk of buying; 'tis the same thing among friends, you know; I present them to you both: you shall give me as good a thing. Put them up, and remember your old friend, when [*singing*] I'm over the hills and far away!   [*They sing and put up the money.*

Enter PLUME, *singing.*

Plume.   *Over the hills, and o'er the main,*
        To Flanders, Portugal, or Spain;
        The queen commands, and we'll obey—
        Over the hill and far away.

Come on, my men of mirth, away with it, I'll make one among ye.—Who are these hearty lads?

Kite.   Off with your hats; 'ouns, off with your hats! This is the captain, the captain.

Appletree.   We have seen captains afore now, mun.

Pearmain.   Aye, and lieutenant-captains too; flesh, I'se keep on my nab!

Appletree.   And I'se scarcely doff mine for any captain in England. My vether's a freeholder.

Plume.   Who are these jolly lads, sergeant?

Kite.   A couple of honest brave fellows, that are willing to serve the Queen: I have entertained them just now as volunteers under your honour's command.

Plume.   And good entertainment they shall have. Volunteers are the men I want, those are the men fit to make soldiers, captains, generals!

Pearmain.   Wauns, Tummas, what's this? Are you listed?

Appletree.   Flesh, not I: are you, Costar?

Pearmain.   Wauns, not I!

Kite.   What, not listed! Ha, ha, ha! a very good jest, faith!

Pearmain.   Come, Tummas, we'll go whome.

Appletree.   Aye, aye, come.

Kite. Home! for shame, gentlemen, behave yourselves better before your captain! Dear Tummas, honest Costar—

Appletree. No, no, we'll be gone.   [*Going.*

Kite. Nay, then I command you to stay: I place you both sentinels in this place for two hours to watch the motion of St. Mary's clock, you; and you the motion of St. Chad's, and he that dare stir from his post till he be relieved, shall have my sword in his guts the next minute.

Plume. What's the matter, sergeant? I'm afraid you're too rough with these gentlemen.

Kite. I'm too mild, sir: they disobey command, sir, and one of them should be shot for an example to the other.

Pearmain. Shot! Tummas.

Plume. Come, gentlemen, what is the matter?

Pearman. We don't know; the noble sergeant is pleased to be in a passion, sir, but—

Kite. They disobey command; they deny their being listed.

Appletree. Nay, sergeant, we don't downright deny it neither; that we dare not do, for fear of being shot; but we humbly conceive in a civil way, and begging your worship's pardon, that we may go home.

Plume. That's easily known. Have either of you received any of the Queen's money?

Pearmain. Not a brass farthing, sir.

Kite. Sir, they have each of 'em received three-and-twenty shillings and sixpence, and 'tis now in their pockets.

Pearmain. Wauns, if I have a penny in my pocket but a bent sixpence, I'll be content to be listed, and shot into the bargain!

Appletree. And I. Look 'e here, sir.

Pearmain. Aye, here's my stock too: nothing but the Queen's picture, that the sergeant gave me just now.

Kite. See there, a broad-piece! three-and-twenty shillings and sixpence; the t'other has the fellow on't.

Plume. The case is plain, gentlemen; the goods are found upon you. Those pieces of gold are worth three-and-twenty and sixpence each.

Pearman. So it seems that *Carolus* is three-and-twenty shillings and sixpence in Latin.

Appletree. 'Tis the same thing in the Greek, for we are listed.

Pearmain. Flesh, but we an't, Tummas!—I desire to be carried before the Mayor, Captain.

[*While they talk, the Captain and Sergeant whisper.*

Plume. 'Twill never do, Kite; your damned tricks will ruin me at last.—I won't lose the fellows though, if I can help it.—Well, gentlemen, there must be some trick in this: my sergeant offers here to take his oath that you're fairly listed.

Appletree. Why, Captain, we know that you soldiers have more liberty of conscience than other folks; but for me or neighbour Costar here to take such an oath, 'twould be a downright perjuration.

Plume. Look 'e, you rascal! you villain! if I find that you have imposed upon these two honest fellows, I'll trample you to death, you dog! Come, how was't?

Appletree. Nay, then, we will speak. Your sergeant, as you say, is a rogue, begging your worship's pardon, and—

Pearmain. Nay, Tummas, let me speak, you
know I can read; and so, sir, he gave us those
two pieces of money for pictures of the Queen by
way of a present.

Plume. How! by way of a present! ... I'll
teach him to abuse honest fellows like you!—
Scoundrel, rogue, villain!

        [*Beats off the* Sergeant, *and follows.*
Both. O brave noble Captain! Huzza! a
brave captain, faith!

Pearmain. Now, Tummas, *Corolus* is Latin for
a beating. This is the bravest captain I ever saw.
Wauns, I have a month's mind to go with him!

Re-enter PLUME.

Plume. A dog! To abuse two such pretty
fellows as you! Look 'e, gentlemen, I love a pretty
fellow: I come among you here as an officer to
list soldiers, not as a kidnapper, to steal slaves.

Pearmain. Mind that, Tummas.

Plume. I desire no man to go with me, but as
I went myself: I went a volunteer, as you or you
may go; for a little time carried a musket, and
now I command a company

Appletree. Mind that, Costar; a sweet gentleman.

Plume. 'Tis true, gentlemen, I might take an
advantage of you; the Queen's money was in
your pockets, my sergeant was ready to take his
oath that you were listed; but I scorn to do
a base thing, you are both of you at your liberty.

Pearmain. Thank you, noble captain.—Ecod,
I cannot find in my heart to leave him, he talks so
finely.

Appletree. Aye, Costar, would he alway hold in this mind.

Plume. Come, my lads, one thing more I'll tell you : you're both young tight fellows, and the army is the place to make you men for ever : every man has his lot, and you have yours. What think you now of a purse full of French gold out of a monsieur's pocket, after you have dashed out his brains with the butt of your firelock, eh ?

Pearmain. Wauns ! I'll have it, Captain—give me a shilling, I'll follow you to the end of the world.

Appletree. Nay, dear Costar, duna ; be advised.

Plume. Here, my hero, here are two guineas for thee, as earnest of what I'll do farther for thee.

Appletree. Duna take it ; duna, dear Costar !
[*Cries, and pulls back his arm.*

Pearmain. I wull ! I wull ! Wauns, my mind gives me, that I shall be a captain myself.—I take your money, sir, and now I'm a gentleman.

Plume. Give me thy hand—And now you and I will travel the world o'er, and command it wherever we tread. Bring your friend with you, if you can. [*Aside.*

Pearmain. Well, Tummas, must we part ?

Appletree. No, Costar, I cannot leave thee.— Come, Captain, [*Crying.*] I'll e'en go along too ; and if you have two honester simpler lads in your company than we twa been—I'll say no more.

Plume. Here, my lad.—[*Gives him money.*] Now, your name ?

Appletree. Tummas Appletree.

Plume. And yours ?

Pearmain. Costar Pearmain.

Plume. Born where?

Appletree. Both in Herefordshire.

Plume. Very well; courage, my lads!—Now we'll sing, *Over the hills and far away.*

> *Courage, boys, 'tis one to ten,*
> *But we return all gentlemen, &c.*

The Recruiting Officer.   1706.

HENRY FIELDING

1707–1754

PARTRIDGE AT THE THEATRE

Mr. Jones having spent three hours in reading
and kissing the aforesaid letter, and being, at last,
in a state of good spirits, from the last-mentioned
considerations, he agreed to carry an appointment,
which he had before made, into execution. This
was to attend Mrs. Miller, and her younger
daughter, into the gallery at the playhouse, and to
admit Mr. Partridge as one of the company. For
as Jones had really that taste for humour which
many affect, he expected to enjoy much entertain
ment in the criticisms of Partridge; from whom
he expected the simple dictates of nature, unim-
proved indeed, but likewise unadulterated by art.

In the first row, then, of the first gallery did Mr.
Jones, Mrs. Miller, her youngest daughter, and
Partridge, take their places. Partridge immediately declared it was the finest place he had ever
been in. When the first music was played, he
said, ' It was a wonder how so many fiddlers
could play at one time, without putting one
another out.' While the fellow was lighting the
upper candles, he cried out to Mrs. Miller, ' Look,
look, madam, the very picture of the man in the
end of the common-prayer book, before the gun-
powder-treason service.' Nor could he help
observing, with a sigh, when all the candles were

lighted, 'That here were candles enough burnt
in one night to keep an honest poor family for
a whole twelvemonth.'

As soon as the play, which was *Hamlet, Prince
of Denmark*, began, Partridge was all attention,
nor did he break silence till the entrance of the
Ghost; upon which he asked Jones, 'What man
that was in the strange dress; something', said he,
'like what I have seen in a picture. Sure it is not
armour, is it?' Jones answered, 'That is the
Ghost.' To which Partridge replied with a smile,
'Persuade me to that, sir, if you can. Though
I can't say I ever actually saw a ghost in my life,
yet I am certain I should know one, if I saw him,
better than that comes to. No, no, sir, ghosts
don't appear in such dresses as that, neither.'
In this mistake, which caused much laughter in
the neighbourhood of Partridge, he was suffered
to continue, till the scene between the Ghost and
Hamlet, when Partridge gave that credit to Mr.
Garrick which he had denied to Jones, and fell
into so violent a trembling, that his knees knocked
against each other. Jones asked him what was
the matter, and whether he was afraid of the
warrior upon the stage? 'O la! sir,' said he,
'I perceive now it is what you told me. I am not
afraid of any thing, for I know it is but a play.
And if it was really a ghost, it could do one no
harm at such a distance, and in so much company; and yet if I was frightened, I am not the
only person.'

'Why, who', cried Jones, 'dost thou take to be
such a coward here besides thyself?'

'Nay, you may call me coward if you will; but
if that little man there upon the stage is not

frightened, I never saw any man frightened in my life. Aye, aye ; *go along with you* ! Aye, to be sure ! Who 's fool then ? Will you ? Lud have mercy upon such fool-hardiness ! Whatever happens it is good enough for you. *Follow you* ?—I'd follow the devil as soon. Nay, perhaps it is the devil,—for they say he can put on what likeness he pleases. Oh ! here he is again. *No farther* ! No, you have gone far enough already ; farther than I'd have gone for all the king's dominions.' Jones offered to speak, but Partridge cried, ' Hush, hush, dear sir, don't you hear him ! ' And during the whole speech of the Ghost, he sat with his eyes fixed partly on the Ghost, and partly on Hamlet, and with his mouth open ; the same passions which succeeded each other in Hamlet succeeding likewise in him.

When the scene was over, Jones said, ' Why, Partridge, you exceed my expectations. You enjoy the play more than I conceived possible.'

' Nay, sir,' answered Partridge, ' if you are not afraid of the devil, I can't help it ; but to be sure it is natural to be surprised at such things, though I know there is nothing in them : not that it was the Ghost that surprised me neither, for I should have known that to have been only a man in a strange dress ; but when I saw the little man so frightened himself, it was that which took hold of me.'

' And dost thou imagine then, Partridge,' cries Jones, ' that he was really frightened ? '

' Nay, sir,' said Partridge, ' did not you yourself observe afterwards, when he found it was his own father's spirit, and how he was murdered in the garden, how his fear forsook him by degrees,

and he was struck dumb with sorrow, as it were,
just as I should have been, had it been my own
case——But hush! O la! What noise is that?
There he is again. Well, to be certain, though I
know there is nothing at all in it, I am glad I am
not down yonder, where those men are.' Then
turning his eyes again upon Hamlet, 'Aye, you
may draw your sword; what signifies a sword
against the power of the devil?'

During the second act, Partridge made very few
remarks. He greatly admired the fineness of the
dresses; nor could he help observing upon the
King's countenance. 'Well,' said he, 'how people
may be deceived by faces? *Nulla fides fronti* is,
I find, a true saying. Who would think, by looking
in the King's face, that he had ever committed a
murder?' He then inquired after the Ghost; but
Jones, who intended he should be surprised, gave
him no other satisfaction than 'that he might
possibly see him again soon, and in a flash of fire.'

Partridge sat in fearful expectation of this; and
now, when the Ghost made his next appearance,
Partridge cried out, 'There, sir, now; what say
you now? Is he frightened now, or no? As
much frightened as you think me; and to be sure
nobody can help some fears. I would not be in
so bad a condition as what's-his-name, Squire
Hamlet, is there, for all the world. Bless me!
What's become of the spirit? As I am a living
soul, I thought I saw him sink into the earth.'

'Indeed, you saw right,' answered Jones.

'Well, well,' cries Partridge, 'I know it is only
a play; and besides, if there was anything in all
this, Madam Miller would not laugh so: for as to
you, sir, you would not be afraid, I believe, if the

devil was here in person. There, there—aye, no wonder you are in such a passion; shake the vile wicked wretch to pieces. If she was my own mother I should serve her so. To be sure, all duty to a mother is forfeited by such wicked doings. Aye, go about your business; I hate the sight of you.'

Our critic was now pretty silent till the play, which Hamlet introduces before the King. This he did not at first understand, till Jones explained it to him; but he no sooner entered into the spirit of it, than he began to bless himself that he had never committed murder. Then, turning to Mrs. Miller, he asked her, 'If she did not imagine the King looked as if he was touched; though he is', said he, 'a good actor, and doth all he can to hide it. Well, I would not have so much to answer for, as that wicked man there hath, to sit upon a much higher chair than he sits upon. No wonder he run away; for your sake I'll never trust an innocent face again.'

The grave-digging scene next engaged the attention of Partridge, who expressed much surprise at the number of skulls thrown upon the stage. To which Jones answered, 'That it was one of the most famous burial-places about town.'

'No wonder then', cries Partridge, 'that the place is haunted. But I never saw in my life a worse grave-digger. I had a sexton, when I was clerk, that should have dug three graves while he is digging one. The fellow handles a spade as if it was the first time he had ever had one in his hand. Aye, aye, you may sing. You had rather sing than work, I believe.' Upon Hamlet's taking up the skull, he cried out, 'Well, it is strange to see how fearless some men are: I never could

bring myself to touch any thing belonging to a
dead man on any account. He seemed frightened
enough, too, at the Ghost, I thought. *Nemo omn-
ibus horis sapit.*'

Little more worth remembering occurred during
the play; at the end of which Jones asked him,
which of the players he had liked best ?

To this he answered, with some appearance of
indignation at the question, ' The King, without
doubt.'

' Indeed, Mr. Partridge,' says Mrs. Miller, ' you
are not of the same opinion as the town; for they
are all agreed that Hamlet is acted by the best
player who ever was on the stage.'

' He the best player ! ' cries Partridge, with
a contemptuous sneer, ' why, I could act as well as
he myself. I am sure if I had seen a ghost, I should
have looked in the very same manner, and done
just as he did. And then, to be sure, in that
scene, as you call it, between him and his mother,
where you told me he acted so fine, why, Lord
help me, any man, that is any good man, that had
had such a mother, would have done exactly the
same. I know you are only joking with me; but
indeed, madam, though I was never at a play in
London, yet I have seen acting before in the
country; and the King for my money; he speaks
all his words distinctly, half as loud again as the
other. Anybody may see he is an actor.'

While Mrs. Miller was thus engaged in conversation with Partridge, a lady came up to Mr. Jones,
whom he immediately knew to be Mrs. Fitzpatrick.
She said she had seen him from the other part of
the gallery, and had taken that opportunity of
speaking to him, as she had something to say,

which might be of great service to himself. She
then acquainted him with her lodgings, and made
him an appointment the next day in the morning,
which, upon recollection she presently changed to
the afternoon ; at which time Jones promised to
attend her.

Thus ended the adventure at the playhouse ;
where Partridge had afforded great mirth, not
only to Jones and Mrs. Miller, but to all who sat
within hearing, who were more attentive to what
he said, than to anything that passed on the stage.

He durst not go to bed all that night for fear of
the Ghost ; and for many nights after, sweat two
or three hours before he went to sleep, with the
same apprehensions ; and waked several times in
great horrors, crying out, ' Lord have mercy upon
us ! there it is.'

Tom Jones. 1749,

SAMUEL JOHNSON

1709–1784

THE ADVENTURES OF THE LADY
PEKUAH

' At what time and in what manner I was forced
away,' said Pekuah, ' your servants have told you.
The suddenness of the event struck me with
surprise, and I was at first rather stupefied, than
agitated with any passion of either fear or sorrow.
My confusion was increased by the speed and
tumult of our flight, while we were followed by
the Turks, who, as it seemed, soon despaired to
overtake us, or were afraid of those whom they
made a show of menacing.

' When the Arabs saw themselves out of danger,
they slackened their course ; and as I was less
harassed by external violence, I began to feel more
uneasiness in my mind. After some time, we
stopped near a spring shaded with trees in a
pleasant meadow, where we were set upon the
ground, and offered such refreshments as our
masters were partaking. I was suffered to sit
with my maids apart from the rest, and none
attempted to comfort or insult us. Here I first
began to feel the full weight of my misery. The
girls sat weeping in silence, and from time to time
looked on me for succour. I knew not to what
condition we were doomed, nor could conjecture

where would be the place of our captivity, or whence to draw any hope of deliverance. I was in the hands of robbers and savages, and had no reason to suppose that their pity was more than their justice, or that they would forbear the gratification of any ardour of desire, or caprice of cruelty. I, however, kissed my maids, and endeavoured to pacify them by remarking that we were yet treated with decency, and that, since we were now carried beyond pursuit, there was no danger of violence to our lives.

'When we were to be set again on horseback, my maids clung round me, and refused to be parted ; but I commanded them not to irritate those who had us in their power. We travelled the remaining part of the day through an unfrequented and pathless country, and came by moonlight to the side of a hill, where the rest of the troop were stationed. Their tents were pitched and their fires kindled, and our chief was welcomed as a man much beloved by his dependants.

'We were received into a large tent, where we found women who had attended their husbands in the expedition. They set before us the supper which they had provided, and I ate it rather to encourage my maids, than to comply with any appetite of my own. When the meat was taken away, they spread the carpets for repose. I was weary, and hoped to find in sleep that remission of distress which nature seldom denies. Ordering myself therefore to be undressed, I observed that the women looked very earnestly upon me, not expecting, I suppose, to see me so submissively attended. When my upper vest was taken off, they were apparently struck with the splendour of my clothes, and one of them timorously laid her hand upon the embroidery. She then went out, and in a short time came back with another woman, who seemed to be of higher rank and greater authority. She did, at her entrance, the usual act of reverence, and taking me by the hand, placed me in a smaller tent, spread with fine carpets, where I spent the night quietly with my maids.

'.In the morning, as I was sitting on the grass, the chief of the troop came towards me. I rose up to receive him, and he bowed with great respect. " Illustrious lady," said he, " my fortune is better than I had presumed to hope : I am told by my women that I have a princess in my camp." " Sir," answered I, " your women have deceived themselves and you ; I am not a princess, but an unhappy stranger, who intended soon to have left this country, in which I am now to be imprisoned for ever." " Whoever or whencesoever you are," returned the Arab, " your dress, and that of your servants, show your rank to be high and your wealth to be great. Why should you, who can so easily procure your ransom, think yourself in danger of perpetual captivity ? The purpose of my incursions is to increase my riches, or, more properly, to gather tribute. The sons of Ishmael are the natural and hereditary lords of this part of the continent, which is usurped by late invaders and low-born tyrants, from whom we are compelled to take by the sword what is denied to justice. The violence of war admits no distinction ; the lance that is lifted at guilt and power, will sometimes fall on innocence and gentleness."

' "How little", said I, "did I expect that yesterday it should have fallen upon me!"

' "Misfortunes", answered the Arab, "should always be expected. If the eye of hostility could learn reverence or pity, excellence like yours had been exempt from injury. But the angels of affliction spread their toils alike for the virtuous and the wicked, for the mighty and the mean. Do not be disconsolate: I am not one of the lawless and cruel rovers of the desert; I know the rules of civil life; I will fix your ransom, give a passport to your messenger, and perform my stipulation with nice punctuality."

' You will easily believe that I was pleased with his courtesy: and finding that his predominant passion was desire of money, I began now to think my danger less, for I knew that no sum would be thought too great for the release of Pekuah. I told him that he should have no reason to charge me with ingratitude, if I was used with kindness, and that any ransom which could be expected for a maid of common rank would be paid; but that he must not persist to rate me as a princess. He said he would consider what he should demand, and then smiling, bowed and retired.

' Soon after, the women came about me, each contending to be more officious than the other, and my maids themselves were served with reverence. We travelled onward by short journeys. On the fourth day, the chief told me that my ransom must be two hundred ounces of gold; which I not only promised him, but told him, that I would add fifty more, if I and my maids were honourably treated.

'I never knew the power of gold before. From that time I was the leader of the troop. The march of every day was longer or shorter as I commanded, and the tents were pitched where I chose to rest. We now had camels and other conveniences for travel; my own women were always at my side; and I amused myself with observing the manners of the vagrant nations, and with viewing remains of ancient edifices, with which these deserted countries appear to have been, in some distant age, lavishly embellished.

'The chief of the band was a man far from illiterate: he was able to travel by the stars or the compass, and had marked, in his erratic expeditions, such places as are most worthy the notice of a passenger. He observed to me, that buildings are always best preserved in places little frequented and difficult of access: for, when once a country declines from its primitive splendour, the more inhabitants are left, the quicker ruin will be made. Walls supply stones more easily than quarries, and palaces and temples will be demolished, to make stables of granite and cottages of porphyry.

'We wandered about in this manner for some weeks, whether, as our chief pretended, for my gratification, or, as I rather suspected, for some convenience of his own. I endeavoured to appear contented, where sullenness and resentment would have been of no use, and that endeavour conduced much to the calmness of my mind: but my heart was always with Nekayah, and the troubles of the night much overbalanced the amusements of the day. My women, who threw all their cares upon their mistress, set their minds at ease from the time when they saw me treated with respect,

and gave themselves up to the incidental allevia-
tions of our fatigue without solicitude or sorrow.
I was pleased with their pleasure, and animated
with their confidence. My condition had lost
much of its terror, since I found that the Arab
ranged the country merely to get riches. Avarice
is a uniform and tractable vice : other intellectual
distempers are different in different constitutions
of mind ; that which soothes the pride of one will
offend the pride of another ; but to the favour of
the covetous there is a ready way ; bring money,
and nothing is denied.

   ' At last we came to the dwelling of our chief,
a strong and spacious house built with stone in an
island of the Nile, which lies, as I was told, under
the tropic. "Lady," said the Arab, "you shall
rest after your journey a few weeks in this place,
where you are to consider yourself as sovereign.
My occupation is war : I have therefore chosen
this obscure residence, from which I can issue
unexpected, and to which I can retire unpursued.
You may now repose in security ; here are few
pleasures, but here is no danger." He then led
me into the inner apartments, and seating me on
the richest couch, bowed to the ground. His
women, who considered me as a rival, looked on
me with malignity ; but being soon informed that
I was a great lady detained only for my ransom,
they began to vie with each other in obsequious-
ness and reverence.

   ' Being again comforted with new assurances of
speedy liberty, I was for some days diverted from
impatience by the novelty of the place. The
turrets overlooked the country to a great distance,
and afforded a view of many windings of the

stream. In the day I wandered from one place to another, as the course of the sun varied the splendour of the prospect, and saw many things which I had never seen before. The crocodiles and river-horses are common in this unpeopled region, and I often looked upon them with terror, though I knew that they could not hurt me. For some time I expected to see mermaids and tritons, which, as Imlac has told me, the European travellers have stationed in the Nile; but no such beings ever appeared, and the Arab, when I inquired after them, laughed at my credulity.

'At night the Arab always attended me to a tower set apart for celestial observations, where he endeavoured to teach me the names and courses of the stars. I had no great inclination to this study, but an appearance of attention was necessary to please my instructor, who valued himself for his skill; and, in a little while, I found some employment requisite to beguile the tediousness of time, which was to be passed always amidst the same objects. I was weary of looking in the morning on things from which I had turned away weary in the evening; I therefore was at last willing to observe the stars rather than do nothing, but could not always compose my thoughts, and was very often thinking on Nekayah, when others imagined me contemplating the sky Soon after, the Arab went upon another expedition, and then my only pleasure was to talk with my maids about the accident by which we were carried away, and the happiness that we should all enjoy at the end of our captivity.'

'There were women in your Arab's fortress,' said the princess: 'why did you not make them your companions, enjoy their conversation, and partake their diversions ? In a place where they found business or amusement, why should you alone sit corroded with idle melancholy ? or why could not you bear for a few months that condition to which they were condemned for life ? '

'The diversions of the women', answered Pekuah, 'were only childish play, by which the mind accustomed to stronger operations could not be kept busy. I could do all which they delighted in doing, by powers merely sensitive, while my intellectual faculites were flown to Cairo. They ran from room to room, as a bird hops from wire to wire in his cage. They danced for the sake of motion, as lambs frisk in a meadow. One some-times pretended to be hurt, that the rest might be alarmed ; or hid herself that another might seek her. Part of their time passed in watching the progress of light bodies that floated on the river, and part in marking the various forms into which clouds broke in the sky.

'Their business was only needlework, in which I and my maids sometimes helped them ; but you know that the mind will easily straggle from the fingers, nor will you suspect that captivity and absence from Nekayah could receive solace from silken flowers.

'Nor was much satisfaction to be hoped from their conversation : for of what could they be expected to talk ? They had seen nothing, for they had lived from early youth in that narrow spot ; of what they had not seen they could have no knowledge, for they could not read. They had no ideas but of the few things that were within their view, and had hardly names for anything but their clothes and their food. As I bore a superior character, I was often called to terminate their quarrels, which I decided as equitably as I could. If it could have amused me to hear the complaints of each against the rest, I might have been often detained by long stories ; but the motives of their animosity were so small, that I could not listen without intercepting the tale.'

'How', said Rasselas, 'can the Arab, whom you represented as a man of more than common accomplishments, take any pleasure in his seraglio, when it is filled only with women like these ? Are they exquisitely beautiful ? '

'They do not', said Pekuah, 'want that unaffecting and ignoble beauty which may subsist without sprightliness or sublimity, without energy of thought or dignity of virtue. But to a man like the Arab such beauty was only a flower casually plucked and carelessly thrown away. Whatever pleasures he might find among them, they were not those of friendship or society. When they were playing about him, he looked on them with inattentive superiority ; when they vied for his regard, he sometimes turned away disgusted. As they had no knowledge, their talk could take nothing from the tediousness of life ; as they had no choice, their fondness, or appearance of fondness, excited in him neither pride nor gratitude ; he was not exalted in his own esteem by the smiles of a woman who saw no other man, nor was much obliged by that regard, of which he could never know the sincerity, and which he might often perceive to be exerted, not so much to delight him as to pain a rival. That which he gave and they received as love, was only a careless distribution of superfluous time, such love as man can bestow upon that which he despises, such as has neither hope nor fear, neither joy nor sorrow.'

'You have reason, lady, to think yourself happy,' said Imlac, 'that you have been thus easily dismissed. How could a mind, hungry for knowledge, be willing, in an intellectual famine, to lose such a banquet as Pekuah's conversation?'

'I am inclined to believe,' answered Pekuah, 'that he was for some time in suspense; for, notwithstanding his promise, whenever I proposed to dispatch a messenger to Cairo, he found some excuse for delay. While I was detained in his house, he made many incursions into the neighbouring countries; and, perhaps, he would have refused to discharge me, had his plunder been equal to his wishes. He returned always courteous, related his adventures, delighted to hear my observations, and endeavoured to advance my acquaintance with the stars. When I importuned him to send away my letters, he soothed me with professions of honour and sincerity; and, when I could be no longer decently denied, put his troop again in motion, and left me to govern in his absence. I was much afflicted by this studied procrastination, and was sometimes afraid that I should be forgotten; that you would leave Cairo, and I must end my days in an island of the Nile.

'I grew at last hopeless and dejected, and cared so little to entertain him, that he for a while more frequently talked with my maids. That he should fall in love with them or with me, might have been equally fatal, and I was not much pleased with the growing friendship. My anxiety was not long

G

for, as I recovered some degree of cheerfulness, he returned to me, and I could not forbear to despise my former uneasiness.

'He still delayed to send for my ransom, and would, perhaps, never have determined, had not your agent found his way to him. The gold, which he would not fetch, he could not reject when it was offered. He hastened to prepare for our journey hither, like a man delivered from the pain of an intestine conflict. I took leave of my companions in the house, who dismissed me with cold indifference.'

Nekayah having heard her favourite's relation, rose and embraced her, and Rasselas gave her an hundred ounces of gold, which she presented to the Arab for the fifty that were promised.

The History of Rasselas. 1759.

OLIVER GOLDSMITH

1728-1774

A VISIT TO WESTMINSTER ABBEY

I AM just returned from Westminster Abbey, the place of sepulture for the philosophers, heroes, and kings of England. What a gloom do monumental inscriptions and all the venerable remains of deceased merit inspire! Imagine a temple marked with the hand of antiquity, solemn as religious awe, adorned with all the magnificence of barbarous profusion, dim windows, fretted pillars, long colonnades, and dark ceilings. Think then, what were my sensations at being introduced to such a scene. I stood in the midst of the temple, and threw my eyes round on the walls, filled with the statues, the inscriptions, and the monuments of the dead.

Alas, I said to myself, how does pride attend the puny child of dust even to the grave! Even humble as I am, I possess more consequence in the present scene than the greatest hero of them all; they have toiled for an hour to gain a transient immortality, and are at length retired to the grave, where they have no attendant but the worm, none to flatter but the epitaph.

As I was indulging such reflections, a gentleman dressed in black, perceiving me to be a stranger, came up, entered into conversation, and politely offered to be my instructor and guide through the temple. If any monument, said he, should

particularly excite your curiosity, I shall endeavour
to satisfy your demands. I accepted with thanks
the gentleman's offer, adding, that ' I was come to
observe the policy, the wisdom, and the justice of
the English, in conferring rewards upon deceased
merit. If adulation like this,' continued I, ' be
properly conducted, as it can no ways injure those
who are flattered, so it may be a glorious incentive
to those who are now capable of enjoying it. It is
the duty of every good government to turn this
monumental pride to its own advantage, to become strong in the aggregate from the weakness of
the individual. If none but the truly great have
a place in this awful repository, a temple like this
will give the finest lessons of morality, and be
a strong incentive to true ambition. I am told
that none have a place here but characters of the
most distinguished merit.' The man in black
seemed impatient at my observations, so I discon-
tinued my remarks, and we walked on together to
take a view of every particular monument in order
as it lay.

As the eye is naturally caught by the finest
objects, I could not avoid being particularly
curious about one monument which appeared more
beautiful than the rest; ' that,' said I to my guide,
' I take to be the tomb of some very great man.
By the peculiar excellence of the workmanship,
and the magnificence of the design, this must be
a trophy raised to the memory of some king who
has saved his country from ruin, or law-giver,
who has reduced his fellow-citizens from anarchy
into just subjection.' ' It is not requisite,' replied
my companion smiling,' to have such qualifications
in order to have a very fine monument here.

More humble abilities will suffice.' 'What, I suppose then, the gaining two or three battles, or the taking half a score towns, is thought a sufficient qualification?' Gaining battles, or taking towns, replied the man in black, may be of service; but a gentleman may have a very fine monument here without ever seeing a battle or a siege. 'This, then, is the monument of some poet, I presume, of one whose wit has gained him immortality?' No, sir, replied my guide, the gentleman who lies here never made verses; and as for wit, he despised it in others, because he had none himself. 'Pray tell me then in a word,' said I peevishly, 'what is the great man who lies here particularly remarkable for?' Remarkable, sir! said my companion; why, sir, the gentleman that lies here is remarkable, very remarkable—for a tomb in Westminster Abbey. 'But, head of my ancestors! how has he got here? I fancy he could never bribe the guardians of the temple to give him a place. Should he not be ashamed to be seen among company, where even moderate merit would look like infamy?' I suppose, replied the man in black, the gentleman was rich, and his friends, as is usual in such a case, told him he was great. He readily believed them; the guardians of the temple, as they got by the self-delusion, were ready to believe him too; so he paid his money for a fine monument; and the workman, as you see, has made him one the most beautiful. Think not, however, that this gentleman is singular in his desire of being buried among the great; there are several others in the temple, who, hated and shunned by the great while alive, have come here, fully resolved to keep them company now they are dead.

As we walked along to a particular part of the
temple, There, says the gentleman, pointing with
his finger, that is the poets' corner; there you see
the monuments of Shakespeare, and Milton, and
Prior, and Drayton. Drayton, I replied; I never
heard of him before; but I have been told of one
Pope : is he there ? It is time enough, replied my
guide, these hundred years; he is not long dead,
people have not done hating him yet. Strange,
cried I, can any be found to hate a man whose life
was wholly spent in entertaining and instructing
his fellow creatures ? Yes, says my guide, they
hate him for that very reason. There are a set of
men called answerers of books, who take upon
them to watch the republic of letters, and distribute reputation by the sheet; they somewhat
resemble the eunuchs in a seraglio, who are incapable of giving pleasure themselves, and hinder
those that would. These answerers have no other
employment but to cry out Dunce, and Scribbler,
to praise the dead, and revile the living, to grant
a man of confessed abilities some small share of
merit, to applaud twenty blockheads in order to
gain the reputation of candour, and to revile the
moral character of the man whose writings they
cannot injure. Such wretches are kept in pay by
some mercenary bookseller, or more frequently,
the bookseller himself takes this dirty work off
their hands, as all that is required is to be very
abusive and very dull; every poet of any genius
is sure to find such enemies; he feels, though he
seems to despise, their malice; they make him
miserable here, and in the pursuit of empty fame,
at last he gains solid anxiety.

'Has this been the case with every poet I see

here ?' cried I.—Yes, with every mother's son of them, replied he, except he happened to be born a mandarin. If he has much money, he may buy reputation from your book-answerers as well as a monument from the guardians of the temple.

'But are there not some men of distinguished taste, as in China, who are willing to patronize men of merit, and soften the rancour of malevolent dullness ?'

I own there are many, replied the man in black; but, alas! Sir, the book-answerers crowd about them, and call themselves the writers of books; and the patron is too indolent to distinguish; thus poets are kept at a distance, while their enemies eat up all their rewards at the mandarin's table.

Leaving this part of the temple, we made up to an iron gate, through which my companion told me we were to pass in order to see the monuments of the kings. Accordingly I marched up without further ceremony, and was going to enter, when a person, who held the gate in his hand, told me I must pay first. I was surprised at such a demand; and asked the man whether the people of England kept a *show* ? Whether the paltry sum he demanded was not a national reproach ? Whether it was not more to the honour of the country to let their magnificence or their antiquities be openly seen, than thus meanly to tax a curiosity which tended to their own honour ? As for your questions,' replied the gate-keeper, ' to be sure they may be very right, because I don't understand them, but as for that there threepence, I farm it from one, who rents it from another, who hires it from a third, who leases it from the guardians of the temple, and we all must live.' I expected upon

paying here, to see something extraordinary, since
what I had seen for nothing filled me with so much
surprise; but in this I was disappointed; there
was little more within than black coffins, rusty
armour, tattered standards, and some few slovenly
figures in wax. I was sorry I had paid, but I comforted myself by considering it would be my last
payment. A person attended us, who, without
once blushing, told a hundred lies; he talked of
a lady who died by pricking her finger, of a king
with a golden head, and twenty such pieces of
absurdity. 'Look ye there, gentlemen,' says he,
pointing to an oak chair, 'there's a curiosity for
ye; in that chair the kings of England were
crowned: you see also a stone underneath, and that
stone is Jacob's pillow.' I could see no curiosity
either in the oak chair or the stone; could I, indeed, behold one of the old kings of England seated
in this, or Jacob's head laid upon the other, there
might be something curious in the sight; but in
the present case, there was no more reason for my
surprise than if I should pick a stone from their
streets, and call it a curiosity, merely because one
of the kings happened to tread upon it as he passed
in a procession.

From hence our conductor led us through
several dark walks and winding ways, uttering lies,
talking to himself, and flourishing a wand which he
held in his hand. He reminded me of the black
magicians of Kobi. After we had been almost
fatigued with a variety of objects, he, at last,
desired me to consider attentively a certain suit of
armour, which seemed to show nothing remarkable.
This armour, said he, belonged to General Monk.
'Very surprising, that a general should wear

armour!' And pray, added he, observe this cap, this is General Monk's cap. 'Very strange indeed, very strange, that a general should have a cap also! Pray, friend, what might this cap have cost originally?' That, Sir, says he, I don't know, but this cap is all the wages I have for my trouble. A very small recompense, truly, said I. Not so very small, replied he, for every gentleman puts some money into it, and I spend the money. 'What, more money! still more money!' Every gentleman gives something, Sir. I'll give thee nothing, returned I; the guardians of the temple should pay you your wages, friend, and not permit you to squeeze thus from every spectator. When we pay our money at the door to see a show, we never give more as we are going out. Sure the guardians of the temple can never think they get enough. Show me the gate; if I stay longer, I may probably meet with more of those ecclesiastical beggars.

Thus leaving the temple precipitately, I returned to my lodgings, in order to ruminate over what was great, and to despise what was mean in the occurrences of the day.

The Citizen of the World. Letter 13. 1762.

AT THE PLAY

THE English are as fond of seeing plays acted as the Chinese; but there is a vast difference in the manner of conducting them. We play our pieces in the open air, the English theirs under cover; we act by daylight, they by the blaze of torches.

One of our plays continues eight or ten days successively; an English piece seldom takes up above four hours in the representation.

My companion in black, with whom I am now beginning to contract an intimacy, introduced me a few nights ago to the play-house, where we placed ourselves conveniently at the foot of the stage. As the curtain was not drawn before my arrival, I had an opportunity of observing the behaviour of the spectators, and indulging those reflections which novelty generally inspires.

The rich in general were placed in the lowest seats, and the poor rose above them in degrees proportioned to their poverty. The order of precedence seemed here inverted; those who were undermost all the day, now enjoyed a temporary eminence, and became masters of the ceremonies. It was they who called for the music, indulging every noisy freedom, and testifying all the insolence of beggary in exaltation.

They who held the middle region seemed not so riotous as those above them, nor yet so tame as those below; to judge by their looks, many of them seemed strangers there as well as myself. They were chiefly employed during this period of expectation in eating oranges, reading the story of the play, or making assignations.

Those who sat in the lowest rows, which are called the pit, seemed to consider themselves as judges of the merits of the poet and the performers; they were assembled partly to be amused, and partly to show their taste; appearing to labour under that restraint which an affectation of superior discernment generally produces. My companion, however, informed me that not one in an hundred of them knew even the first principles of criticism; that they assumed the right of being censors because there was none to contradict their pretensions; and that every man who now called himself a connoisseur, became such to all intents and purposes.

Those who sat in the boxes appeared in the most unhappy situation of all. The rest of the audience came merely for their own amusement; these rather to furnish out a part of the entertainment themselves. I could not avoid considering them as acting parts in dumb show—not a curtsy or nod that was not the result of art; not a look nor a smile that was not designed for murder. Gentlemen and ladies ogled each other through spectacles; for my companion observed, that blindness was of late become fashionable; all affected indifference and ease, while their hearts at the same time burned for conquest. Upon the whole, the lights, the music, the ladies in their gayest dresses, the men with cheerfulness and expectation in their looks, all conspired to make a most agreeable picture, and to fill an heart that sympathises at human happiness with an inexpressible serenity.

The expected time for the play to begin at last arrived, the curtain was drawn, and the actors came on. A woman, who personated a queen, came in curtsying to the audience, who clapped their hands upon her appearance. Clapping of hands is, it seems, the manner of applauding in England: the manner is absurd; but every country, you know, has its peculiar absurdities. I was equally surprised, however, at the submission of the actress, who should have considered herself as a queen, as at the little discernment of

the audience who gave her such marks of applause
before she attempted to deserve them. Preliminaries between her and the audience being thus
adjusted, the dialogue was supported between her
and a most hopeful youth, who acted the part of
her confidant. They both appeared in extreme
distress, for it seems the queen had lost a child
some fifteen years before, and still keeps its dear
resemblance next to her heart, while her kind
companion bore a part in her sorrows.

Her lamentations grew loud. Comfort is offered,
but she detests the very sound. She bids them
preach comfort to the winds. Upon this her
husband comes in, who, seeing the queen so much
afflicted, can himself hardly refrain from tears or
avoid partaking in the soft distress. After thus
grieving through three scenes, the curtain dropped
for the first act.

Truly, said I to my companion, these kings and
queens are very much disturbed at no very great
misfortune ; certain I am, were people of humbler
stations to act in this manner, they would be
thought divested of common sense. I had scarce
finished this observation, when the curtain rose,
and the king came on in a violent passion. His
wife had, it seems, refused his proffered tenderness,
had spurned his royal embrace ; and he seemed
resolved not to survive her fierce disdain. After
he had thus fretted, and the queen had fretted
through the second act, the curtain was let down
once more.

Now, says my companion, you perceive the king
to be a man of spirit, he feels at every pore ; one
of your phlegmatic sons of clay would have given
the queen her own way, and let her come to herself

by degrees; but the king is for immediate tenderness, or instant death: death and tenderness are leading passions of every modern buskined hero; this moment they embrace, and the next stab, mixing daggers and kisses in every period.

I was going to second his remarks, when my attention was engrossed by a new object; a man came in balancing a straw upon his nose, and the audience were clapping their hands in all the raptures of applause. To what purpose, cried I, does this unmeaning figure make his appearance; is he a part of the plot? Unmeaning do you call him? replied my friend in black; this is one of the most important characters of the whole play; nothing pleases the people more than the seeing a straw balanced; there is a great deal of meaning in the straw; there is something suited to every apprehension in the sight; and a fellow possessed of talents like these is sure of making his fortune.

The third act now began with an actor who came to inform us that he was the villain of the play, and intended to show strange things before all was over. He was joined by another, who seemed as much disposed for mischief as he; their intrigues continued through this whole division. If that be a villain, said I, he must be a very stupid one, to tell his secrets without being asked; such soliloquies of late are never admitted in China.

The noise of clapping interrupted me once more; a child of six years old was learning to dance on the stage, which gave the ladies and mandarins infinite satisfaction. I am sorry, said I, to see the pretty creature so early learning so very bad a trade; dancing being, I presume, as contemptible here as in China. Quite the reverse, interrupted my companion ; dancing is a very reputable and genteel employment here ; men have a greater chance for encouragement from the merit of their heels than their heads. One who jumps up and flourishes his toes three times before he comes to the ground, may have three hundred a year ; he who flourishes them four times, get four hundred ; but he who arrives at five is inestimable, and may demand what salary he thinks proper. The female dancers too are valued for this sort of jumping and crossing ; and 'tis a cant word among them, that she deserves most who shows highest. But the fourth act is begun, let us be attentive.

In the fourth act the queen finds her long-lost child, now grown up into a youth of smart parts and great qualifications ; wherefore she wisely considers that the crown will fit his head better than that of her husband, whom she knows to be a driveller. The king discovers her design, and here comes on the deep distress ; he loves the queen, and he loves the kingdom ; he resolves, therefore, in order to possess both, that her son must die. The queen exclaims at his barbarity ; is frantic with rage, and at length, overcome with sorrow, falls into a fit ; upon which the curtain drops, and the act is concluded.

Observe the art of the poet, cries my companion ; when the queen can say no more, she falls into a fit. While thus her eyes are shut, while she is supported in the arms of Abigail, what horrors do we not fancy, we feel it in every nerve ; take my word for it, that fits are the true aposiopesis of modern tragedy.

The fifth act began, and a busy piece it was. Scenes shifting, trumpets sounding, mobs hallooing, carpets spreading, guards bustling from one door to another; gods, daemons, daggers, racks, and ratsbane. But whether the king was killed, or the queen was drowned, or the son was poisoned, I have absolutely forgotten.

When the play was over, I could not avoid observing, that the persons of the drama appeared in as much distress in the first act as the last: How is it possible, said I, to sympathize with them through five long acts; pity is but a short-lived passion; I hate to hear an actor mouthing trifles; neither startings, strainings, nor attitudes affect me unless there be cause: after I have been once or twice deceived by those unmeaning alarms, my heart sleeps in peace, probably unaffected by the principal distress. There should be one great passion aimed at by the actor as well as the poet, all the rest should be subordinate, and only contribute to make that the greater; if the actor therefore exclaims upon every occasion in the tones of despair, he attempts to move us too soon; he anticipates the blow, he ceases to affect though he gains our applause.

I scarce perceived that the audience were almost all departed; wherefore mixing with the crowd, my companion and I got into the street; where essaying an hundred obstacles from coach-wheels and palanquin poles like birds in their flight through the branches of a forest, after various turnings, we both at length got home in safety.

The Citizen of the World. Letter 21. 1762.

A WHITE-ELEPHANT

My wife and daughters happening to return
a visit to neighbour Flamborough's, found that
family had lately got their pictures drawn by
a limner, who travelled the country, and took
likenesses for fifteen shillings a head. As this
family and ours had long a sort of rivalry in point
of taste, our spirit took the alarm at this stolen
march upon us, and notwithstanding all I could
say, and I said much, it was resolved that we
should have our pictures done too. Having,
therefore, engaged the limner, for what could I do ?
our next deliberation was to show the superiority
of our taste in the attitudes. As for our neighbour's family, there were seven of them, and they
were drawn with seven oranges, a thing quite out
of taste, no variety in life, no composition in the
world. We desired to have something in a brighter
style, and, after many debates, at length came to
an unanimous resolution of being drawn together
in one large historical family piece. This would
be cheaper, since one frame would serve for all,
and it would be infinitely more genteel ; for all
families of any taste were now drawn in the same
manner. As we did not immediately recollect
an historical subject to hit us, we were contented
each with being drawn as independent historical
figures. My wife desired to be represented as
Venus, and the painter was desired not to be too
frugal of his diamonds in her stomacher and hair.
Her two little ones were to be as Cupids by her
side, while I, in my gown and band, was to present
her with my books on the Whistonian contro-

versy. Olivia would be drawn as an Amazon, sitting upon a bank of flowers, drest in a green joseph, richly laced with gold, and a whip in her hand; Sophia was to be a shepherdess, with as many sheep as the painter could put in for nothing; and Moses was to be drest out with an hat and white feather. Our taste so much pleased the 'Squire, that he insisted on being put in as one of the family in the character of Alexander the Great, at Olivia's feet. This was considered by us all as an indication of his desire to be introduced into the family, nor could we refuse his request. The painter was therefore set to work, and as he wrought with assiduity and expedition, in less than four days the whole was compleated. The piece was large, and it must be owned he did not spare his colours; for which my wife gave him great encomiums. We were all perfectly satisfied with his performance; but an unfortunate circumstance had not occurred till the picture was finished, which now struck us with dismay. It was so very large that we had no place in the house to fix it. How we all came to disregard so material a point is inconceivable; but certain it is, we had been all greatly overseen. The picture, therefore, instead of gratifying our vanity, as we hoped, leaned, in a most mortifying manner, against the kitchen wall, where the canvas was stretched and painted, much too large to be got through any of the doors, and the jest of all our neighbours. One compared it to Robinson Crusoe's long-boat, too large to be removed; another thought it more resembled a reel in a bottle; some wondered how it could be got out, but still more were amazed how it ever got in. *The Vicar of Wakefield.* 1766.

BLACKMAIL

Enter CROAKER.

Croaker. Death and destruction! Are all the horrors of air, fire and water to be levelled only at me! Am I only to be singled out for gunpowder-plots, combustibles and conflagration! Here it is —An incendiary letter dropped at my door. 'To muster Croaker, these with speed.' Aye, aye, plain enough the direction: all in the genuine incendiary spelling, and as cramp as the devil. 'With speed.' O, confound your speed. But let me read it once more. (*Reads.*) 'Mustar Croaker as sone as yowe see this leve twenty gunnes at the bar of the Talbot tell called for, or yowe and yower experetion will be all blown up.' Ah, but too plain. Blood and gunpowder in every line of it. Blown up! murderous dog! All blown up! Heavens! what have I and my poor family done, to be all blown up! (*Reads.*) 'Our pockets are low, and money we must have.' Aye, there's the reason; they'll blow us up, because they have got low pockets. (*Reads.*) 'It is but a short time you have to consider; for if this takes wind, the house will quickly be all of a flame.' Inhuman monsters! blow us up, and then burn us. The earthquake at Lisbon was but a bonfire to it. (*Reads.*) 'Make quick despatch, and so no more at present. But may Cupid, the little god of love, go with you wherever you go.' The little god of love! Cupid, the little god of love go with me! Go you to the devil, you and your little Cupid together; I'm so frightened, I scarce know whether

I sit, stand, or go. Perhaps this moment I'm treading on lighted matches, blazing brimstone, and barrels of gunpowder. They are preparing to blow me into up the clouds. Murder! We shall be all burnt in our beds; we shall be all burnt in our beds.

To HONEYWOOD, *enter* CROAKER, *with the letter in his hand, and Mrs.* CROAKER.

Mrs. Croaker. Ha! ha! ha! And so, my dear, it's your supreme wish that I should be quite wretched upon this occasion? ha! ha!

Croaker. (*Mimicking.*) Ha! ha! ha! And so, my dear, it's your supreme pleasure to give me no better consolation?

Mrs. Croaker. Positively, my dear; what is this incendiary stuff and trumpery to me? our house may travel through the air like the house of Loretto, for aught I care, if I am to be miserable in it.

Croaker. Would to heaven it were converted into a house of correction for your benefit. Have we not every thing to alarm us? Perhaps this very moment the tragedy is beginning.

Mrs. Croaker. Then let us reserve our distress till the rising of the curtain, or give them the money they want, and have done with them.

Croaker. Give them my money!—And **pray,** what right have they to my money?

Mrs. Croaker. And pray, what right then have you to my good humour?

Croaker. And so your good humour advises me to part with my money? Why then, to tell your good humour a piece of my mind, I'd sooner part with my wife. Here's Mr. Honeywood, see what he'll say to it. My dear Honeywood, look at this incendiary letter dropped at my door. It will freeze you with terror; and yet lovey here can read it—can read it, and laugh.

Mrs. Croaker. Yes, and so will Mr. Honeywood.

Croaker. If he does, I'll suffer to be hanged the next minute in the rogue's place, that's all.

Mrs. Croaker. Speak, Mr. Honeywood; is there any thing more foolish than my husband's fright upon this occasion?

Honeywood. It would not become me to decide, madam; but doubtless, the greatness of his terrors, now, will but invite them to renew their villany another time.

Mrs. Croaker. I told you, he'd be of my opinion.

Croaker. How, Sir! do you maintain that I should lie down, under such an injury, and show, neither by my tears nor complaints, that I have something of the spirit of a man in me?

Honeywood. Pardon me, Sir. You ought to make the loudest complaints, if you desire redress. The surest way to have redress, is to be earnest in the pursuit of it.

Croaker. Aye, whose opinion is he of now?

Mrs. Croaker. But don't you think that laughing-off our fears is the best way?

Honeywood. What is the best, madam, few can say; but I'll maintain it to be a very wise way.

Croaker. But we're talking of the best. Surely the best way is to face the enemy in the field, and not wait till he plunders us in our very bed-chamber.

Honeywood. Why, Sir, as to the best, that—that's a very wise way too.

Mrs. Croaker. But can any thing be more absurd, than to double our distresses by our apprehensions, and put it in the power of every low fellow that can scrawl ten words of wretched spelling, to torment us ?

Honeywood. Without doubt, nothing more absurd.

Croaker. How ! would it not be more absurd to despise the rattle till we are bit by the snake ?

Honeywood. Without doubt, perfectly absurd.

Croaker. Then you are of my opinion ?

Honeywood. Entirely.

Mrs. Croaker. And you reject mine ?

Honeywood. Heavens forbid, madam ! No sure, no reasoning can be more just than yours. We ought certainly to despise malice if we cannot oppose it, and not make the incendiary's pen as fatal to our repose as the highwayman's pistol.

Mrs. Croaker. O ! then you think I'm quite right ?

Honeywood. Perfectly right,

Croaker. A plague of plagues, we can't be both right. I ought to be sorry, or I ought to be glad. My hat must be on my head, or my hat must be off.

Mrs. Croaker. Certainly, in two opposite opinions, if one be perfectly reasonable, the other can't be perfectly right.

Honeywood. And why may not both be right. madam ? Mr. Croaker in earnestly seeking redress, and you in waiting the event with good humour ? Pray let me see the letter again. I have it. This letter requires twenty guineas to be left at the bar of the Talbot Inn. If it be indeed an incendiary letter, what if you and I, Sir, go there ; and, when the writer comes to be paid his expected booty, seize him?

Croaker. My dear friend, it's the very thing; the very thing. While I walk by the door, you shall plant yourself in ambush near the bar; burst out upon the miscreant like a masqued battery; extort a confession at once, and so hang him up by surprise.

Honeywood. Yes, but I would not chuse to exercise too much severity. It is my maxim, Sir, that crimes generally punish themselves.

Croaker. Well, but we may upbraid him a little. I suppose?   [*Ironically.*

Honeywood. Aye, but not punish him too rigidly.

Croaker. Well, well, leave that to my own benevolence.

Honeywood. Well, I do; but remember that universal benevolence is the first law of nature.

                    [*Exeunt* HONEYWOOD *and Mrs.* CROAKER

Croaker. Yes; and my universal benevolence will hang the dog, if he had as many necks as a hydra.

                    The Good-natur'd Man. 1768.

EDMUND BURKE

1729-1797

THE AMERICAN WHALE FISHERY

As to the wealth which the Colonies have drawn from the sea by their fisheries, you had all that matter fully opened at your bar. You surely thought those acquisitions of value, for they seemed even to excite your envy; and yet the spirit by which that enterprising employment has been exercised, ought rather, in my opinion, to have raised your esteem and admiration. And pray, Sir, what in the world is equal to it? Pass by the other parts, and look at the manner in which the people of New England have of late carried on the Whale Fishery. Whilst we follow them among the tumbling mountains of ice, and behold them penetrating into the deepest frozen recesses of Hudson's Bay and Davis's Straits, whilst we are looking for them beneath the Arctic Circle, we hear that they have pierced into the opposite region of polar cold, that they are at the antipodes, and engaged under the frozen Serpent of the south. Falkland Island, which seemed too remote and romantic an object for the grasp of national ambition, is but a stage and resting-place in the progress of their victorious industry. Nor is the equinoctial heat more discouraging to them, than the accumulated winter of both the poles. We know that whilst some of them draw the line and strike the harpoon on the coast of Africa, others run the longitude, and pursue their gigantic game along the coast of Brazil. No sea but what is vexed by their fisheries. No climate that is not witness to their toils. Neither the perseverance of Holland, nor the activity of France, nor the dexterous and firm sagacity of English enterprise, ever carried this most perilous mode of hardy industry to the extent to which it has been pushed by this recent people; a people who are still, as it were, but in the gristle, and not yet hardened into the bone of manhood. When I contemplate these things; when I know that the Colonies in general owe little or nothing to any care of ours, and that they are not squeezed into this happy form by the constraints of watchful and suspicious government, but that, through a wise and salutary neglect, a generous nature has been suffered to take her own way to perfection; when I reflect upon these effects, when I see how profitable they have been to us, I feel all the pride of power sink, and all presumption in the wisdom of human contrivances melt and die away within me. My rigour relents. I pardon something to the spirit of liberty.

Conciliation with the Colonies. 1775.

HYDER ALI AND THE CARNATIC

AMONG the victims to this magnificent plan of universal plunder, worthy of the heroic avarice of the projectors, you have all heard (and he has made himself to be well remembered) of an Indian chief called Hyder Ali Khan. This man possessed the western, as the Company under the name of

the Nabob of Arcot does the eastern division of
the Carnatic. It was among the leading measures
in the design of this cabal (according to their own
emphatic language) to *extirpate* this Hyder Ali.
They declared the Nabob of Arcot to be his
sovereign, and himself to be a rebel, and publicly
invested their instrument with the sovereignty
of the kingdom of Mysore. But their victim was
not of the passive kind. They were soon obliged
to conclude a treaty of peace and close alliance
with this rebel, at the gates of Madras. Both
before and since that treaty, every principle of
policy pointed out this power as a natural alliance;
and on his part, it was courted by every sort of
amicable office. But the cabinet council of English creditors would not suffer their Nabob of Arcot
to sign the treaty, nor even to give to a prince,
at least his equal, the ordinary titles of respect
and courtesy. From that time forward, a continued
plot was carried on within the divan, black and
white, of the Nabob of Arcot, for the destruction
of Hyder Ali. As to the outward members of the
double, or rather treble government of Madras,
which had signed the treaty, they were always
prevented by some over-ruling influence (which
they do not describe, but which cannot be mis-
understood) from performing what justice and
interest combined so evidently to enforce.

When at length Hyder Ali found that he had to
do with men who either would sign no convention,
or whom no treaty, and no signature could bind,
and who were the determined enemies of human
intercourse itself, he decreed to make the country
possessed by these incorrigible and predestinated
criminals a memorable example to mankind. He

resolved, in the gloomy recesses of a mind capacious of such things, to leave the whole Carnatic an everlasting monument of vengeance ; and to put perpetual desolation as a barrier between him and those against whom the faith which holds the moral elements of the world together was no protection. He became at length so confident of his force, so collected in his might, that he made no secret whatsoever of his dreadful resolution. Having terminated his disputes with every enemy, and every rival, who buried their mutual animosities in their common detestation against the creditors of the Nabob of Arcot, he drew from every quarter whatever a savage ferocity could add to his new rudiments in the arts of destruction ; and compounding all the materials of fury, havoc, and desolation, into one black cloud, he hung for a while on the declivities of the mountains. Whilst the authors of all these evils were idly and stupidly gazing on this menacing meteor, which blackened all their horizon, it suddenly burst, and poured down the whole of its contents upon the plains of the Carnatic. Then ensued a scene of woe, the like of which no eye had seen, no heart conceived, and which no tongue can adequately tell. All the horrors of war before known or heard of, were mercy to that new havoc. A storm of universal fire blasted every field, consumed every house, destroyed every temple. The miserable inhabitants flying from their flaming villages, in part were slaughtered; others, without regard to sex, to age, to the respect of rank, or sacredness of function; fathers torn from children, husbands from wives, enveloped in a whirlwind of cavalry, and amidst the goading spears of drivers, and the trampling of pursuing horses, were swept into captivity, in an unknown and hostile land. Those who were able to evade this tempest, fled to the walled cities. But escaping from fire, sword, and exile, they fell into the jaws of famine.

The alms of the settlement, in this dreadful exigency, were certainly liberal; and all was done by charity that private charity could do: but it was a people in beggary; it was a nation which stretched out its hands for food. For months together these creatures of sufferance, whose very excess and luxury in their most plenteous days, had fallen short of the allowance of our austerest fasts, silent, patient, resigned, without sedition or disturbance, almost without complaint, perished by an hundred a day in the streets of Madras; every day seventy at least laid their bodies in the streets, or on the glacis of Tanjore, and expired of famine in the granary of India. I was going to awake your justice towards this unhappy part of our fellow citizens, by bringing before you some of the circumstances of this plague of hunger. Of all the calamities which beset and waylay the life of man, this comes the nearest to our heart, and is that wherein the proudest of us all feels himself to be nothing more than he is: but I find myself unable to manage it with decorum; these details are of a species of horror so nauseous and disgusting; they are so degrading to the sufferers and to the hearers; they are so humiliating to human nature itself, that, on better thoughts, I find it more advisable to throw a pall over this hideous object, and to leave it to your general conceptions.

For eighteen months, without intermission, this destruction raged from the gates of Madras to the

gates of Tanjore; and so completely did these
masters in their art, Hyder Ali, and his more
ferocious son, absolve themselves of their impious
vow, that when the British armies traversed, as
they did, the Carnatic for hundreds of miles in all
directions, through the whole line of their march
they did not see one man, not one woman, not
one child, not one four-footed beast of any description whatever. One dead uniform silence reigned
over the whole region. With the inconsiderable
exceptions of the narrow vicinage of some few
forts, I wish to be understood as speaking literally.
I mean to produce to you more than three witnesses,
above all exception, who will support this assertion
in its full extent. That hurricane of war passed
through every part of the central provinces of the
Carnatic. Six or seven districts to the north and
to the south (and these not wholly untouched)
escaped the general ravage.

The Carnatic is a country not much inferior in
extent to England. Figure to yourself, Mr. Speaker,
the land in whose representative chair you sit;
figure to yourself the form and fashion of your
sweet and cheerful country from Thames to Trent,
north and south, and from the Irish to the German
sea, east and west, emptied and embowelled (may
God avert the omen of our crimes!) by so accomplished a desolation. Extend your imagination
a little further, and then suppose your ministers
taking a survey of this scene of waste and desolation; what would be your thoughts if you should
be informed, that they were computing how much
had been the amount of the excises, how much the
customs, how much the land and malt tax, in order
that they should charge (take it in the most

favourable light) for public service, upon the relics of the satiated vengeance of relentless enemies, the whole of what England had yielded in the most exuberant seasons of peace and abundance ? What would you call it ? To call it tyranny, sublimed into madness, would be too faint an image ; yet this very madness is the principle upon which the ministers at your right hand have proceeded in their estimate of the revenues of the Carnatic, when they were providing, not supply for the establishment of its protection, but rewards for the authors of its ruin.

Every day you are fatigued and disgusted with this cant, ' the Carnatic is a country that will soon recover, and become instantly as prosperous as ever.' They think they are talking to innocents, who will believe that by sowing of dragons' teeth, men may come up ready grown and ready armed. They who will give themselves the trouble of considering (for it requires no great reach of thought, no very profound knowledge) the manner in which mankind are increased, and countries cultivated, will regard all this raving as it ought to be regarded. In order that the people, after a long period of vexation and plunder, may be in a condition to maintain government, government must begin by maintaining them. Here the road to economy lies not through receipt, but through expense ; and in that country nature has given no short cut to your object. Men must propagate, like other animals, by the mouth. Never did oppression light the nuptial torch ; never did extortion and usury spread out the genial bed. Does any of you think that England, so wasted, would, under such a nursing attendance, so rapidly and cheaply

recover ? But he is meanly acquainted with either
England or India, who does not know that England
would a thousand times sooner resume population,
fertility, and what ought to be the ultimate secre-
tion from both, revenue, than such a country as
the Carnatic.

The Carnatic is not by the bounty of nature
a fertile soil. The general size of its cattle is proof
enough that it is much otherwise. It is some days
since I moved, that a curious and interesting map,
kept in the India House, should be laid before you.[1]
The India House is not yet in readiness to send it ;
I have therefore brought down my own copy, and
there it lies for the use of any gentleman who may
think such a matter worthy of his attention. It is
indeed a noble map, and of noble things ; but it
is decisive against the golden dreams and sanguine
speculations of avarice run mad. In addition to
what you know must be the case in every part of
the world (the necessity of a previous provision of
habition, seed, stock, capital), that map will show
you, that the uses of the influences of Heaven itself
are in that country a work of art. The Carnatic
is refreshed by few or no living brooks or running
streams, and it has rain only at a season ; but its
product of rice exacts the use of water subject to
perpetual command. This is the national bank
of the Carnatic, on which it must have a
perpetual credit, or it perishes irretrievably.
For that reason, in the happier times of India,
a number almost incredible of reservoirs have
been made in chosen places throughout the whole
country ; they are formed, for the greater part,
of mounds of earth and stones, with sluices of

[1] Mr. Barnard's map of the Jaghire.

solid masonry ; the whole constructed with admirable skill and labour, and maintained at a mighty charge. In the territory contained in that map alone, I have been at the trouble of reckoning the reservoirs, and they amount to upwards of eleven hundred, from the extent of two or three acres to five miles in circuit. From these reservoirs currents are occasionally drawn over the fields, and these watercourses again call for a considerable expense to keep them properly scoured and duly levelled. Taking the district in that map as a measure, there cannot be in the Carnatic and Tanjore fewer than ten thousand of these reservoirs of the larger and middling dimensions, to say nothing of those for domestic services, and the use of religious purification. These are not the enterprises of your power, nor in a style of magnificence suited to the taste of your minister. These are the monuments of real kings, who were the fathers of their people ; testators to a posterity which they embraced as their own. These are the grand sepulchres built by ambition ; but by the ambition of an unsatiable benevolence, which, not contented with reigning in the dispensation of happiness during the contracted term of human life, had strained, with all the reachings and graspings of a vivacious mind, to extend the dominion of their bounty beyond the limits of nature, and to perpetuate themselves through generations of generations, the guardians, the protectors, the nourishers of mankind.

Long before the late invasion, the persons who are objects of the grant of public money now before you had so diverted the supply of the pious funds of culture and population, that everywhere the

reservoirs were fallen into a miserable decay.
But after those domestic enemies had provoked
the entry of a cruel foreign foe into the country, he
did not leave it until his revenge had completed
the destruction begun by their avarice. Few,
very few indeed, of these magazines of water that
are not either totally destroyed, or cut through
with such gaps, as to require a serious attention
and much cost to re-establish them, as the means
of present subsistence to the people, and of future
revenue to the state.

What, Sir, would a virtuous and enlightened
ministry do on the view of the ruins of such works
before them ? on the view of such a chasm of
desolation as that which yawned in the midst of
those countries to the north and south, which still
bore some vestiges of cultivation ? They would
have reduced all their most necessary establish-
ments ; they would have suspended the justest
payments ; they would have employed every
shilling derived from the producing to reanimate
the powers of the unproductive parts. While they
were performing this fundamental duty, whilst
they were celebrating these mysteries of justice
and humanity, they would have told the corps of
fictitious creditors, whose crimes were their claims,
that they must keep an awful distance ; that
they must silence their inauspicious tongues ; that
they must hold off their profane unhallowed paws
from this holy work ; they would have proclaimed
with a voice that should make itself heard, that
on every country the first creditor is the plough ;
that this original, indefeasible claim supersedes
every other demand.

This is what a wise and virtuous ministry

would have done and said. This, therefore, is what our minister could never think of saying or doing. A ministry of another kind would have first improved the country, and have thus laid a solid foundation for future opulence and future force. But on this grand point of the restoration of the country, there is not one syllable to be found in the correspondence of our ministers, from the first to the last : they felt nothing for a land desolated by fire, sword, and famine ; their sympathies took another direction ; they were touched with pity for bribery, so long tormented with a fruitless itching of its palms ; their bowels yearned for usury, that had long missed the harvest of its returning months ;[1] they felt for peculation, which had been for so many years raking in the dust of an empty treasury ; they were melted into compassion for rapine and oppression, licking their dry, parched, unbloody jaws. These were the objects of their solicitude. These were the necessities for which they were studious to provide.

Speech on the Nabob of Arcot's Debts. 1785.

[1] Interest is rated in India by the month.

EDWARD GIBBON

1737–1794

THE SEVEN SLEEPERS

AMONG the insipid legends of ecclesiastical history, I am tempted to distinguish the memorable fable of the Seven Sleepers; whose imaginary date corresponds with the reign of the younger Theodosius and the conquest of Africa by the Vandals. When the emperor Decius persecuted the Christians, seven noble youths of Ephesus concealed themselves in a spacious cavern in the side of an adjacent mountain; where they were doomed to perish by the tyrant, who gave orders that the entrance should be firmly secured with a pile of huge stones. They immediately fell into a deep slumber, which was miraculously prolonged, without injuring the powers of life, during a period of one hundred and eighty-seven years. At the end of that time, the slaves of Adolius, to whom the inheritance of the mountain had descended, removed the stones, to supply materials for some rustic edifice; the light of the sun darted into the cavern, and the seven sleepers were permitted to awake. After a slumber, as they thought, of a few hours, they were pressed by the calls of hunger; and resolved that Jamblichus, one of their number, should secretly return to the city, to purchase bread for the use of his companions. The youth (if we may still employ that appellation) could no longer recognize the once familiar aspect of his native country; and his surprise was increased by the appearance of a large cross, triumphantly erected over the principal gate of Ephesus. His singular dress and obsolete language confounded the baker, to whom he offered an ancient medal of Decius as the current coin of the empire; and Jamblichus, on the suspicion of a secret treasure, was dragged before the judge. Their mutual inquiries produced the amazing discovery that two centuries were almost elapsed since Jamblichus and his friends had escaped from the rage of a Pagan tyrant. The bishop of Ephesus, the clergy, the magistrates, the people, and, as it is said, the emperor Theodosius himself, hastened to visit the cavern of the Seven Sleepers; who bestowed their benediction, related their story, and at the same instant peaceably expired. The origin of this marvellous fable cannot be ascribed to the pious fraud and credulity of the *modern* Greeks, since the authentic tradition may be traced within half a century of the supposed miracle. James of Sarug, a Syrian bishop, who was born only two years after the death of the younger Theodosius, has devoted one of his two hundred and thirty homilies to the praise of the young men of Ephesus. Their legend, before the end of the sixth century, was translated from the Syriac into the Latin language, by the care of Gregory of Tours. The hostile communions of the East preserve their memory with equal reverence; and their names are honourably inscribed in the Roman, the Abyssinian, and the Russian calendar. Nor has their reputation been confined to the Christian world. This popular tale, which Mahomet might learn when he drove his camels to the fairs

of Syria, is introduced, as a divine revelation, into
the Koran. The story of the Seven Sleepers has
been adopted, and adorned, by the nations, from
Bengal to Africa, who profess the Mahometan
religion; and some vestiges of a similar tradition
have been discovered in the remote extremities
of Scandinavia. This easy and universal belief,
so expressive of the sense of mankind, may be
ascribed to the genuine merit of the fable itself.
We imperceptibly advance from youth to age,
without observing the gradual, but incessant,
change of human affairs, and, even in our larger
experience of history, the imagination is accustomed, by a perpetual series of causes and effects,
to unite the most distant revolutions. But, if the
interval between two memorable eras could be
instantly annihilated; if it were possible, after
a momentary slumber of two hundred years, to
display the *new* world to the eyes of a spectator,
who still retained a lively and recent impression
of the *old*; his surprise and his reflections would
furnish the pleasing subject of a philosophical
romance. The scene could not be more advantage-
ously placed than in the two centuries which
elapsed between the reigns of Decius and of
Theodosius the younger. During this period, the
seat of government had been transported from
Rome to a new city on the banks of the Thracian
Bosphorus; and the abuse of military spirit had
been suppressed by an artificial system of tame
and ceremonious servitude. The throne of the
persecuting Decius was filled by a succession of
Christian and orthodox princes, who had extirpated
the fabulous gods of antiquity; and the public
devotion of the age was impatient to exalt the

saints and martyrs of the Catholic Church on the
altars of Diana and Hercules. The union of the
Roman empire was dissolved; its genius was
humbled in the dust; and armies of unknown
Barbarians, issuing from the frozen regions of the
North, had established their victorious reign over
the fairest provinces of Europe and Africa.

*The Decline and Fall of the
Roman Empire.* 1776–88.

ARABIA AND ITS INHABITANTS

In the vacant space between Persia, Syria,
Egypt, and Aethiopia, the Arabian peninsula may
be conceived as a triangle of spacious but irregular
dimensions. From the northern point of Beles on
the Euphrates, a line of fifteen hundred miles is
terminated by the straits of Babelmandel and the
land of frankincense. About half this length may
be allowed for the middle breadth from east to west,
from Bassora to Suez, from the Persian Gulf to the
Red Sea. The sides of the triangle are gradually
enlarged, and the southern basis presents a front
of a thousand miles to the Indian Ocean. The
entire surface of the peninsula exceeds in a fourfold
proportion that of Germany or France; but the
far greater part has been justly stigmatized with
the epithets of the *stony* and the *sandy*. Even
the wilds of Tartary are decked by the hand of
nature with lofty trees and luxuriant herbage;
and the lonesome traveller derives a sort of comfort
and society from the presence of vegetable life.
But in the dreary waste of Arabia, a boundless

level of sand is intersected by sharp and naked
mountains, and the face of the desert, without
shade or shelter, is scorched by the direct and
intense rays of a tropical sun. Instead of refreshing
breezes, the winds, particularly from the south-
west, diffuse a noxious and even deadly vapour;
the hillocks of sand which they alternately raise
and scatter are compared to the billows of the
ocean; and whole caravans, whole armies, have
been lost and buried in the whirlwind. The
common benefits of water are an object of desire
and contest; and such is the scarcity of wood that
some art is requisite to preserve and propagate the
element of fire. Arabia is destitute of navigable
rivers, which fertilize the soil and convey its
produce to the adjacent regions; the torrents
that fall from the hills are imbibed by the thirsty
earth; the rare and hardy plants, the tamarind
or the acacia, that strike their roots into the clefts
of the rocks, are nourished by the dews of the
night; a scanty supply of rain is collected in
cisterns and aqueducts; the wells and springs are
the secret treasure of the desert; and the pilgrim
of Mecca, after many a dry and sultry march, is
disgusted by the taste of the waters, which have
rolled over a bed of sulphur or salt. Such is the
general and genuine picture of the climate of
Arabia. The experience of evil enhances the
value of any local or partial enjoyments. A shady
grove, a green pasture, a stream of fresh water,
are sufficient to attract a colony of sedentary
Arabs to the fortunate spots which can afford
food and refreshment to themselves and their
cattle, and which encourage their industry in the
cultivation of the palm-tree and the vine. The

high lands that border on the Indian Ocean are distinguished by their superior plenty of wood and water; the air is more temperate, the fruits are more delicious, the animals and the human race more numerous; the fertility of the soil invites and rewards the toil of the husbandman; and the peculiar gifts of frankincense and coffee have attracted, in different ages, the merchants of the world. If it be compared with the rest of the peninsula, this sequestrated region may truly deserve the appellation of the *happy*; and the splendid colouring of fancy and fiction has been suggested by contrast and countenanced by distance. It was for this earthly paradise that nature had reserved her choicest favours and her most curious workmanship; the incompatible blessings of luxury and innocence were ascribed to the natives; the soil was impregnated with gold and gems, and both the land and sea were taught to exhale the odours of aromatic sweets. This division of the *sandy*, the *stony*, and the *happy*, so familiar to the Greeks and Latins, is unknown to the Arabians themselves; and it is singular enough that a country, whose language and inhabitants had ever been the same, should scarcely retain a vestige of its ancient geography. The maritime districts of *Bahrein* and *Oman* are opposite to the realm of Persia. The kingdom of *Yemen* displays the limits, or at least the situation, of Arabia Felix; the name *Neged* is extended over the inland space; and the birth of Mahomet has illustrated the province of *Hejaz* along the coast of the Red Sea.

The measure of population is regulated by the means of subsistence; and the inhabitants of this vast peninsula might be outnumbered by the subjects of a fertile and industrious province. Along the shores of the Persian Gulf, of the ocean, and even of the Red Sea, the *Ichthyophagi*, or fish-eaters, continued to wander in quest of their precarious food. In this primitive and abject state, which ill deserves the name of society, the human brute, without arts or laws, almost without sense or language, is poorly distinguished from the rest of the animal creation. Generations and ages might roll away in silent oblivion, and the helpless savage was restrained from multiplying his race by the wants and pursuits which confined his existence to the narrow margin of the sea-coast. But in an early period of antiquity the great body of the Arabs had emerged from this scene of misery; and, as the naked wilderness could not maintain a people of hunters, they rose at once to the more secure and plentiful condition of the pastoral life. The same life is uniformly pursued by the roving tribes of the desert, and in the portrait of the modern *Bedoweens* we may trace the features of their ancestors, who, in the age of Moses or Mahomet, dwelt under similar tents, and conducted their horses and camels and sheep to the same springs and the same pastures. Our toil is lessened, and our wealth is increased, by our dominion over the useful animals; and the Arabian shepherd had acquired the absolute possession of a faithful friend and a laborious slave. Arabia, in the opinion of the naturalist, is the genuine and original country of the *horse*; the climate most propitious, not indeed to the size, but to the spirit and swiftness, of that generous animal. The merit of the Barb, the Spanish, and the English breed is derived from a mixture of Arabian blood; the Bedoweens preserve, with superstitious care, the honours and the memory of the purest race; the males are sold at a high price, but the females are seldom alienated; and the birth of a noble foal was esteemed, among the tribes, as a subject of joy and mutual congratulation. These horses are educated in the tents, among the children of the Arabs, with a tender familiarity, which trains them in the habits of gentleness and attachment. They are accustomed only to walk and to gallop; their sensations are not blunted by the incessant abuse of the spur and the whip; their powers are reserved for the moments of flight and pursuit; but no sooner do they feel the touch of the hand or the stirrup than they dart away with the swiftness of the wind; and, if their friend be dismounted in the rapid career, they instantly stop till he has recovered his seat. In the sands of Africa and Arabia the *camel* is a sacred and precious gift. That strong and patient beast of burthen can perform, without eating or drinking, a journey of several days; and a reservoir of fresh water is preserved in a large bag, a fifth stomach of the animal, whose body is imprinted with the marks of servitude. The larger breed is capable of transporting a weight of a thousand pounds; and the dromedary, of a lighter and more active frame, outstrips the fleetest courser in the race. Alive or dead, almost every part of the camel is serviceable to man; her milk is plentiful and nutritious; the young and tender flesh has the taste of veal; a valuable salt is extracted from the urine; the dung supplies the deficiency of fuel; and the long hair, which falls each year and is renewed, is coarsely manufactured into the garments, the furniture, and the tents, of the Bedoweens. In the rainy seasons they consume the rare and insufficient herbage of the desert; during the heats of summer and the scarcity of winter, they remove their encampments to the sea-coast, the hills of Yemen, or the neighbourhood of the Euphrates, and have often extorted the dangerous licence of visiting the banks of the Nile and the villages of Syria and Palestine. The life of a wandering Arab is a life of danger and distress; and, though sometimes, by rapine or exchange, he may appropriate the fruits of industry, a private citizen in Europe is in the possession of more solid and pleasing luxury than the proudest emir who marches in the field at the head of ten thousand horse.

The Decline and Fall of the
Roman Empire. 1776–88.

THE BEGINNING AND THE COMPLETION OF A GREAT WORK

No sooner was I settled in my house and library, than I undertook the composition of the first volume of my *History*. At the outset all was dark and doubtful; even the title of the work, the true era of the *Decline and Fall of the Empire*, the limits of the introduction, the division of the chapters, and the order of the narrative; and I was often tempted to cast away the labour of seven years. The style of an author should be the image of his mind, but the choice and command of language is the fruit of exercise. Many experi-

ments were made before I could hit the middle
tone between a dull chronicle and a rhetorical
declamation : three times did I compose the first
chapter, and twice the second and third, before
I was tolerably satisfied with their effect In the
remainder of the way I advanced with a more
equal and easy pace ; but the fifteenth and
sixteenth chapters have been reduced by three
successive revisals from a large volume to their
present size ; and they might still be compressed,
without any loss of facts or sentiments. An
opposite fault may be imputed to the concise
and superficial narrative of the first reigns from
Commodus to Alexander ; a fault of which I have
never heard, except from Mr. Hume in his last
journey to London. Such an oracle might have
been consulted and obeyed with rational devotion ;
but I was soon disgusted with the modest practice
of reading the manuscript to my friends. Of such
friends some will praise from politeness, and some
will criticize from vanity. The author himself is
the best judge of his own performance ; no one
has so deeply meditated on the subject ; no one
is so sincerely interested in the event. . . .

I have presumed to mark the moment of
conception : I shall now commemorate the hour
of my final deliverance. It was on the day, or
rather night, of the 27th of June, 1787, between
the hours of eleven and twelve, that I wrote the
last lines of the last page, in a summer-house in
my garden. After laying down my pen, I took
several turns in a *berceau*, or covered walk of
acacias, which commands a prospect of the country,
the lake, and the mountains. The air was temperate,
the sky was serene, the silver orb of the moon was

reflected from the waters, and all nature was silent. I will not dissemble the first emotions of joy on the recovery of my freedom, and, perhaps, the establishment of my fame. But my pride was soon humbled, and a sober melancholy was spread over my mind, by the idea that I had taken an ever-lasting leave of an old and agreeable companion, and that whatsoever might be the future date of my *History*, the life of the historian must be short and precarious. I will add two facts, which have seldom occurred in the composition of six, or at least of five, quartos. (1) My first rough manuscript, without any intermediate copy, has been sent to the press. (2) Not a sheet has been seen by any human eyes, excepting those of the author and the printer: the faults and the merits are exclusively my own.

Autobiography. 1796.

RICHARD BRINSLEY SHERIDAN

1751–1816

LADY TEAZLE BEHIND THE SCREEN

A Library

JOSEPH SURFACE *and a* SERVANT.

Joseph Surface. No letter from Lady Teazle ?

Servant. No, sir.

Joseph Surface. I am surprised she has not sent, if she is prevented from coming. Sir Peter certainly does not suspect me. Yet, I wish I may not lose the heiress, through the scrape I have drawn myself into with the wife ; however, Charles's imprudence and bad character are great points in my favour. [*Knocking heard without.*

Servant. Sir, I believe that must be Lady Teazle.

Joseph Surface. Hold !—See whether it is or not before you go to the door : I have a particular message for you, if it should be my brother.

Servant. 'Tis her ladyship, sir ; she always leaves her chair at the milliner's in the next street.

Joseph Surface. Stay, stay ; draw that screen before the window—that will do ;—my opposite neighbour is a maiden lady of so anxious a temper. [SERVANT *draws the screen, and exit.*]—I have a difficult hand to play in this affair. Lady Teazle has lately suspected my views on Maria ; but she must by no means be let into that secret,—at least, till I have her more in my power.

Enter LADY TEAZLE.

Lady Teazle. What, sentiment in soliloquy now? Have you been very impatient?—O Lud! don't pretend to look grave. I vow I couldn't come before.

Joseph Surface. Oh, madam, punctuality is a species of constancy, a very unfashionable quality in a lady.

Lady Teazle. Upon my word you ought to pity me. Do you know Sir Peter is grown so ill-natured to me of late, and so jealous of Charles, too—that's the best of the story, isn't it?

Joseph Surface. I am glad my scandalous friends keep that up. [*Aside.*

Lady Teazle. I am sure I wish he would let Maria marry him, and then perhaps he would be convinced; don't you, Mr. Surface?

Joseph Surface. Indeed I do not. [*Aside.*]— Oh, certainly I do! for then my dear Lady Teazle would also be convinced how wrong her suspicions were of my having any design on the silly girl.

Lady Teazle. Well, well, I'm inclined to believe you. But isn't it provoking, to have the most ill-natured things said of one?—And there's my friend Lady Sneerwell has circulated I don't know how many scandalous tales of me, and all without any foundation too—that's what vexes me.

Joseph Surface. Aye, madam, to be sure, that is the provoking circumstance—without foundation; yes, yes, there's the mortification, indeed; for when a scandalous story is believed against one, there certainly is no comfort like the consciousness of having deserved it.

Lady Teazle. No, to be sure, then I'd forgive their malice; but to attack me, who am really so innocent, and who never say an ill-natured thing of anybody—that is, of any friend; and then Sir Peter too, to have him so peevish, and so suspicious, when I know the integrity of my own heart— indeed 'tis monstrous !

Joseph Surface. But, my dear Lady Teazle, 'tis your own fault if you suffer it. When a husband entertains a groundless suspicion of his wife, and withdraws his confidence from her, the original compact is broken, and she owes it to the honour of her sex to outwit him.

Lady Teazle. Indeed !—so that if he suspects me without cause, it follows, that the best way of curing his jealousy is to give him reason for 't.

Joseph Surface. Undoubtedly—for your husband should never be deceived in you,—and in that case it becomes you to be frail in compliment to his discernment.

Lady Teazle. To be sure, what you say is very reasonable, and when the consciousness of my innocence——

Joseph Surface. Ah! my dear madam, there is the great mistake : 'tis this very conscious innocence that is of the greatest prejudice to you. What is it makes you negligent of forms, and careless of the world's opinion ?—why, the consciousness of your own innocence. What makes you thoughtless in your conduct, and apt to run into a thousand little imprudences ?—why, the consciousness of your own innocence. What makes you impatient of Sir Peter's temper, and outrageous at his suspicions ?—why, the consciousness of your innocence.

Lady Teazle. 'Tis very true!

Joseph Surface. Now, my dear Lady Teazle, if you would but once make a trifling *faux pas*, you can't conceive how cautious you would grow, and how ready to humour and agree with your husband.

Lady Teazle. Do you think so?

Joseph Surface. Oh! I am sure on't; and then you would find all scandal would cease at once, for, in short, your character at present is like a person in a plethora, absolutely dying from too much health.

Lady Teazle. So, so; then I perceive your prescription is, that I must sin in my own defence, and part with my virtue to secure my reputation?

Joseph Surface. Exactly so, upon my credit, ma'am.

Lady Teazle. Well, certainly this is the oddest doctrine, and the newest receipt for avoiding calumny!

Joseph Surface. An infallible one, believe me. Prudence, like experience, must be paid for.

Lady Teazle. Why, if my understanding were once convinced——

Joseph Surface. Oh, certainly, madam, your understanding should be convinced. Yes, yes— Heaven forbid I should persuade you to do anything you thought wrong. No, no, I have too much honour to desire it.

Lady Teazle. Don't you think we may as well leave *honour* out of the question?

Joseph Surface. Ah! the ill effects of your country education, I see, still remain with you.

Lady Teazle. I doubt they do indeed; and I will fairly own to you, that if I could be persuaded to do wrong, it would be by Sir Peter's ill usage sooner than your *honourable logic*, after all.

Joseph Surface. Then, by this hand, which he is unworthy of—— [*Taking her hand.*

Enter SERVANT.

'Sdeath, you blockhead—what do you want?

Servant. I beg your pardon, sir, but I thought you would not choose Sir Peter to come up without announcing him.

Joseph Surface. Sir Peter!—Oons—the devil!

Lady Teazle. Sir Peter! O Lud—I'm ruined—I'm ruined!

Servant. Sir, 'twasn't I let him in.

Lady Teazle. Oh! I'm quite undone! What will become of me? Now, Mr. Logic—Oh! he's on the stairs—I'll get behind here—and if ever I'm so imprudent again—— [*Goes behind the screen.*

Joseph Surface. Give me that book.

[*Sits down. Servant pretends to adjust his hair.*

Enter SIR PETER.

Sir Peter Teazle. Aye, ever improving himself—Mr. Surface, Mr. Surface——

Joseph Surface. Oh! my dear Sir Peter, I beg your pardon—[*Gaping—throws away the book.*]—I have been dozing over a stupid book.—Well, I am much obliged to you for this call. You haven't been here, I believe, since I fitted up this room.—Books, you know, are the only things in which I am a coxcomb.

Sir Peter Teazle. 'Tis very neat indeed.—Well, well, that's proper; and you can make even your screen a source of knowledge—hung, I perceive, with maps?

Joseph Surface. Oh, yes, I find great use in that screen.

Sir Peter Teazle. I dare say you must, certainly, when you want to find anything in a hurry.

Joseph Surface. Aye, or to hide anything in a hurry either.   [*Aside.*

Sir Peter Teazle. Well, I have a little private business——

Joseph Surface. You need not stay [*to the* SERVANT].

Servant. No, sir.   [*Exit.*

Joseph Surface. Here's a chair, Sir Peter—I beg——

Sir Peter Teazle. Well, now we are alone, there is a subject, my dear friend, on which I wish to unburthen my mind to you—a point of the greatest moment to my peace ; in short, my dear friend, Lady Teazle's conduct of late has made me extremely unhappy.

Joseph Surface. Indeed ! I am very sorry to hear it.

Sir Peter Teazle. Aye, 'tis too plain she has not the least regard for me ; but, what 's worse, I have pretty good authority to suppose she has formed an attachment to another.

Joseph Surface. Indeed ! you astonish me !

Sir Peter Teazle. Yes ; and, between ourselves, I think I've discovered the person.

Joseph Surface. How ! you alarm me exceedingly.

Sir Peter Teazle. Aye, my dear friend, I knew you would sympathize with me !

Joseph Surface. Yes—believe me, Sir Peter, such a discovery would hurt me just as much as it would you.

Sir Peter Teazle. I am convinced of it.—Ah! it is a happiness to have a friend whom we can trust even with one's family secrets. But have you no guess who I mean?

Joseph Surface. I haven't the most distant idea. It can't be Sir Benjamin Backbite!

Sir Peter Teazle. Oh, no! What say you to Charles?

Joseph Surface. My brother! impossible!

Sir Peter Teazle. Oh! my dear friend, the goodness of your own heart misleads you. You judge of others by yourself.

Joseph Surface. Certainly, Sir Peter, the heart that is conscious of its own integrity is ever slow to credit another's treachery.

Sir Peter Teazle. True—but your brother has no sentiment—you never hear him talk so.

Joseph Surface. Yet, I can't but think Lady Teazle herself has too much principle.

Sir Peter Teazle. Aye,—but what is principle against the flattery of a handsome, lively young fellow?

Joseph Surface. That's very true.

Sir Peter Teazle. And there's, you know, the difference of our ages makes it very improbable that she should have any very great affection for me; and if she were to be frail, and I were to make it public, why the town would only laugh at me, the foolish old bachelor, who had married a girl.

Joseph Surface. That's true, to be sure—they *would* laugh.

Sir Peter Teazle. Laugh—aye, and make ballads, and paragraphs, and the devil knows what of me.

Joseph Surface. No—you must never make it public.

Sir Peter Teazle. But then again—that the nephew of my old friend, Sir Oliver, should be the person to attempt such a wrong, hurts me more nearly.

Joseph Surface. Aye, there's the point. When ingratitude barbs the dart of injury, the wound has double danger in it.

Sir Peter Teazle. Aye—I, that was, in a manner, left his guardian; in whose house he had been so often entertained; who never in my life denied him—my advice.

Joseph Surface. Oh, 'tis not to be credited. There may be a man capable of such baseness, to be sure; but, for my part, till you can give me positive proofs, I cannot but doubt it. However, if it should be proved on him, he is no longer a brother of mine—I disclaim kindred with him: for the man who can break the laws of hospitality, and tempt the wife of his friend, deserves to be branded as the pest of society.

Sir Peter Teazle. What a difference there is between you! What noble sentiments!

Joseph Surface. Yet, I cannot suspect Lady Teazle's honour.

Sir Peter Teazle. I am sure I wish to think well of her, and to remove all ground of quarrel between us. She has lately reproached me more than once with having made no settlement on her; and, in our last quarrel, she almost hinted that she should not break her heart if I was dead. Now, as we seem to differ in our ideas of expense, I have resolved she shall have her own way, and be her own mistress in that respect for the future; and if I were to die, she will find I have not been inattentive to her interest while living. Here, my

friend, are the drafts of two deeds, which I wish
to have your opinion on. By one, she will enjoy
eight hundred a year independent while I live ;
and, by the other, the bulk of my fortune at my
death.

Joseph Surface. This conduct, Sir Peter, is
indeed truly generous.——I wish it may not
corrupt my pupil.   [*Aside.*

Sir Peter Teazle. Yes, I am determined she
shall have no cause to complain, though I would
not have her acquainted with the latter instance of
my affection yet awhile.

Joseph Surface. Nor I, if I could help it.
                                               [*Aside.*

Sir Peter Teazle. And now, my dear friend, if
you please, we will talk over the situation of your
affairs with Maria.

Joseph Surface. [*Softly.*]—Oh, no, Sir Peter ;
another time, if you please.

Sir Peter Teazle. I am sensibly chagrined at
the little progress you seem to make in her affections.

Joseph Surface. I beg you will not mention it.
What are my disappointments when your happiness is in debate ! [*Softly.*]—'Sdeath, I shall be
ruined every way.   [*Aside.*

Sir Peter Teazle. And though you are so averse
to my acquainting Lady Teazle with your passion
for Maria, I'm sure she 's not your enemy in the
affair.

Joseph Surface. Pray, Sir Peter, now, oblige
me. I am really too much affected by the subject
we have been speaking of, to bestow a thought on
my own concerns. The man who is entrusted
with his friend's distresses can never——

Enter SERVANT.

Well, sir ?

Servant. Your brother, sir, is speaking to a gentleman in the street, and says he knows you are within.

Joseph Surface. 'Sdeath, blockhead, I'm not within—I'm out for the day.

Sir Peter Teazle. Stay—hold—a thought has struck me :—you shall be at home.

Joseph Surface. Well, well, let him up. [*Exit* SERVANT.] He'll interrupt Sir Peter, however.

[*Aside.*

Sir Peter Teazle. Now, my good friend, oblige me, I entreat you. Before Charles comes, let me conceal myself somewhere—then do you tax him on the point we have been talking, and his answer may satisfy me at once.

Joseph Surface. Oh, fie, Sir Peter ! would you have me join in so mean a trick ?—to trepan my brother too ?

Sir Peter Teazle. Nay, you tell me you are sure he is innocent ; if so, you do him the greatest service by giving him an opportunity to clear himself, and you will set my heart at rest. Come, you shall not refuse me : here, behind this screen will be—Hey ! what the devil ! there seems to be one listener there already—I'll swear I saw a petticoat !

Joseph Surface. Ha ! ha ! ha ! Well, this is ridiculous enough. I'll tell you, Sir Peter, though I hold a man of intrigue to be a most despicable character, yet, you know, it does not follow that one is to be an absolute Joseph either ! Hark'ee, 'tis a little French milliner—a silly rogue that plagues me,—and having some character to lose, on your coming, sir, she ran behind the screen.

Sir Peter Teazle. Ah! you rogue! But, egad, she has overheard all I have been saying of my wife.

Joseph Surface. Oh, 'twill never go any farther, you may depend upon it.

Sir Peter Teazle. No! then, faith, let her hear it out.—Here's a closet will do as well.

Joseph Surface. Well, go in there.

Sir Peter Teazle. Sly rogue! sly rogue!

[*Going into the closet.*

Joseph Surface. A narrow escape, indeed! and a curious situation I'm in, to part man and wife in this manner.

Lady Teazle. [*Peeping.*]—Couldn't I steal off?

Joseph Surface. Keep close, my angel!

Sir Peter Teazle. [*Peeping.*] Joseph, tax him home.

Joseph Surface. Back, my dear friend!

Lady Teazle. Couldn't you lock Sir Peter in?

Joseph Surface. Be still, my life!

Sir Peter Teazle. [*Peeping.*] You're sure the little milliner won't blab?

Joseph Surface. In, in, my good Sir Peter.— 'Fore Gad, I wish I had a key to the door.

Enter CHARLES SURFACE.

Charles Surface. Holla! brother, what has been the matter? Your fellow would not let me up at first. What! have you had a Jew or a wench with you?

Joseph Surface. Neither, brother, I assure you.

Charles Surface. But what has made Sir Peter steal off? I thought he had been with you.

Joseph Surface. He *was*, brother; but hearing you were coming, he did not choose to stay.

Charles Surface. What! was the old gentleman afraid I wanted to borrow money of him?

Joseph Surface. No, sir: but I am sorry to find, Charles, you have lately given that worthy man grounds for great uneasiness.

Charles Surface. Yes, they tell me I do that to a great many worthy men.—But how so, pray?

Joseph Surface. To be plain with you, brother—he thinks you are endeavouring to gain Lady Teazle's affections from him.

Charles Surface. Who, I? O Lud! not I, upon my word. Ha! ha! ha! ha! so the old fellow has found out that he has got a young wife, has he? —or, what is worse, Lady Teazle has found out she has an old husband?

Joseph Surface. This is no subject to jest on, brother. He who can laugh—

Charles Surface. True, true, as you were going to say—then, seriously, I never had the least idea of what you charge me with, upon my honour.

Joseph Surface. Well, it will give Sir Peter great satisfaction to hear this.   [*Aloud.*

Charles Surface. To be sure, I once thought the lady seemed to have taken a fancy to me; but, upon my soul, I never gave her the least encouragement:—besides, you know my attachment to Maria.

Joseph Surface. But sure, brother, even if Lady Teazle had betrayed the fondest partiality for you——

Charles Surface. Why, look'ee, Joseph, I hope I shall never deliberately do a dishonourable action; but if a pretty woman was purposely to throw herself in my way—and that pretty woman married to a man old enough to be her father——

Joseph Surface. Well——

Charles Surface. Why, I believe I should be obliged to borrow a little of your morality, that 's all.—But, brother, do you know now that you surprise me exceedingly, by naming *me* with Lady Teazle; for, 'faith, I always understood *you* were her favourite.

Joseph Surface. Oh, for shame, Charles! This retort is foolish.

Charles Surface. Nay, I swear I have seen you exchange such significant glances——

Joseph Surface. Nay, nay, sir, this is no jest.

Charles Surface. Egad, I'm serious. Don't you remember one day when I called here——

Joseph Surface. Nay, prithee, Charles——

Charles Surface. And found you together——

Joseph Surface. Zounds, sir! I insist——

Charles Surface. And another time when your servant——

Joseph Surface. Brother, brother, a word with you!—Gad, I must stop him.   [*Aside.*

Charles Surface. Informed, I say, that——

Joseph Surface. Hush! I beg your pardon, but Sir Peter has overheard all we have been saying. I knew you would clear yourself, or I should not have consented.

Charles Surface. How, Sir Peter! Where is he?

Joseph Surface. Softly; there!

                      [*Points to the closet.*

Charles Surface. Oh, 'fore Heaven, I'll have him out. Sir Peter, come forth!

Joseph Surface. No, no——

Charles Surface. I say, Sir Peter, come into

court.—[*Pulls in* SIR PETER.]—What, my old
guardian!—What! turn inquisitor, and take
evidence incog?

Sir Peter Teazle. Give me your hand, Charles—
I believe I have suspected you wrongfully; but
you mustn't be angry with Joseph—'twas my
plan!

Charles Surface. Indeed!

Sir Peter Teazle. But I acquit you. I promise
you I don't think near so ill of you as I did: what
I have heard has given me great satisfaction.

Charles Surface. Egad, then, 'twas lucky you
didn't hear any more—wasn't it, Joseph?
[*Apart to* JOSEPH.

Sir Peter Teazle. Ah! you would have retorted on him.

Charles Surface. Aye, aye, that was a joke.

Sir Peter Teazle. Yes, yes, I know his honour
too well.

Charles Surface. But you might as well have
suspected *him* as *me* in this matter, for all that—
mightn't he, Joseph? [*Apart to* JOSEPH.

Sir Peter Teazle. Well, well, I believe you.

Joseph Surface. Would they were both well
out of the room! [*Aside.*

Enter SERVANT, *and whispers* JOSEPH SURFACE.

Sir Peter Teazle. And in future perhaps we
may not be such strangers.

Joseph Surface. Gentlemen, I beg pardon—
I must wait on you downstairs: here is a person
come on particular business.

Charles Surface. Well, you can see him in
another room. Sir Peter and I have not met
a long time, and I have something to say to him.

Joseph Surface. They must not be left together. [*Aside.*] I'll send this man away, and return directly.——Sir Peter, not a word of the French milliner. [*Apart to* SIR PETER, *and goes out.*

Sir Peter Teazle. I! not for the world!—[*Apart to* JOSEPH.]—Ah! Charles, if you associated more with your brother, one might indeed hope for your reformation. He is a man of sentiment.—Well, there is nothing in the world so noble as a man of sentiment!

Charles Surface. Pshaw! he is too moral by half—and so apprehensive of his good name, as he calls it, that I suppose he would as soon let a priest into his house as a girl.

Sir Peter Teazle. No, no,—come, come,—you wrong him.—No, no! Joseph is no rake, but he is no such saint either in that respect.——I have a great mind to tell him—we should have a laugh at Joseph. [*Aside.*

Charles Surface. Oh, hang him! He's a very anchorite, a young hermit.

Sir Peter Teazle. Hark'ee—you must not abuse him: he may chance to hear of it again, I promise you.

Charles Surface. Why, you won't tell him?

Sir Peter Teazle. No—but—this way. Egad, I'll tell him.—[*Aside.*] Hark'ee—have you a mind to have a good laugh at Joseph?

Charles Surface. I should like it of all things.

Sir Peter Teazle. Then, i' faith, we will—I'll be quit with him for discovering me.—He had a girl with him when I called.

Charles Surface. What! Joseph? you jest.

Sir Peter Teazle. Hush!—a little French milliner—and the best of the jest is—she's in the room now.

Charles Surface. The devil she is!

Sir Peter Teazle. Hush! I tell you! [*Points.*

Charles Surface. Behind the screen! 'Slife, let's unveil her!

Sir Peter Teazle. No, no—he's coming—you shan't, indeed!

Charles Surface. Oh, egad, we'll have a peep at the little milliner!

Sir Peter Teazle. Not for the world—Joseph will never forgive me——

Charles Surface. I'll stand by you——

Sir Peter Teazle. Odds, here he is—[JOSEPH SURFACE *enters just as* CHARLES SURFACE *throws down the screen.*]

Charles Surface. Lady Teazle, by all that's wonderful!

Sir Peter Teazle. Lady Teazle, by all that's damnable!

Charles Surface. Sir Peter, this is one of the smartest French milliners I ever saw. Egad, you seem all to have been diverting yourselves here at hide and seek, and I don't see who is out of the secret.—Shall I beg your ladyship to inform me? Not a word!—Brother, will you be pleased to explain this matter? What! is Morality dumb too? —Sir Peter, though I found you in the dark, perhaps you are not so now! All mute!—Well— though I can make nothing of the affair, I suppose you perfectly understand one another—so I'll leave you to yourselves—[*Going.*] Brother, I'm sorry to find you have given that worthy man cause for so much uneasiness.—Sir Peter! there's nothing in the world so noble as a man of sentiment!

[*Exit* CHARLES. *They stand for some time looking at each other.*

Joseph Surface. Sir Peter—notwithstanding—I confess—that appearances are against me—if you will afford me your patience—I make no doubt—but I shall explain everything to your satisfaction.

Sir Peter Teazle. If you please, sir.

Joseph Surface. The fact is, sir, that Lady Teazle, knowing my pretensions to your ward, Maria—I say, sir,—Lady Teazle, being apprehensive of the jealousy of your temper—and knowing my friendship to the family—she, sir, I say—called here—in order that—I might explain these pretensions—but on your coming—being apprehensive—as I said—of your jealousy—she withdrew—and this, you may depend on it, is the whole truth of the matter.

Sir Peter Teazle. A very clear account, upon my word ; and I dare swear the lady will vouch for every article of it.

Lady Teazle. For not one word of it, Sir Peter !

Sir Peter Teazle. How ! don't you think it worth while to agree in the lie ?

Lady Teazle. There is not one syllable of truth in what that gentleman has told you.

Sir Peter Teazle. I believe you, upon my soul, ma'am !

Joseph Surface. [*Aside.*]—'Sdeath, madam, will you betray me ?

Lady Teazle. Good Mr. Hypocrite, by your leave, I'll speak for myself.

Sir Peter Teazle. Aye, let her alone, sir ; you'll find she'll make out a better story than you, without prompting.

Lady Teazle. Hear me, Sir Peter !—I came hither on no matter relating to your ward, and even ignorant of this gentleman's pretensions to her. But I came seduced by his insidious arguments, at least to listen to his pretended passion, if not to sacrifice your honour to his baseness.

Sir Peter Teazle. Now, I believe, the truth is coming indeed !

Joseph Surface. The woman's mad !

Lady Teazle. No, sir,—she has recovered her senses, and your own arts have furnished her with the means.—Sir Peter, I do not expect you to credit me—but the tenderness you expressed for me, when I am sure you could not think I was a witness to it, has penetrated so to my heart, that had I left the place without the shame of this discovery, my future life should have spoken the sincerity of my gratitude. As for that smooth-tongued hypocrite, who would have seduced the wife of his too credulous friend, while he affected honourable addresses to his ward—I behold him now in a light so truly despicable, that I shall never again respect myself for having listened to him.

[*Exit* LADY TEAZLE.

Joseph Surface. Notwithstanding all this, Sir Peter, Heaven knows——

Sir Peter Teazle. That you are a villain ! and so I leave you to your conscience.

Joseph Surface. You are too rash, Sir Peter; you *shall* hear me. The man who shuts out conviction by refusing to——

[*Exeunt* SIR PETER *and* SURFACE *talking.*

The School for Scandal. 1777.

SIR FRETFUL PLAGIARY

Enter SERVANT *to* MR. *and* MRS. DANGLE
and SNEER.

Servant. Sir Fretful Plagiary, sir.

Dangle. Beg him to walk up.—[*Exit* SERVANT.]
Now, Mrs. Dangle, Sir Fretful Plagiary is an author
to your own taste.

Mrs. Dangle. I confess he is a favourite of mine,
because everybody else abuses him.

Sneer. Very much to the credit of your charity,
madam, if not of your judgement.

Dangle. But, egad, he allows no merit to any
author but himself, that's the truth on't—though
he's my friend.

Sneer. Never. He is as envious as an old maid
verging on the desperation of six-and-thirty : and
then the insidious humility with which he seduces
you to give a free opinion on any of his works, can
be exceeded only by the petulant arrogance with
which he is sure to reject your observations.

Dangle. Very true, egad—though he's my
friend.

Sneer. Then his affected contempt of all newspaper strictures ; though, at the same time, he is
the sorest man alive, and shrinks like scorched
parchment from the fiery ordeal of true criticism :
yet is he so covetous of popularity, that he had
rather be abused than not mentioned at all.

Dangle. There's no denying it—though he is
my friend.

Sneer. You have read the tragedy he has just
finished, haven't you ?

Dangle. Oh, yes ; he sent it to me yesterday.

Sneer. Well, and you think it execrable, don't you ?

Dangle. Why, between ourselves, egad, I must own—though he's my friend—that it is one of the most——He's here [*Aside*]—finished and most admirable perform——

Sir Fretful. [*without.*] Mr. Sneer with him, did you say ?

Enter SIR FRETFUL.

Dangle. Ah, my dear friend !—Egad, we were just speaking of your tragedy. Admirable, Sir Fretful, admirable!

Sneer. You never did anything beyond it, Sir Fretful—never in your life.

Sir Fretful. You make me extremely happy ; for without a compliment, my dear Sneer, there isn't a man in the world whose judgement I value as I do yours—and Mr. Dangle's.

Mrs. Dangle. They are only laughing at you, Sir Fretful ; for it was but just now that——

Dangle. Mrs. Dangle ! Ah, Sir Fretful, you know Mrs. Dangle. My friend Sneer was rallying just now. He knows how she admires you, and——

Sir Fretful. O Lord, I am sure Mr. Sneer has more taste and sincerity than to——A damned double-faced fellow ! [*Aside.*

Dangle. Yes, yes,—Sneer *will* jest—but a better-humoured——

Sir Fretful. Oh, I know——

Dangle. He has a ready turn for ridicule—his wit costs him nothing.

Sir Fretful. No, egad,—or I should wonder how he came by it. [*Aside.*

Mrs. Dangle. Because his jest is always at the xpense of his friend.

Dangle. But, Sir Fretful, have you sent your lay to the managers yet ?—or can I be of any ervice to you ?

Sir Fretful. No, no, I thank you ; I believe he piece had sufficient recommendation with it. thank you, though—I sent it to the manager of 'ovent Garden Theatre this morning.

Sneer. I should have thought, now, that it night have been cast (as the actors call it) better t Drury Lane.

Sir Fretful. O Lud ! no—never send a play here while I live—hark'ee ! [*Whispers* SNEER.

Sneer. Writes himself !—I know he does——

Sir Fretful. I say nothing—I take away from no nan's merit—I am hurt at no man's good fortune —I say nothing—But this I will say—through all ny knowledge of life, I have observed—that there ᵴ not a passion so strongly rooted in the human eart as envy !

Sneer. I believe you have reason for what you ay, indeed.

Sir Fretful. Besides, I can tell you it is not lways so safe to leave a play in the hands of those ʼho write themselves.

Sneer. What, they may steal from them, hey, ny dear Plagiary ?

Sir Fretful. Steal !—to be sure they may ; and, gad, serve your best thoughts as gipsies do stolen hildren, disfigure them to make 'em pass for their wn.

Sneer. But your present work is a sacrifice to lelpomene, and *he,* you know, never——

Sir Fretful. That 's no security. A dexterous

plagiarist may do anything. Why, sir, for aug[h]
I know, he might take out some of the best things i[n]
my tragedy and put them into his own comedy.

Sneer. That might be done, I dare be sworn.

Sir Fretful. And then, if such a person give[s]
you the least hint or assistance, he is devilish ap[t]
to take the merit of the whole——

Dangle. If it succeeds.

Sir Fretful. Aye,—but with regard to this piec[e]
I think I can hit that gentleman, for I can safel[y]
swear he never read it.

Sneer. I'll tell you how you may hurt hi[m]
more.

Sir Fretful. How ?

Sneer. Swear he wrote it.

Sir Fretful. Plague on't now, Sneer, I sha[ll]
take it ill. I believe you want to take away m[y]
character as an author !

Sneer. Then I am sure you ought to be ver[y]
much obliged to me.

Sir Fretful. Hey !—Sir !——

Dangle. Oh, you know, he never means wha[t]
he says.

Sir Fretful. Sincerely then—you do like th[e]
piece ?

Sneer. Wonderfully !

Sir Fretful. But come now, there must b[e]
something that you think might be mended, hey[?]
—Mr. Dangle, has nothing struck you ?

Dangle. Why, faith, it is but an ungraciou[s]
thing for the most part to——

Sir Fretful. With most authors it is just s[o]
indeed ; they are in general strangely tenacious [;]
But, for my part, I am never so well pleased a[s]
when a judicious critic points out any defect t[o]

SIR FRETFUL PLAGIARY   227

ne; for what is the purpose of showing a work to
a friend, if you don't mean to profit by his
opinion?

Sneer. Very true. Why, then, though I seriously admire the piece upon the whole, yet there is
one small objection; which, if you'll give me leave,
I'll mention.

Sir Fretful. Sir, you can't oblige me more.

Sneer. I think it wants incident.

Sir Fretful. Good God!—you surprise me!—
wants incident!

Sneer. Yes; I own I think the incidents are
too few.

Sir Fretful. Good God! Believe me, Mr.
Sneer, there is no person for whose judgement
I have a more implicit deference. But I protest to
you, Mr. Sneer, I am only apprehensive that the
incidents are too crowded.—My dear Dangle, how
does it strike you?

Dangle. Really, I can't agree with my friend
Sneer. I think the plot quite sufficient; and the
four first acts by many degrees the best I ever read
or saw in my life. If I might venture to suggest
anything, it is that the interest rather falls off in
the fifth.

Sir Fretful. Rises, I believe you mean, sir.

Dangle. No, I don't, upon my word.

Sir Fretful. Yes, yes, you do, upon my soul—it
certainly don't fall off, I assure you. No, no, it
don't fall off!

Dangle. Now, Mrs. Dangle, didn't you say it
struck you in the same light?

Mrs. Dangle No, indeed, I did not—I did not
see a fault in any part of the play from the beginning to the end.

Sir Fretful. Upon my soul, the women are the best judges after all!

Mrs. Dangle. Or if I made any objection, I am sure it was to nothing in the piece! but that I was afraid it was, on the whole, a little too long.

Sir Fretful. Pray, madam, do you speak as to duration of time; or do you mean that the story is tediously spun out?

Mrs. Dangle. O Lud! no. I speak only with reference to the usual length of acting plays.

Sir Fretful. Then I am very happy—very happy indeed—because the play is a short play, a remarkably short play. I should not venture to differ with a lady on a point of taste; but, on these occasions, the watch, you know, is the critic.

Mrs. Dangle. Then, I suppose, it must have been Mr. Dangle's drawling manner of reading it to me.

Sir Fretful. Oh, if Mr. Dangle read it, that's quite another affair! But I assure you, Mrs. Dangle, the first evening you can spare me three hours and a half, I'll undertake to read you the whole from beginning to end, with the prologue and epilogue, and allow time for the music between the acts.

Mrs. Dangle. I hope to see it on the stage next.

Dangle. Well, Sir Fretful, I wish you may be able to get rid as easily of the newspaper criticisms as you do of ours.

Sir Fretful. The *newspapers*! Sir, they are the most villanous—licentious—abominable—infernal—Not that I ever read them—No—I make it a rule never to look into a newspaper.

Dangle. You are quite right, for it certainly must hurt an author of delicate feelings to see the liberties they take.

Sir Fretful. No!—quite the contrary; their abuse is, in fact, the best panegyric—I like it of all things. An author's reputation is only in danger from their support.

Sneer. Why, that's true—and that attack now on you the other day——

Sir Fretful What? where?

Dangle. Aye, you mean in a paper of Thursday; it was completely ill-natured, to be sure.

Sir Fretful. Oh, so much the better. Ha! ha! ha! I wouldn't have it otherwise.

Dangle. Certainly it is only to be laughed at; for——

Sir Fretful. You don't happen to recollect what the fellow said, do you?

Sneer. Pray, Dangle—Sir Fretful seems a little anxious——

Sir Fretful. O Lud, no!—anxious,—not I,—not the least.—I—But one may as well hear, you know.

Dangle. Sneer, do *you* recollect?—Make out something.   [*Aside.*

Sneer. I will. [*To* DANGLE.]—Yes, yes, I remember perfectly.

Sir Fretful. Well, and pray now—not that it signifies—what might the gentleman say?

Sneer. Why, he roundly asserts that you have not the slightest invention, or original genius whatever; though you are the greatest traducer of all other authors living.

Sir Fretful. Ha! ha! ha!—very good!

Sneer. That as to Comedy, you have not one

idea of your own, he believes, even in your common-
place book, where stray jokes and pilfered witti-
cisms are kept with as much method as the ledger
of the Lost-and-Stolen Office.

Sir Fretful. Ha! ha! ha!—very pleasant!

Sneer. Nay, that you are so unlucky as not to
have the skill even to *steal* with taste : but that
you glean from the refuse of obscure volumes,
where more judicious plagiarists have been before
you; so that the body of your work is a composition
of dregs and sediments—like a bad tavern's worst
wine.

Sir Fretful. Ha! ha!

Sneer. In your more serious efforts, he says,
your bombast would be less intolerable, if the
thoughts were ever suited to the expression ; but
the homeliness of the sentiment stares through the
fantastic encumbrance of its fine language, like
a clown in one of the new uniforms !

Sir Fretful. Ha! ha!

Sneer. That your occasional tropes and flowers
suit the general coarseness of your style, as tam-
bour sprigs would a ground of linsey-woolsey ;
while your imitations of Shakespeare resemble the
mimicry of Falstaff's page, and are about as near
the standard of the original.

Sir Fretful. Ha!—

Sneer. In short, that even the finest passages
you steal are of no service to you ; for the poverty
of your own language prevents their assimilating ;
so that they lie on the surface like lumps of marl on
a barren moor, encumbering what it is not in their
power to fertilize !

Sir Fretful. [*After great agitation.*] Now another
person would be vexed at this.

Sneer. Oh ! but I wouldn't have told you, only to divert you.

Sir Fretful. I know it—I *am* diverted—ha ! ha ! ha !—not the least invention ! Ha ! ha ! ha ! very good !—very good !

Sneer. Yes—no genius ! Ha ! ha ! ha !

Dangle. A severe rogue ! ha ! ha ! ha ! But you are quite right, Sir Fretful, never to read such nonsense.

Sir Fretful. To be sure—for if there is anything to one's praise, it is a foolish vanity to be gratified at it, and if it is abuse—why one is always sure to hear of it from one damned good-natured friend or another !

Enter SERVANT.

Servant. Sir, there is an Italian gentleman with a French interpreter, and three young ladies, and a dozen musicians, who say they are sent by Lady Rondeau and Mrs. Fuge.

Dangle. Gadso ! they come by appointment. Dear Mrs. Dangle, do let them know I'll see them directly.

Mrs. Dangle. You know, Mr. Dangle, I shan't understand a word they say.

Dangle. But you hear there's an interpreter.

Mrs. Dangle. Well, I'll try to endure their complaisance till you come. [*Exit.*

Servant. And Mr. Puff, sir, has sent word that the last rehearsal is to be this morning, and that he'll call on you presently.

Dangle. That's true—I shall certainly be at home. [*Exit* SERVANT.] Now, Sir Fretful, if you have a mind to have justice done you in the way of answer—egad, Mr. Puff's your man.

Sir Fretful. Pshaw! sir, why should I wish to have it answered, when I tell you I am pleased at it!

Dangle. True, I had forgot that. But I hope you are not fretted at what Mr. Sneer——

Sir Fretful. Zounds! no, Mr. Dangle, don't I tell you these things never fret me in the least.

Dangle. Nay, I only thought——

Sir Fretful. And let me tell you, Mr. Dangle, 'tis damned affronting in you to suppose that I am hurt, when I tell you I am not.

Sneer. But why so warm, Sir Fretful?

Sir Fretful. Gad's life! Mr. Sneer, you are as absurd as Dangle; how often must I repeat it to you, that nothing can vex me but your supposing it possible for me to mind the damned nonsense you have been repeating to me!—and let me tell you, if you continue to believe this, you must mean to insult me, gentlemen—and then your disrespect will affect me no more than the newspaper criticisms—and I shall treat it—with exactly the same calm indifference and philosophic contempt—and so, your servant.   [*Exit.*

Sneer. Ha! ha! ha! Poor Sir Fretful! Now will he go and vent his philosophy in anonymous abuse of all modern critics and authors. But, Dangle, you must get your friend Puff to take me to the rehearsal of his tragedy.

Dangle. I'll answer for't, he'll thank you for desiring it. But come and help me to judge of this musical family; they are recommended by people of consequence, I assure you.

Sneer. I am at your disposal the whole morning—but I thought you had been a decided critic in music, as well as in literature.

Dangle. So I am—but I have a bad ear. I'faith, Sneer, though, I am afraid we were a little too severe on Sir Fretful—though he is my friend.

Sneer. Why, 'tis certain, that unnecessarily to mortify the vanity of any writer, is a cruelty which mere dullness never can deserve ; but where a base and personal malignity usurps the place of literary emulation, the aggressor deserves neither quarter nor pity.

Dangle. That's true, egad !—though he's my friend !

The Critic. 1779.

SIR WALTER SCOTT

1771–1832

ESCAPE OF SIR ARTHUR WARDOUR

The information of Davy Dibble, which had spread such general alarm at Monkbarns, proved to be strictly correct. Sir Arthur and his daughter had set out, according to their first proposal, to return to Knockwinnock by the turnpike road; but when they reached the head of the loaning, as it was called, or great lane, which on one side made a sort of avenue to the house of Monkbarns, they discerned, a little way before them, Lovel, who seemed to linger on the way as if to give him an opportunity to join them. Miss Wardour immediately proposed to her father that they should take another direction; and, as the weather was fine, walk home by the sands, which, stretching below a picturesque ridge of rocks, afforded at almost all times a pleasanter passage between Knockwinnock and Monkbarns than the highroad. Sir Arthur acquiesced willingly. 'It would be unpleasant', he said, 'to be joined by that young fellow, whom Mr. Oldbuck had taken the freedom to introduce them to.' And his old-fashioned politeness had none of the ease of the present day, which permits you, if you have a mind, to *cut* the person you have associated with for a week, the instant you feel or suppose yourself in a situation which makes it disagreeable to own him. Sir

Arthur only stipulated, that a little ragged boy, for the guerdon of one penny sterling, should run to meet his coachman, and turn his equipage back to Knockwinnock.

When this was arranged, and the emissary dispatched, the knight and his daughter left the highroad, and following a wandering path among sandy hillocks, partly grown over with furze and the long grass called bent, soon attained the side of the ocean. The tide was by no means so far out as they had computed; but this gave them no alarm;—there were seldom ten days in the year when it approached so near the cliffs as not to leave a dry passage. But, nevertheless, at periods of spring-tide, or even when the ordinary flood was accelerated by high winds, this road was altogether covered by the sea; and tradition had recorded several fatal accidents which had happened on such occasions. Still, such dangers were considered as remote and improbable; and rather served, with other legends, to amuse the hamlet fireside, than to prevent any one from going between Knockwinnock and Monkbarns by the sands.

As Sir Arthur and Miss Wardour paced along, enjoying the pleasant footing afforded by the cool moist hard sand, Miss Wardour could not help observing that the last tide had risen considerably above the usual water-mark. Sir Arthur made the same observation, but without its occurring to either of them to be alarmed at the circumstance. The sun was now resting his huge disk upon the edge of the level ocean, and gilded the accumulation of towering clouds through which he had travelled the livelong day, and which now

assembled on all sides, like misfortunes and
disasters around a sinking empire and falling
monarch. Still, however, his dying splendour
gave a sombre magnificence to the massive
congregation of vapours, forming out of their
unsubstantial gloom the show of pyramids and
towers, some touched with gold, some with purple,
some with a hue of deep and dark red. The
distant sea, stretched beneath this varied and
gorgeous canopy, lay almost portentously still,
reflecting back the dazzling and level beams of the
descending luminary, and the splendid colouring
of the clouds amidst which he was setting. Nearer
to the beach, the tide rippled onward in waves
of sparkling silver, that imperceptibly, yet rapidly,
gained upon the sand.

With a mind employed in admiration of the
romantic scene, or perhaps on some more agitating
topic, Miss Wardour advanced in silence by her
father's side, whose recently offended dignity did
not stoop to open any conversation. Following
the windings of the beach, they passed one projecting point of headland or rock after another,
and now found themselves under a huge and
continued extent of the precipices by which that
iron-bound coast is in most places defended.
Long projecting reefs of rock, extending under
water, and only evincing their existence by here
and there a peak entirely bare, or by the breakers
which foamed over those that were partially
covered, rendered Knockwinnock bay dreaded by
pilots and ship-masters. The crags which rose
between the beach and the mainland, to the
height of two or three hundred feet, afforded in
their crevices shelter for unnumbered seafowl, in

situations seemingly secured by their dizzy height from the rapacity of man. Many of these wild tribes, with the instinct which sends them to seek the land before a storm arises, were now winging towards their nests with the shrill and dissonant clang which announces disquietude and fear. The disk of the sun became almost totally obscured ere he had altogether sunk below the horizon, and an early and lurid shade of darkness blotted the serene twilight of a summer evening. The wind began next to arise; but its wild and moaning sound was heard for some time, and its effects became visible on the bosom of the sea, before the gale was felt on shore. The mass of waters, now dark and threatening, began to lift itself in larger ridges, and sink in deeper furrows, forming waves that rose high in foam upon the breakers, or burst upon the beach with a sound resembling distant thunder.

Appalled by this sudden change of weather Miss Wardour drew close to her father, and held his arm fast. ' I wish,' at length she said, but almost in a whisper, as if ashamed to express her increasing apprehensions, ' I wish we had kept the road we intended, or waited at Monkbarns for the carriage.'

Sir Arthur looked round, but did not see, or would not acknowledge, any signs of an immediate storm. They would reach Knockwinnock, he said, long before the tempest began. But the speed with which he walked, and with which Isabella could hardly keep pace, indicated a feeling that some exertion was necessary to accomplish his consolatory prediction.

They were now near the centre of a deep but

narrow bay, or recess, formed by two projecting capes of high and inaccessible rock, which shot out into the sea like the horns of a crescent ;— and neither durst communicate the apprehension which each began to entertain, that, from the unusually rapid advance of the tide, they might be deprived of the power of proceeding by doubling the promontory which lay before them, or of retreating by the road which brought them thither.

As they thus pressed forward, longing doubtless to exchange the easy curving line, which the sinuosities of the bay compelled them to adopt, for a straighter and more expeditious path, though less conformable to the line of beauty, Sir Arthur observed a human figure on the beach advancing to meet them. 'Thank God,' he exclaimed, 'we shall get round Halket Head!—that person must have passed it'; thus giving vent to the feeling of hope, though he had suppressed that of apprehension.

'Thank God, indeed!' echoed his daughter, half audibly, half internally, as expressing the gratitude which she strongly felt.

The figure which advanced to meet them made many signs, which the haze of the atmosphere, now disturbed by wind and by a drizzling rain, prevented them from seeing or comprehending distinctly.—Some time before they met, Sir Arthur could recognize the old blue-gowned beggar, Edie Ochiltree. It is said that even the brute creation lay aside their animosities and antipathies when pressed by an instant and common danger. The beach under Halket Head, rapidly diminishing in extent by the encroach-

ments of a spring-tide and a north-west wind,
was in like manner a neutral field, where even
a justice of peace and a strolling mendicant might
meet upon terms of mutual forbearance.

'Turn back! turn back!' exclaimed the
vagrant; 'why did ye not turn when I waved
to you?'

'We thought,' replied Sir Arthur, in great
agitation, 'we thought we could get round
Halket Head.'

'Halket Head!—the tide will be running on
Halket Head by this time like the Fall of Fyers!—
it was a' I could do to get round it twenty minutes
since—it was coming in three feet abreast. We
will maybe get back by Bally-Burgh Ness Point
yet. The Lord help us!—it's our only chance.
We can but try.'

'My God, my child!'—'My father! my dear
father!' exclaimed the parent and daughter, as,
fear lending them strength and speed, they turned
to retrace their steps and endeavoured to double
the point, the projection of which formed the
southern extremity of the bay.

'I heard ye were here, frae the bit callant ye
sent to meet your carriage,' said the beggar, as he
trudged stoutly on a step or two behind Miss
Wardour; 'and I couldna bide to think o' the
dainty young leddy's peril, that has ay been kind
to ilka forlorn heart that cam near her. Sae
I lookit at the lift and the rin o' the tide, till
I settled it that if I could get down time enough
to gie you warning, we wad do weel yet. But
I doubt, I doubt, I have been beguiled! for what
mortal ee ever saw sic a race as the tide is rinning
e'en now? See, yonder's the Ratton's Skerry—

he ay held his neb abune the water in my day—
but he 's aneath it now.'

Sir Arthur cast a look in the direction in which
the old man pointed. A huge rock, which in
general, even in spring-tides, displayed a hulk
like the keel of a large vessel, was now quite under
water, and its place only indicated by the boiling
and breaking of the eddying waves which encoun-
tered its submarine resistance.

'Mak haste, mak haste, my bonny leddy,' continued the old man—'mak haste, and we may
do yet! Take haud o' my arm—an auld and
frail arm it 's now, but it 's been in as sair stress
as this is yet. Take haud o' my arm, my win-
some leddy! D'ye see yon wee black speck
amang the wallowing waves yonder? This morning it was as high as the mast o' a brig—it 's sma'
eneugh now—but, while I see as muckle black
about it as the crown o' my hat, I winna believe
but we'll get round the Bally-Burgh Ness, for a'
that 's come and gane yet.'

Isabella, in silence, accepted from the old man
the assistance which Sir Arthur was less able to
afford her. The waves had now encroached so
much upon the beach, that the firm and smooth
footing which they had hitherto had on the sand
must be exchanged for a rougher path close to
the foot of the precipice, and in some places even
raised upon its lower ledges. It would have been
utterly impossible for Sir Arthur Wardour, or his
daughter, to have found their way along these
shelves without the guidance and encouragement
of the beggar, who had been there before in high
tides, though never, he acknowledged, 'in sae
awsome a night as this.'

It was indeed a dreadful evening. The howling of the storm mingled with the shrieks of the sea-fowl, and sounded like the dirge of the three devoted beings, who, pent between two of the most magnificent, yet most dreadful objects of nature—a raging tide and an insurmountable precipice—toiled along their painful and dangerous path, often lashed by the spray of some giant billow, which threw itself higher on the beach than those that had preceded it. Each minute did their enemy gain ground perceptibly upon them! Still, however, loath to relinquish the last hopes of life, they bent their eyes on the black rock pointed out by Ochiltree. It was yet distinctly visible among the breakers, and continued to be so, until they came to a turn in their precarious path, where an intervening projection of rock hid it from their sight. Deprived of the view of the beacon on which they had relied, they now experienced the double agony of terror and suspense. They struggled forward, however; but, when they arrived at the point from which they ought to have seen the crag, it was no longer visible: the signal of safety was lost among a thousand white breakers, which, dashing upon the point of the promontory, rose in prodigious sheets of snowy foam, as high as the mast of a first-rate man-of-war, against the dark brow of the precipice.

The countenance of the old man fell. Isabella gave a faint shriek, and, 'God have mercy upon us!' which her guide solemnly uttered, was piteously echoed by Sir Arthur—'My child! my child!—to die such a death!'

'My father! my dear father!' his daughter

exclaimed, clinging to him—'and you too, who have lost your own life in endeavouring to save ours!'

'That's not worth the counting,' said the old man. 'I hae lived to be weary o' life; and here or yonder—at the back o' a dyke, in a wreath o' snaw, or in the wame o' a wave, what signifies how the auld gaberlunzie dies?'

'Good man,' said Sir Arthur, 'can you think of nothing?—of no help?—I'll make you rich—I'll give you a farm—I'll'——

'Our riches will be soon equal,' said the beggar, looking out upon the strife of the waters—'they are sae already; for I hae nae land, and you would give your fair bounds and barony for a square yard of rock that would be dry for twal hours.'

While they exchanged these words, they paused upon the highest ledge of rock to which they could attain; for it seemed that any further attempt to move forward could only serve to anticipate their fate. Here, then, they were to await the sure though slow progress of the raging element, something in the situation of the martyrs of the early church, who, exposed by heathen tyrants to be slain by wild beasts, were compelled for a time to witness the impatience and rage by which the animals were agitated, while awaiting the signal for undoing their grates and letting them loose upon the victims.

Yet even this fearful pause gave Isabella time to collect the powers of a mind naturally strong and courageous, and which rallied itself at this terrible juncture. 'Must we yield life', she said, 'without a struggle? Is there no path, however dreadful, by which we could climb the crag, or at least attain some height above the tide, where we could remain till morning, or till help comes? They must be aware of our situation, and will raise the country to relieve us.'

Sir Arthur, who heard but scarcely comprehended his daughter's question, turned, nevertheless, instinctively and eagerly to the old man, as if their lives were in his gift. Ochiltree paused— 'I was a bauld craigsman', he said, 'ance in my life, and mony a kittywake's and lungie's nest hae I harried up amang thae very black rocks; but it's lang, lang syne, and nae mortal could speel them without a rope—and if I had ane, my ee-sight, and my footstep, and my hand-grip, hae a' failed mony a day sinsyne—And then, how could I save *you*? But there was a path here ance, though maybe, if we could see it, ye would rather bide where we are—His name be praised!' he ejaculated suddenly, 'there's ane coming down the crag e'en now!'—Then, exalting his voice, he hilloa'd out to the daring adventurer such instructions as his former practice, and the remembrance of local circumstances, suddenly forced upon his mind: 'Ye're right—ye're right!—that gate— that gate!—fasten the rope weel round Crummie's-horn, that's the muckle black stane—cast twa plies round it—that's it!—now, weize yoursell a wee easel-ward—a wee mair yet to that ither stane—we ca'd it the Cat's-lug—there used to be the root o' an aik tree there—that will do!— canny now, lad—canny now—tak tent and tak time—Lord bless ye, tak time.—Vera weel!—Now ye maun get to Bessy's Apron, that's the muckle braid flat blue stane—and then, I think, wi' your help and the tow thegither, I'll win at ye, and

then we'll be able to get up the young leddy and
Sir Arthur.'

The adventurer, following the directions of old
Edie, flung him down the end of the rope, which
he secured around Miss Wardour, wrapping her
previously in his own blue gown, to preserve her
as much as possible from injury. Then, availing
himself of the rope, which was made fast at the
other end, he began to ascend the face of the crag—
a most precarious and dizzy undertaking, which,
however, after one or two perilous escapes, placed
him safe on the broad flat stone beside our friend
Lovel. Their joint strength was able to raise
Isabella to the place of safety which they had
attained. Lovel then descended in order to assist
Sir Arthur, around whom he adjusted the rope ;
and again mounting to their place of refuge, with
the assistance of old Ochiltree, and such aid as
Sir Arthur himself could afford, he raised himself
beyond the reach of the billows.

The sense of reprieve from approaching and
apparently inevitable death, had its usual effect.
The father and daughter threw themselves into
each other's arms, kissed and wept for joy,
although their escape was connected with the
prospect of passing a tempestuous night upon
a precipitous ledge of rock, which scarce afforded
footing for the four shivering beings, who now,
like the sea-fowl around them, clung there in hopes
of some shelter from the devouring element which
raged beneath. The spray of the billows, which
attained in fearful succession the foot of the precipice, overflowing the beach on which they so
lately stood, flew as high as their place of temporary refuge ; and the stunning sound with which

they dashed against the rocks beneath, seemed as
if they still demanded the fugitives in accents of
thunder as their destined prey. It was a summer
night, doubtless; yet the probability was slender
that a frame so delicate as that of Miss Wardour
should survive till morning the drenching of the
spray; and the dashing of the rain which now
burst in full violence, accompanied with deep and
heavy gusts of wind, added to the constrained and
perilous circumstances of their situation.

'The lassie!—the puir sweet lassie!' said the
old man: 'mony such a night have I weathered
at hame and abroad, but, God guide us, how can
she ever win through it!'

His apprehension was communicated in smothered
accents to Lovel; for, with the sort of free-
masonry by which bold and ready spirits correspond
in moments of danger, and become almost instinctively known to each other, they had established a
mutual confidence.—'I'll climb up the cliff again,'
said Lovel—'there's daylight enough left to see my
footing; I'll climb up, and call for more assistance.'

'Do so, do so, for heaven's sake!' said Sir
Arthur, eagerly.

'Are ye mad?' said the mendicant: 'Francie
o' Fowlsheugh, and he was the best craigsman that
ever speel'd heugh (mair by token, he brake his
neck upon the Dunbuy of Slaines), wadna hae
ventured upon the Halket Head craigs after sundown—It's God's grace, and a great wonder
besides, that ye are not in the middle o' that
roaring sea wi' what ye hae done already—I didna
think there was the man left alive would hae come
down the craigs as ye did. I question an I could
hae done it mysell, at this hour and in this weather,

in the youngest and yaldest of my strength—But to venture up again—it's a mere and a clear tempting o' Providence.'

'I have no fear,' answered Lovel; 'I marked all the stations perfectly as I came down, and there is still light enough left to see them quite well—I am sure I can do it with perfect safety. Stay here, my good friend, by Sir Arthur and the young lady.'

'Deil be in my feet then,' answered the bedesman, sturdily; 'if ye gang, I'll gang too; for between the twa o' us, we'll hae mair than wark eneugh to get to the tap o' the heugh.'

'No, no—stay you here and attend to Miss Wardour—you see Sir Arthur is quite exhausted.'

'Stay yoursell then, and I'll gae,' said the old man;—'let death spare the green corn and take the ripe.'

'Stay both of you, I charge you,' said Isabella, faintly; 'I am well, and can spend the night very well here—I feel quite refreshed.' So saying, her voice failed her—she sank down, and would have fallen from the crag had she not been supported by Lovel and Ochiltree, who placed her in a posture half sitting, half reclining, beside her father, who, exhausted by fatigue of body and mind so extreme and unusual, had already sat down on a stone in a sort of stupor.

'It is impossible to leave them,' said Lovel— 'What is to be done?—Hark! hark!—did I not hear a hallo?'

'The skreigh of a Tammie Norie,' answered Ochiltree—'I ken the skirl weel.'

'No, by Heaven!' replied Lovel, 'it was a human voice.'

A distant hail was repeated, the sound plainly distinguishable among the various elemental noises, and the clang of the sea-mews by which they were surrounded. The mendicant and Lovel exerted their voices in a loud hallo, the former waving Miss Wardour's handkerchief on the end of his staff to make them conspicuous from above. Though the shouts were repeated, it was some time before they were in exact response to their own, leaving the unfortunate sufferers uncertain whether, in the darkening twilight and increasing storm, they had made the persons who apparently were traversing the verge of the precipice to bring them assistance, sensible of the place in which they had found refuge. At length their hallo was regularly and distinctly answered, and their courage confirmed, by the assurance that they were within hearing, if not within reach, of friendly assistance.

The shout of human voices from above was soon augmented, and the gleam of torches mingled with those lights of evening which still remained amidst the darkness of the storm. Some attempt was made to hold communication between the assistants above and the sufferers beneath, who were still clinging to their precarious place of safety ; but the howling of the tempest limited their intercourse to cries as inarticulate as those of the winged denizens of the crag, which shrieked in chorus, alarmed by the reiterated sound of human voices, where they had seldom been heard.

On the verge of the precipice an anxious group had now assembled. Oldbuck was the foremost and most earnest, pressing forward with unwonted desperation to the very brink of the crag, and extending his head (his hat and wig secured by a handkerchief under his chin) over the dizzy height, with an air of determination which made his more timorous assistants tremble.

'Haud a care, haud a care, Monkbarns!' cried Caxon, clinging to the skirts of his patron, and withholding him from danger as far as his strength permitted — 'God's sake, haud a care! — Sir Arthur's drowned already, and an ye fa' over the cleugh too, there will be but ae wig left in the parish, and that's the minister's.'

'Mind the peak there,' cried Mucklebackit, an old fisherman and smuggler—'mind the peak—Steenie, Steenie Wilks, bring up the tackle—I'se warrant we'll sune heave them on board, Monkbarns, wad ye but stand out o' the gate.'

'I see them,' said Oldbuck—'I see them low down on that flat stone—Hilli-hilloa, hilli-ho-a!'

'I see them mysell weel eneugh,' said Mucklebackit; 'they are sitting down yonder like hoodie-craws in a mist; but d'ye think ye'll help them wi' skirling that gate like an auld skart before a flaw o' weather?—Steenie, lad, bring up the mast—Od, I'se hae them up as we used to bouse up the kegs o' gin and brandy lang syne.— Get up the pickaxe, make a step for the mast— make the chair fast with the rattlin—haul taut and belay!'

The fishers had brought with them the mast of a boat, and as half of the country fellows about had now appeared, either out of zeal or curiosity, it was soon sunk in the ground, and sufficiently secured. A yard across the upright mast, and a rope stretched along it, and reeved through a block at each end, formed an extempore crane, which afforded the means of lowering an arm-chair, well secured and fastened, down to the flat shelf on which the sufferers had roosted. Their joy at hearing the preparations going on for their deliverance was considerably qualified when they beheld the precarious vehicle by means of which they were to be conveyed to upper air. It swung about a yard free of the spot which they occupied, obeying each impulse of the tempest, the empty air all around it, and depending upon the security of a rope, which, in the increasing darkness, had dwindled to an almost imperceptible thread. Besides the hazard of committing a human being to the vacant atmosphere in such a slight means of conveyance, there was the fearful danger of the chair and its occupant being dashed, either by the wind or the vibrations of the cord, against the rugged face of the precipice. But to diminish the risk as much as possible, the experienced seaman had let down with the chair another line, which, being attached to it, and held by the persons beneath, might serve by way of _gy_, as Muckle-backit expressed it, to render its descent in some measure steady and regular. Still, to commit one's self in such a vehicle, through a howling tempest of wind and rain, with a beetling precipice above and a raging abyss below, required that courage which despair alone can inspire. Yet wild as the sounds and sights of danger were, both above, beneath, and around, and doubtful and dangerous as the mode of escaping appeared to be, Lovel and the old mendicant agreed, after a moment's consultation, and after the former, by a sudden strong pull, had, at his own imminent risk, ascertained the security of the rope, that it

would be best to secure Miss Wardour in the chair,
and trust to the tenderness and care of those
above for her being safely craned up to the top
of the crag.

'Let my father go first,' exclaimed Isabella;
'for God's sake, my friends, place him first in
safety!'

'It cannot be, Miss Wardour,' said Lovel;—
'your life must be first secured—the rope which
bears your weight may——'

'I will not listen to a reason so selfish!'

'But ye maun listen to it, my bonny lassie,'
said Ochiltree, 'for a' our lives depend on it—
besides, when ye get on the tap o' the heugh
yonder, ye can gie them a round guess o' what's
ganging on in this Patmos o' ours—and Sir
Arthur's far by that, as I am thinking.'

Struck with the truth of this reasoning, she
exclaimed, 'True, most true; I am ready and
willing to undertake the first risk—What shall
I say to our friends above?'

'Just to look that their tackle does not graze
on the face o' the crag, and to let the chair down
and draw it up hooly and fairly;—we will halloo
when we are ready.'

With the sedulous attention of a parent to
a child, Lovel bound Miss Wardour with his
handkerchief, neckcloth, and the mendicant's
leathern belt, to the back and arms of the chair,
ascertaining accurately the security of each knot,
while Ochiltree kept Sir Arthur quiet. 'What are
ye doing wi' my bairn?—what are ye doing?—
She shall not be separated from m —Isabel, stay
with me, I command you!'

'Lordsake, Sir Arthur, haud your tongue, and

be thankful to God that there's wiser folk than you to manage this job,' cried the beggar, worn out by the unreasonable exclamations of the poor Baronet.

'Farewell, my father!' murmured Isabella— 'farewell, my—my friends!' and, shutting her eyes, as Edie's experience recommended, she gave the signal to Lovel, and he to those who were above. She rose, while the chair in which she sat was kept steady by the line which Lovel managed beneath. With a beating heart he watched the flutter of her white dress, until the vehicle was on a level with the brink of the precipice.

'Canny now, lads, canny now!' exclaimed old Mucklebackit, who acted as commodore; 'swerve the yard a bit—Now—there! there she sits safe on dry land.'

A loud shout announced the successful experiment to her fellow sufferers beneath, who replied with a ready and cheerful hallo. Monkbarns, in his ecstasy of joy, stripped his greatcoat to wrap up the young lady, and would have pulled off his coat and waistcoat for the same purpose, had he not been withheld by the cautious Caxon. 'Haud a care o' us! your honour will be killed wi' the hoast—ye'll no get out o' your night-cowl this fortnight—and that will suit us unco ill.— Na, na—there's the chariot down by; let twa o' the folk carry the young leddy there.'

'You're right,' said the Antiquary, readjusting the sleeves and collar of his coat, 'you're right, Caxon; this is a naughty night to swim in.— Miss Wardour, let me convey you to the chariot.'

'Not for worlds, till I see my father safe.'

In a few distinct words, evincing how much her

resolution had surmounted even the mortal fear of so agitating a hazard, she explained the nature of the situation beneath, and the wishes of Lovel and Ochiltree.

'Right, right, that's right too—I should like to see the son of Sir Gamelyn de Guardover on dry land myself—I have a notion he would sign the abjuration oath, and the Ragman-roll to boot, and acknowledge Queen Mary to be nothing better than she should be, to get alongside my bottle of old port that he ran away from, and left scarce begun. But he's safe now, and here a' comes' (for the chair was again lowered, and Sir Arthur made fast in it, without much consciousness on his own part)—'here a' comes—Bowse away, my boys! canny wi' him—a pedigree of a hundred links is hanging on a tenpenny tow—the whole barony of Knockwinnock depends on three plies of hemp—*respice finem, respice funem*—look to your end—look to a rope's end.—Welcome, welcome, my good old friend, to firm land, though I cannot say to warm land or to dry land. A cord for ever against fifty fathom of water, though not in the sense of the base proverb—a fico for the phrase—better *sus. per funem*, than *sus. per coll.*'

While Oldbuck ran on in this way, Sir Arthur was safely wrapped in the close embraces of his daughter, who, assuming that authority which the circumstances demanded, ordered some of the assistants to convey him to the chariot, promising to follow in a few minutes. She lingered on the cliff, holding an old countryman's arm, to witness probably the safety of those whose dangers she had shared.

'What have we here?' said Oldbuck, as the

vehicle once more ascended—'what patched and weather-beaten matter is this?' Then, as the torches illumed the rough face and grey hairs of old Ochiltree,—'What! is it thou?—Come, old Mocker, I must needs be friends with thee.—But who the devil makes up your party besides?'

'Ane that's weel worth ony twa o' us, Monkbarns;—it's the young stranger lad they ca' Lovel—and he's behaved this blessed night as if he had three lives to rely on, and was willing to waste them a' rather than endanger ither folks. Ca' hooly, sirs, as ye wad win an auld man's blessing!—mind there's naebody below now to haud the gy—Hae a care o' the Cat's-lug corner—bide weel aff Crummie's-horn!'

'Have a care indeed,' echoed Oldbuck. 'What! is it my *rara avis*—my black swan—my phoenix of companions in a post-chaise?—take care of him, Mucklebackit.'

'As muckle care as if he were a greybeard o' brandy; and I canna take mair if his hair were like John Harlowe's.—Yo ho, my hearts! bowse away with him!'

Lovel did, in fact, run a much greater risk than any of his precursors. His weight was not sufficient to render his ascent steady amid such a storm of wind, and he swung like an agitated pendulum at the mortal risk of being dashed against the rocks. But he was young, bold, and active, and, with the assistance of the beggar's stout piked staff, which he had retained by advice of the proprietor, contrived to bear himself from the face of the precipice, and the yet more hazardous projecting cliffs which varied its surface. Tossed in empty space, like an idle and

unsubstantial feather, with a motion that agitated
the brain at once with fear and with dizziness, he
retained his alertness of exertion and presence of
mind ; and it was not until he was safely grounded
upon the summit of the cliff, that he felt temporary and giddy sickness. As he recovered from
a sort of half swoon, he cast his eyes eagerly
around. The object which they would most
willingly have sought was already in the act of
vanishing. Her white garment was just discernible as she followed on the path which her father
had taken. She had lingered till she saw the last
of their company rescued from danger, and until
she had been assured by the hoarse voice of
Mucklebackit, that ' the callant had come off wi'
unbrizzed banes, and that he was but in a kind of
dwam '. But Lovel was not aware that she had
expressed in his fate even this degree of interest,—
which, though nothing more than was due to
a stranger who had assisted her in such an hour of
peril, he would have gladly purchased by braving
even more imminent danger than he had that
evening been exposed to. The beggar she had
already commanded to come to Knockwinnock
that night. He made an excuse.—' Then to-
morrow let me see you.'

The old man promised to obey. Oldbuck thrust
something into his hand—Ochiltree looked at it
by the torchlight, and returned it—' Na, na !
I never tak gowd—besides, Monkbarns, ye wad
maybe be rueing it the morn.' Then turning to the
group of fishermen and peasants—' Now, sirs, wha
will gie me a supper and some clean pease-strae ? '

' I,' ' and I,' ' and I,' answered many a ready
voice.

'Aweel, since sae it is, and I can only sleep in ae barn at ance, I'll gae down wi' Saunders Mucklebackit—he has ay a soup o' something comfortable about his bigging—and, bairns, I'll maybe live to put ilka ane o' ye in mind some ither night that ye hae promised me quarters and my awmous'; and away he went with the fisherman.

Oldbuck laid the hand of strong possession on Lovel—'Deil a stride ye's go to Fairport this night, young man—you must go home with me to Monkbarns. Why, man, you have been a hero— a perfect Sir William Wallace, by all accounts. Come, my good lad, take hold of my arm;—I am not a prime support in such a wind—but Caxon shall help us out—here, you old idiot, come on the other side of me.—And how the deil got you down to that infernal Bessy's Apron, as they call it? Bess, said they? Why, curse her, she has spread out that vile pennon or banner of woman-kind, like all the rest of her sex, to allure her votaries to death and headlong ruin.'

'I have been pretty well accustomed to climbing, and I have long observed fowlers practise that pass down the cliff.'

'But how, in the name of all that is wonderful, came you to discover the danger of the pettish Baronet and his far more deserving daughter?'

'I saw them from the verge of the precipice.'

'From the verge!—umph—And what possessed you, *dumosa pendere procul de rupe?*—though *dumosa* is not the appropriate epithet—what the deil, man, tempted ye to the verge of the craig?'

'Why—I like to see the gathering and growling of a coming storm—or, in your own classical

language, Mr. Oldbuck, *suave mari magno*—and
so forth—but here we reach the turn to Fairport.
I must wish you good-night.'

'Not a step, not a pace, not an inch, not a
shathmont, as I may say,—the meaning of which
word has puzzled many that think themselves
antiquaries. I am clear we should read *salmon-
length* for *shathmont's-length*. You are aware that
the space allotted for the passage of a salmon
through a dam, dike, or weir, by statute, is the
length within which a full-grown pig can turn
himself round. Now I have a scheme to prove,
that, as terrestrial objects were thus appealed to
for ascertaining submarine measurement, so it
must be supposed that the productions of the
water were established as gauges of the extent of
land.—Shathmont—salmont—you see the close
alliance of the sounds; dropping out two *h's*, and
a *t*, and assuming an *l*, makes the whole difference
—I wish to Heaven no antiquarian derivation had
demanded heavier concessions.'

'But, my dear sir, I really must go home—I am
wet to the skin.'

'Shalt have my night-gown, man, and slippers,
and catch the antiquarian fever as men do the
plague, by wearing infected garments. Nay, I
know what you would be at—you are afraid to
put the old bachelor to charges. But is there
not the remains of that glorious chicken-pie—
which, *meo arbitrio*, is better cold than hot—and
that bottle of my oldest port, out of which the
silly brain-sick Baronet (whom I cannot pardon,
since he has escaped breaking his neck) had just
taken one glass, when his infirm noddle went
a wool-gathering after Gamelyn de Guardover?'

So saying, he dragged Lovel forward, till the Palmer's Port of Monkbarns received them. Never, perhaps, had it admitted two pedestrians more needing rest; for Monkbarns's fatigue had been in a degree very contrary to his usual habits, and his more young and robust companion had that evening undergone agitation of mind which had harassed and wearied him even more than his extraordinary exertions of body.

The Antiquary. 1815.

ROB ROY IN THE TOLBOOTH

THE magistrate took the light out of his servant-maid's hand, and advanced to his scrutiny, like Diogenes in the street of Athens, lantern in hand, and probably with as little expectation as that of the cynic, that he was likely to encounter any especial treasure in the course of his researches. The first whom he approached was my mysterious guide, who, seated on a table as I have already described him, with his eyes firmly fixed on the wall, his features arranged into the utmost inflexibility of expression, his hands folded on his breast with an air betwixt carelessness and defiance, his heel patting against the foot of the table, to keep time with the tune which he continued to whistle, submitted to Mr. Jarvie's investigation with an air of absolute confidence and assurance, which, for a moment, placed at fault the memory and sagacity of the acute investigator.

'Ah!—Eh!—Oh!' exclaimed the Bailie. 'My conscience!—it's impossible—and yet—no!—Conscience, it canna be!—and yet again—Deil hae me! that I suld say sae—Ye robber—ye cateran—ye born deevil that ye are, to a' bad ends and nae gude ane—can this be you?'

'E'en as ye see, Bailie,' was the laconic answer.

'Conscience! if I am na clean bumbaized—*you*, ye cheat-the-wuddy rogue, *you* here on your venture in the Tolbooth o' Glasgow?—What d'ye think's the value o' your head?'

'Umph!—why, fairly weighed, and Dutch weight, it might weigh down one provost's, four bailies', a town-clerk's, six deacons', besides stent-masters'——

'Ah, ye reiving villain!' interrupted Mr. Jarvie. 'But tell ower your sins, and prepare ye, for if I say the word'——

'True, Bailie,' said he who was thus addressed, folding his hands behind him with the utmost nonchalance, 'but ye will never say that word.'

'And why suld I not, sir?' exclaimed the magistrate—'Why suld I not? Answer me that —why suld I not?'

'For three sufficient reasons, Bailie Jarvie.— First, for auld langsyne;—second, for the sake of the auld wife ayont the fire at Stuckavrallachan, that made some mixture of our bluids, to my own proper shame be it spoken! that has a cousin wi' accounts, and yarn winnles, and looms, and shuttles, like a mere mechanical person;—and lastly, Bailie, because if I saw a sign o' your betraying me, I would plaster that wa' with your harns ere the hand of man could rescue you!'

'Ye're a bauld desperate villain, sir,' retorted the undaunted Bailie; 'and ye ken that I ken ye to be sae, and that I wadna stand a moment for my ain risk.'

' I ken weel,' said the other, ' ye hae gentle bluid in your veins, and I wad be laith to hurt my ain kinsman. But I'll gang out here as free as I came in, or the very wa's o' Glasgow Tolbooth shall tell o't these ten years to come.'

. ' Weel, weel,' said Mr. Jarvie, ' bluid's thicker than water ; and it liesna in kith, kin, and ally, to see motes in ilk other's een if other een see them no. It wad be sair news to the auld wife below the Ben of Stuckavrallachan, that you, ye Hieland limmer, had knockit out my harns, or that I had kilted you up in a tow. But ye'll own, ye dour deevil, that were it no your very sell, I wad hae grippit the best man in the Hielands.'

' Ye wad hae tried, cousin,' answered my guide, ' that I wot weel ; but I doubt ye wad hae come aff wi' the short measure ; for we gang-there-out Hieland bodies are an unchancy generation when you speak to us o' bondage. We downa bide the coercion of gude braid-claith about our hinderlans ; let a be breeks o' freestone, and garters o' iron.'

' Ye'll find the stane breeks and the airn garters, ay, and the hemp cravat, for a' that, neighbour,' replied the Bailie. ' Nae man in a civilized country ever played the pliskies ye hae done— but e'en pickle in your ain pockneuk—I hae gi'en ye warning.'

' Well, cousin,' said the other, ' ye'll wear black at my burial ? '

' Deil a black cloak will be there, Robin, but the corbies and the hoodie-craws, I'se gie ye my hand on that. But whar's the gude thousand pund Scots that I lent ye, man, and when am I to see it again ? '

' Where it is,' replied my guide, after the

affectation of considering for a moment, 'I cannot justly tell—probably where last year's snaw is.'

'And that's on the tap of Schehallion, ye Hieland dog,' said Mr. Jarvie; 'and I look for payment frae you where ye stand.'

'Ay,' replied the Highlander, 'but I keep neither snaw nor dollars in my sporran. And as to when you'll see it—why, just when the king enjoys his ain again, as the auld sang says.'

'Warst of a', Robin,' retorted the Glaswegian,—'I mean, ye disloyal traitor—Warst of a'!—Wad ye bring popery in on us, and arbitrary power, and a foist and a warming-pan, and the set forms, and the curates, and the auld enormities o' surplices and cearments? Ye had better stick to your auld trade o' theft-boot, blackmail, spreaghs, and gillravaging—better stealing nowte than ruining nations.'

'Hout, man, whisht wi' your whiggery,' answered the Celt, 'we hae kend ane anither mony a lang day. I'se take care your counting-room is no cleaned out when the Gillon-a-naillie come to redd up the Glasgow buiths, and clear them o' their auld shop-wares. And, unless it just fa' in the preceese way o' your duty, ye maunna see me oftener, Nicol, than I am disposed to be seen.'

'Ye are a dauring villain, Rob,' answered the Bailie; 'and ye will be hanged, that will be seen and heard tell o''; but I'se ne'er be the ill bird and foul my nest, set apart strong necessity and the skreigh of duty, which no man should hear and be inobedient.—And wha the deevil's this?' he continued, turning to me—'Some gillravager that ye hae listed, I daur say. He looks as if he had a bauld heart to the highway, and a lang craig for the gibbet.'

' This, good Mr. Jarvie,' said Owen, who, like myself, had been struck dumb during this strange recognition, and no less strange dialogue, which took place betwixt these extraordinary kinsmen—' This, good Mr. Jarvie, is young Mr. Frank Osbaldistone, only child of the head of our house, who should have been taken into our firm at the time Mr. Rashleigh Osbaldistone, his cousin, had the luck to be taken into it '—(Here Owen could not suppress a groan)—' But, howsoever '——

' O, I have heard of that smaik,' said the Scotch merchant, interrupting him ; ' it is he whom your principal, like an obstinate auld fule, wad make a merchant o', wad he or wad he no, and the lad turned a strolling stage-player, in pure dislike to the labour an honest man should live by.—Weel, sir, what say you to your handiwark ? Will Hamlet the Dane, or Hamlet's ghost, be good security for Mr. Owen, sir ? '

' I don't deserve your taunt,' I replied, ' though I respect your motive, and am too grateful for the assistance you have afforded Mr. Owen, to resent it. My only business here was to do what I could (it is perhaps very little) to aid Mr. Owen in the management of my father's affairs. My dislike of the commercial profession is a feeling of which I am the best and sole judge.'

' I protest,' said the Highlander, ' I had some respect for this callant even before I kend what was in him ; but now I honour him for his contempt of weavers and spinners, and sic-like mechanical persons and their pursuits.'

'Ye're mad, Rob,' said the Bailie—'mad as a March hare,—though wherefore a hare suld be mad at March mair than at Martinmas, is mair than I can weel say. Weavers! Deil shake ye out o' the web the weaver craft made. Spinners! —ye'll spin and wind yoursell a bonny pirn. And this young birkie here, that ye're hoying and hounding on the shortest road to the gallows and the deevil, will his stage-plays and his poetries help him here, d'ye think, ony mair than your deep oaths and drawn dirks, ye reprobate that ye are?— Will *Tityre tu patulae*, as they ca' it, tell him where Rashleigh Osbaldistone is? or Macbeth, and all his kernes and galloglasses, and your awn to boot, Rob, procure him five thousand pounds to answer the bills which fall due ten days hence, were they a' rouped at the Cross, basket-hilts, Andra-Ferraras, leather targets, brogues, brochan, and sporrans?'

'Ten days?' I answered, and instinctively drew out Diana Vernon's packet; and the time being elapsed during which I was to keep the seal sacred, I hastily broke it open. A sealed letter fell from a blank enclosure, owing to the trepidation with which I opened the parcel. A slight current of wind, which found its way through a broken pane of the window, wafted the letter to Mr. Jarvie's feet, who lifted it, examined the address with unceremonious curiosity, and, to my astonishment, handed it to his Highland kinsman, saying, 'Here's a wind has blown a letter to its right owner, though there were ten thousand chances against its coming to hand.'

The Highlander, having examined the address, broke the letter open without the least ceremony. I endeavoured to interrupt his proceeding.

' You must satisfy me, sir,' said I, ' that the
letter is intended for you before I can permit you
to peruse it.'

' Make yourself quite easy, Mr. Osbaldistone,'
replied the mountaineer, with great composure ;—
' remember Justice Inglewood, Clerk Jobson, Mr.
Morris—above all, remember your vera humble
servant, Robert Cawmil, and the beautiful Diana
Vernon. Remember all this, and doubt no longer
that the letter is for me.'

I remained astonished at my own stupidity.
Through the whole night, the voice, and even the
features of this man, though imperfectly seen,
haunted me with recollections to which I could
assign no exact local or personal associations.
But now the light dawned on me at once,—this
man was Campbell himself. His whole peculiar-
ities flashed on me at once,—the deep strong
voice,—the inflexible, stern, yet considerate cast
of features,—the Scottish brogue, with its corresponding dialect and imagery, which, although he
possessed the power at times of laying them aside,
recurred at every moment of emotion, and gave
pith to his sarcasm, or vehemence to his expostu-
lation. Rather beneath the middle size than
above it, his limbs were formed upon the very
strongest model that is consistent with agility,
while, from the remarkable ease and freedom of
his movements, you could not doubt his possessing
the latter quality in a high degree of perfection.
Two points in his person interfered with the rules
of symmetry—his shoulders were so broad in
proportion to his height, as, notwithstanding the
lean and lathy appearance of his frame, gave him
something the air of being too square in respect

to his stature; and his arms, though round, sinewy, and strong, were so very long as to be rather a deformity. I afterwards heard that this length of arm was a circumstance on which he prided himself; that when he wore his native Highland garb, he could tie the garters of his hose without stooping; and that it gave him great advantage in the use of the broadsword, at which he was very dexterous. But certainly this want of symmetry destroyed the claim he might otherwise have set up, to be accounted a very handsome man; it gave something wild, irregular, and, as it were, unearthly, to his appearance, and reminded me involuntarily, of the tales which Mabel used to tell of the old Picts who ravaged Northumberland in ancient times, who, according to her tradition, were a sort of half-goblin half-human beings, distinguished, like this man, for courage, cunning, ferocity, the length of their arms, and the squareness of their shoulders.

When, however, I recollected the circumstances in which we formerly met, I could not doubt that the billet was most probably designed for him. He had made a marked figure among those mysterious personages over whom Diana seemed to exercise an influence, and from whom she experienced an influence in her turn. It was painful to think that the fate of a being so amiable was involved in that of desperadoes of this man's description; yet it seemed impossible to doubt it. Of what use, however, could this person be to my father's affairs?—I could think only of one. Rashleigh Osbaldistone had, at the instigation of Miss Vernon, certainly found means to produce Mr. Campbell when his presence was necessary to exculpate me from Morris's accusation—Was it not possible that her influence, in like manner, might prevail on Campbell to produce Rashleigh ? Speaking on this supposition, I requested to know where my dangerous kinsman was, and when Mr. Campbell had seen him. The answer was indirect.

' It 's a kittle cast she has gien me to play; but yet it 's fair play, and I winna balk her. Mr. Osbaldistone, I dwell not very far from hence—my kinsman can show you the way—Leave Mr. Owen to do the best he can in Glasgow—do you come and see me in the glens, and it 's like I may pleasure you, and stead your father in his extremity. I am but a poor man; but wit 's better than wealth—and, cousin ' (turning from me to address Mr. Jarvie), ' if ye daur venture sae muckle as to eat a dish of Scotch collops, and a leg o' red-deer venison wi' me, come ye wi' this Sassenach gentleman as far as Drymen or Bucklivie, or the Clachan of Aberfoil will be better than ony o' them, and I'll hae somebody waiting to weise ye the gate to the place where I may be for the time—What say ye, man ?—There 's my thumb, I'll ne'er beguile thee.'

' Na, na, Robin,' said the cautious burgher, ' I seldom like to leave the Gorbals ; I have nae freedom to gang amang your wild hills, Robin, and your kilted red-shanks—it disna become my place, man.'

' The devil damn your place and you baith ! ' reiterated Campbell. ' The only drap o' gentle bluid that 's in your body was our great-grand-uncle's that was justified at Dumbarton, and you set yourself up to say ye wad derogate frae your place to visit me !—Hark thee, man, I owe thee a day in harst—I'll pay up your thousan pund Scots, plack and bawbee, gin ye'll be an honest fallow for anes, and just daiker up the gate wi' this Sassenach.'

' Hout awa' wi' your gentility,' replied the Bailie ; ' carry your gentle bluid to the Cross, and see what ye'll buy wi't.—But, if I *were* to come, wad ye really and soothfastly pay me the siller ? '

' I swear to ye,' said the Highlander, ' upon the halidome of him that sleeps beneath the grey stane at Inch-Cailleach.'

' Say nae mair, Robin,—say nae mair—We'll see what may be dune.—But ye maunna expect me to gang ower the Highland line—I'll gae beyond the line at no rate. Ye maun meet me about Bucklivie or the Clachan of Aberfoil, and dinna forget the needful.'

' Nae fear—nae fear,' said Campbell ; ' I'll be as true as the steel blade that never failed its master. —But I must be budging, cousin, for the air o' Glasgow Tolbooth is no that ower salutary to a Highlander's constitution.'

' Troth,' replied the merchant, ' and if my duty were to be dune, ye couldna change your atmosphere, as the minister ca's it, this ae wee while.— Ochon, that I sud ever be concerned in aiding and abetting an escape frae justice ! it will be a shame and disgrace to me and mine, and my very father's memory, for ever.'

' Hout tout, man, let that flee stick in the wa',' answered his kinsman ; ' when the dirt's dry it will rub out—Your father, honest man, could look ower a friend's fault as weel as anither.'

' Ye may be right, Robin,' replied the Bailie,

after a moment's reflection; ' he was a considerate man the deacon; he kend we had a' our frailties, and he lo'ed his friends—Ye'll no hae forgotten him, Robin?' This question he put in a softened tone, conveying as much at least of the ludicrous as the pathetic.

' Forgotten him!' replied his kinsman, ' what suld ail me to forget him?—a wapping weaver he was, and wrought my first pair o' hose.—But come awa', kinsman—

> Come fill up my cup, come fill up my cann,
> Come saddle my horses, and call up my man;
> Come open your gates, and let me gae free,
> I daurna stay langer in bonny Dundee.'

' Whisht, sir!' said the magistrate, in an authoritative tone—' lilting and singing sae near the latter end o' the Sabbath! This house may hear ye sing anither tune yet—Aweel, we hae a' backslidings to answer for—Stanchells, open the door.'

The jailer obeyed, and we all sallied forth. Stanchells looked with some surprise at the two strangers, wondering, doubtless, how they came into these premises without his knowledge; but Mr. Jarvie's 'Friends o' mine, Stanchells—friends o' mine,' silenced all disposition to inquiries. We now descended into the lower vestibule, and hallooed more than once for Dougal, to which summons no answer was returned; when Campbell observed, with a sardonic smile, ' That if Dougal was the lad he kent him, he would scarce wait to get thanks for his ain share of the night's wark, but was in all probability on the full trot to the pass of Ballamaha '——

' And left us—and, abune a', me, mysell, locked

up in the Tolbooth a' night!' exclaimed the Bailie, in ire and perturbation. 'Ca' for fore-hammers, sledge-hammers, pinches, and coulters; send for Deacon Yettlin, the smith, and let him ken that Bailie Jarvie's shut up in the Tolbooth by a Hieland blackguard, whom he'll hang up as high as Haman'——

'When ye catch him,' said Campbell, gravely; 'but stay, the door is surely not locked.'

Indeed, on examination, we found that the door was not only left open, but that Dougal in his retreat had, by carrying off the keys along with him, taken care that no one should exercise his office of porter in a hurry.

'He has glimmerings o' common sense now, that creature Dougal,' said Campbell; 'he kend an open door might hae served me at a pinch.'

We were by this time in the street.

'I tell you, Robin,' said the magistrate, 'in my puir mind, if ye live the life ye do, ye shuld hae ane o' your gillies door-keeper in every jail in Scotland, in case o' the warst.'

'Ane o' my kinsmen a bailie in ilka burgh will just do as weel, cousin Nicol—so, gude night or gude morning to ye; and forget not the Clachan of Aberfoil.'

Rob Roy. 1817.

JANE AUSTEN

1775–1817

AN OFFER OF MARRIAGE

THE next day opened a new scene at Longbourn.
Mr. Collins made his declaration in form. Having
resolved to do it without loss of time, as his leave
of absence extended only to the following Saturday,
and having no feelings of diffidence to make it
distressing to himself even at the moment, he
set about it in a very orderly manner, with all the
observances which he supposed a regular part of
the business. On finding Mrs. Bennet, Elizabeth,
and one of the younger girls together, soon after
breakfast, he addressed the mother in these
words:

' May I hope, madam, for your interest with your
fair daughter Elizabeth, when I solicit for the
honour of a private audience with her in the course
of this morning ? '

Before Elizabeth had time for anything but
a blush of surprise, Mrs. Bennet instantly answered:

' Oh dear !—Yes—certainly.—I am sure Lizzy
will be very happy—I am sure she can have no
objection.—Come, Kitty, I want you upstairs.' And
gathering her work together, she was hastening
away, when Elizabeth called out:

' Dear ma'am, do not go.—I beg you will not go.
—Mr. Collins must excuse me.—He can have

nothing to say to me that anybody need not hear. I am going away myself.'

'No, no, nonsense, Lizzy.—I desire you will stay where you are.'—And upon Elizabeth's seeming really, with vexed and embarrassed looks, about to escape, she added, 'Lizzy, I *insist* upon your staying and hearing Mr. Collins.'

Elizabeth would not oppose such an injunction— and a moment's consideration making her also sensible that it would be wisest to get it over as soon and as quietly as possible, she sat down again, and tried to conceal by incessant employment the feelings which were divided between distress and diversion. Mrs. Bennet and Kitty walked off, and as soon as they were gone Mr. Collins began.

'Believe me, my dear Miss Elizabeth, that your modesty, so far from doing you any disservice, rather adds to your other perfections. You would have been less amiable in my eyes had there *not* been this little unwillingness; but allow me to assure you that I have your respected mother's permission for this address. You can hardly doubt the purport of my discourse, however your natural delicacy may lead you to dissemble; my attentions have been too marked to be mistaken. Almost as soon as I entered the house I singled you out as the companion of my future life. But before I am run away with by my feelings on this subject, perhaps it would be advisable for me to state my reasons for marrying—and moreover for coming into Hertfordshire with the design of selecting a wife, as I certainly did.'

The idea of Mr. Collins, with all his solemn composure, being run away with by his feelings, made Elizabeth so near laughing that she could not use the short pause he allowed in any attempt to stop him farther, and he continued :

'My reasons for marrying are, first, that I think it a right thing for every clergyman in easy circumstances (like myself) to set the example of matrimony in his parish. Secondly, that I am convinced it will add very greatly to my happiness ; and thirdly—which perhaps I ought to have mentioned earlier, that it is the particular advice and recommendation of the very noble lady whom I have the honour of calling patroness. Twice has she condescended to give me her opinion (unasked too !) on this subject ; and it was but the very Saturday night before I left Hunsford—between our pools at quadrille, while Mrs. Jenkinson was arranging Miss de Bourgh's foot-stool, that she said, "Mr. Collins, you must marry. A clergyman like you must marry.—Choose properly, choose a gentlewoman for *my* sake ; and for your *own*, let her be an active, useful sort of person, not brought up high, but able to make a small income go a good way. This is my advice. Find such a woman as soon as you can, bring her to Hunsford, and I will visit her." Allow me, by the way, to observe, my fair cousin, that I do not reckon the notice and kindness of Lady Catherine de Bourgh as among the least of the advantages in my power to offer. You will find her manners beyond anything I can describe ; and your wit and vivacity I think must be acceptable to her, especially when tempered with the silence and respect which her rank will inevitably excite. Thus much for my general intention in favour of matrimony ; it remains to be told why my views were directed to Longbourn instead of my own neighbourhood, where I assure you there are many amiable young women. But the fact is, that being, as I am, to inherit this estate after the death of your honoured father (who, however, may live many years longer), I could not satisfy myself without resolving to choose a wife from among his daughters, that the loss to them might be as little as possible, when the melancholy event takes place—which, however, as I have already said, may not be for several years. This has been my motive, my fair cousin, and I flatter myself it will not sink me in your esteem. And now nothing remains for me but to assure you in the most animated language of the violence of my affection. To fortune I am perfectly indifferent, and shall make no demand of that nature on your father, since I am well aware that it could not be complied with; and that one thousand pounds in the 4 per cents. which will not be yours till after your mother's decease, is all that you may ever be entitled to. On that head, therefore, I shall be uniformly silent; and you may assure yourself that no ungenerous reproach shall ever pass my lips when we are married.'

It was absolutely necessary to interrupt him now.

'You are too hasty, sir,' she cried. 'You forget that I have made no answer. Let me do it without further loss of time. Accept my thanks for the compliment you are paying me. I am very sensible of the honour of your proposals, but it is impossible for me to do otherwise than decline them.'

'I am not now to learn,' replied Mr. Collins, with a formal wave of the hand, 'that it is usual with young ladies to reject the addresses of the man whom they secretly mean to accept, when he first applies for their favour ; and that sometimes the refusal is repeated a second or even a third time. I am therefore by no means discouraged by what you have just said, and shall hope to lead you to the altar ere long.'

'Upon my word, sir,' cried Elizabeth, 'your hope is rather an extraordinary one after my declaration. I do assure you that I am not one of those young ladies (if such young ladies there are) who are so daring as to risk their happiness on the chance of being asked a second time. I am perfectly serious in my refusal.—You could not make *me* happy, and I am convinced that I am the last woman in the world who would make *you* so.— Nay, were your friend Lady Catherine to know me, I am persuaded she would find me in every respect ill qualified for the situation.'

'Were it certain that Lady Catherine would think so,' said Mr. Collins very gravely—' but I cannot imagine that her ladyship would at all disapprove of you. And you may be certain that when I have the honour of seeing her again I shall speak in the highest terms of your modesty, economy, and other amiable qualifications.'

'Indeed, Mr. Collins, all praise of me will be unnecessary. You must give me leave to judge for myself, and pay me the compliment of believing what I say. I wish you very happy and very rich, and by refusing your hand, do all in my power to prevent your being otherwise. In making me the offer, you must have satisfied the delicacy of your feelings with regard to my family, and may take possession of Longbourn estate whenever it falls, without any self-reproach This matter may be considered, therefore, as finally settled.' And rising as she thus spoke, she would have quitted the room, had not Mr. Collins thus addressed her :

'When I do myself the honour of speaking to you next on the subject I shall hope to receive a more favourable answer than you have now given me ; though I am far from accusing you of cruelty at present, because I know it to be the established custom of your sex to reject a man on the first application, and perhaps you have even now said as much to encourage my suit as would be consistent with the true delicacy of the female character.'

'Really, Mr. Collins,' cried Elizabeth with some warmth, 'you puzzle me exceedingly. If what I have hitherto said can appear to you in the form of encouragement, I know not how to express my refusal in such a way as may convince you of its being one.'

'You must give me leave to flatter myself, my dear cousin, that your refusal of my addresses is merely words of course. My reasons for believing it are briefly these : It does not appear to me that my hand is unworthy your acceptance, or that the establishment I can offer would be any other than highly desirable. My situation in life, my connexions with the family of De Bourgh, and my relationship to your own, are circumstances highly in my favour ; and you should take it into further consideration that in spite of your manifold attractions, it is by no means certain that another offer of marriage may ever be made you. Your portion is unhappily so small that it will in all likelihood undo the effects of your loveliness and amiable qualifications. As I must therefore conclude that you are not serious in your rejection of me, I shall choose to attribute it to your wish of increasing my love by suspense, according to the usual practice of elegant females.'

'I do assure you, sir, that I have no pretensions whatever to that kind of elegance which consists in tormenting a respectable man. I would rather be paid the compliment of being believed sincere. I thank you again and again for the honour you have done me in your proposals, but to accept them is absolutely impossible. My feelings in every respect forbid it. Can I speak plainer? Do not consider me now as an elegant female intending to plague you, but as a rational creature speaking the truth from her heart.'

'You are uniformly charming!' cried he, with an air of awkward gallantry; 'and I am persuaded that when sanctioned by the express authority of both your excellent parents, my proposals will not fail of being acceptable.'

To such perseverance in wilful self-deception Elizabeth would make no reply, and immediately and in silence withdrew; determined, that if he persisted in considering her repeated refusals as flattering encouragement, to apply to her father, whose negative might be uttered in such a manner as must be decisive, and whose behaviour at least could not be mistaken for the affectation and coquetry of an elegant female.

Mr. Collins was not left long to the silent contemplation of his successful love; for Mrs. Bennet, having dawdled about in the vestibule to watch for the end of the conference, no sooner saw Elizabeth open the door and with quick step pass her towards the staircase, than she entered the breakfast-room, and congratulated both him and herself in warm terms on the happy prospect of their nearer connexion. Mr. Collins received and returned these felicitations with equal pleasure, and then proceeded to relate the particulars of their interview, with the result of which he trusted he had every reason to be satisfied, since the refusal which his cousin had steadfastly given him would naturally flow from her bashful modesty and the genuine delicacy of her character.

This information, however, startled Mrs. Bennet ; —she would have been glad to be equally satisfied that her daughter had meant to encourage him by protesting against his proposals, but she dared not believe it, and could not help saying so.

'But depend upon it, Mr. Collins,' she added, 'that Lizzy shall be brought to reason. I will speak to her about it myself directly. She is a very headstrong foolish girl, and does not know her own interest ; but I will *make* her know it.'

'Pardon me for interrupting you, madam,' cried Mr. Collins ; 'but if she is really headstrong and foolish, I know not whether she would altogether be a very desirable wife to a man in my situation, who naturally looks for happiness in the marriage state. If therefore she actually persists in rejecting my suit, perhaps it were better not to force her into accepting me, because if liable to such defects of temper, she could not contribute much to my felicity.'

'Sir, you quite misunderstand me,' said Mrs. Bennet, alarmed. 'Lizzy is only headstrong in such matters as these. In everything else she is as good-natured a girl as ever lived. I will go directly to Mr. Bennet, and we shall very soon settle it with her, I am sure.'

She would not give him time to reply, but hurrying instantly to her husband, called out as she entered the library.

'Oh! Mr. Bennet, you are wanted immediately; we are all in an uproar. You must come and make Lizzy marry Mr. Collins, for she vows she will not have him, and if you do not make haste he will change his mind and not have *her*.'

Mr. Bennet raised his eyes from his book as she entered, and fixed them on her face with a calm unconcern which was not in the least altered by her communication.

'I have not the pleasure of understanding you,' said he, when she had finished her speech. 'Of what are you talking?'

'Of Mr. Collins and Lizzy. Lizzy declares she will not have Mr. Collins, and Mr. Collins begins to say that he will not have Lizzy.'

'And what am I to do on the occasion?—It seems an hopeless business.'

'Speak to Lizzy about it yourself. Tell her that you insist upon her marrying him.'

'Let her be called down. She shall hear my opinion.'

Mrs. Bennet rang the bell, and Miss Elizabeth was summoned to the library.

'Come here, child,' cried her father as she appeared. 'I have sent for you on an affair of importance. I understand that Mr. Collins has made you an offer of marriage. Is it true?' Elizabeth replied that it was. 'Very well—and this offer of marriage you have refused?'

'I have, sir.'

' Very well. We now come to the point. Your mother insists upon your accepting it. Is it not so, Mrs. Bennet ? '

' Yes, or I will never see her again.'

' An unhappy alternative is before you, Elizabeth. From this day you must be a stranger to one of your parents.—Your mother will never see you again if you do *not* marry Mr. Collins, and I will never see you again if you *do*.'

Elizabeth could not but smile at such a conclusion of such a beginning ; but Mrs. Bennet, who had persuaded herself that her husband regarded the affair as she wished, was excessively disappointed.

' What do you mean, Mr. Bennet, by talking in this way ? You promised me to *insist* upon her marrying him.'

' My dear,' replied her husband, ' I have two small favours to request. First, that you will allow me the free use of my understanding on the present occasion ; and secondly, of my room. I shall be glad to have the library to myself as soon as may be.'

Not yet, however, in spite of her disappointment in her husband, did Mrs. Bennet give up the point. She talked to Elizabeth again and again ; coaxed and threatened her by turns. She endeavoured to secure Jane in her interest, but Jane with all possible mildness declined interfering ;—and Elizabeth sometimes with real earnestness and sometimes with playful gaiety replied to her attacks. Though her manner varied, however, her determination never did.

Mr. Collins, meanwhile, was meditating in solitude on what had passed. He thought too well of himself to comprehend on what motive his cousin could refuse him; and though his pride was hurt, he suffered in no other way. His regard for her was quite imaginary; and the possibility of her deserving her mother's reproach prevented his feeling any regret.

While the family were in this confusion, Charlotte Lucas came to spend the day with them. She was met in the vestibule by Lydia, who, flying to her, cried in a half whisper, 'I am glad you are come, for there is such fun here!—What do you think has happened this morning?—Mr. Collins has made an offer to Lizzy, and she will not have him.'

Charlotte had hardly time to answer, before they were joined by Kitty, who came to tell the same news, and no sooner had they entered the breakfast-room, where Mrs. Bennet was alone, than she likewise began on the subject, calling on Miss Lucas for her compassion, and entreating her to persuade her friend Lizzy to comply with the wishes of all her family. 'Pray do, my dear Miss Lucas,' she added in a melancholy tone, 'for nobody is on my side, nobody takes part with me, I am cruelly used, nobody feels for my poor nerves.'

Charlotte's reply was spared by the entrance of Jane and Elizabeth.

'Aye, there she comes,' continued Mrs. Bennet, 'looking as unconcerned as may be, and caring no more for us than if we were at York, provided she can have her own way.—But I tell you what, Miss Lizzy, if you take it into your head to go on refusing every offer of marriage in this way, you will never get a husband at all—and I am sure I do not know who is to maintain you when your father is dead.— *I* shall not be able to keep you—and so I warn you. —I have done with you from this very day.—

I told you in the library, you know, that I should never speak to you again, and you will find me as good as my word. I have no pleasure in talking to undutiful children.—Not that I have much pleasure indeed in talking to anybody. People who suffer as I do from nervous complaints can have no great inclination for talking. Nobody can tell what I suffer!—But it is always so. Those who do not complain are never pitied.'

Her daughters listened in silence to this effusion, sensible that any attempt to reason with or soothe her would only increase the irritation. She talked on, therefore, without interruption from any of them till they were joined by Mr. Collins, who entered with an air more stately than usual, and on perceiving whom, she said to the girls:

'Now, I do insist upon it, that you, all of you, hold your tongues, and let Mr. Collins and me have a little conversation together.'

Elizabeth passed quietly out of the room, Jane and Kitty followed, but Lydia stood her ground, determined to hear all she could; and Charlotte, detained first by the civility of Mr. Collins, whose inquiries after herself and all her family were very minute, and then by a little curiosity, satisfied herself with walking to the window and pretending not to hear. In a doleful voice Mrs. Bennet thus began the projected conversation.—'Oh! Mr. Collins!'—

'My dear madam,' replied he, 'let us be for ever silent on this point. Far be it from me', he presently continued in a voice that marked his displeasure, 'to resent the behaviour of your daughter. Resignation to inevitable evils is the duty of us all; the peculiar duty of a young man who has been so fortunate as I have been in early preferment; and I trust I am resigned. Perhaps not the less so from feeling a doubt of my positive happiness had my fair cousin honoured me with her hand; for I have often observed that resignation is never so perfect as when the blessing denied begins to lose somewhat of its value in our estimation. You will not, I hope, consider me as showing any disrespect to your family, my dear madam, by thus withdrawing my pretensions to your daughter's favour, without having paid yourself and Mr. Bennet the compliment of requesting you to interpose your authority in my behalf. My conduct may, I fear, be objectionable in having accepted my dismission from your daughter's lips instead of your own. But we are all liable to error. I have certainly meant well through the whole affair. My object has been to secure an amiable companion for myself, with due consideration for the advantage of all your family, and if my *manner* has been at all reprehensible, I here beg leave to apologize.'

Pride and Prejudice. 1813.

CHARLES LAMB

1775–1834

SPARTAN TREATMENT AT SCHOOL

IN Mr. Lamb's *Works*, published a year or two since, I find a magnificent eulogy on my old school, such as it was, or now appears to him to have been, between the years 1782 and 1789. It happens, very oddly, that my own standing at Christ's was nearly corresponding with his; and, with all gratitude to him for his enthusiasm for the cloisters, I think he has contrived to bring together whatever can be said in praise of them, dropping all the other side of the argument most ingeniously.

I remember L. at school; and can well recollect that he had some peculiar advantages, which I and others of his schoolfellows had not. His friends lived in town, and were near at hand; and he had the privilege of going to see them, almost as often as he wished, through some invidious distinction, which was denied to us. The present worthy sub-treasurer to the Inner Temple can explain how that happened. He had his tea and hot rolls in a morning, while we were battening upon our quarter of a penny loaf—our *crug*—moistened with attenuated small beer, in wooden piggins, smacking of the pitched leathern jack it was poured from. Our Monday's milk porritch, blue and tasteless, and the pease soup of Saturday, coarse and choking, were enriched for him with a slice of ' extraordinary bread and butter', from the hot-loaf of the Temple. The Wednesday's mess of millet, somewhat less repugnant (we had three banyan to four meat days in the week) was endeared to his palate with a lump of double-refined, and a smack of ginger (to make it go down the more glibly) or the fragrant cinnamon. In lieu of our *half-pickled* Sundays, or *quite fresh* boiled beef on Thursdays (strong as *caro equina*), with detestable marigolds floating in the pail to poison the broth, our scanty mutton crags on Fridays—and rather more savoury, but grudging, portions of the same flesh, rotten, roasted or rare, on the Tuesdays (the only dish which excited our appetites, and disappointed our stomachs, in almost equal proportion)—he had his hot plate of roast veal, or the more tempting griskin (exotics unknown to our palates), cooked in the paternal kitchen (a great thing), and brought him daily by his maid or aunt ! I remember the good old relative (in whom love forbade pride) squatting down upon some odd stone in a by-nook of the cloisters, disclosing the viands (of higher regale than those cakes which the ravens ministered to the Tishbite) ; and the contending passions of L. at the unfolding. There was love for the bringer ; shame for the thing brought, and the manner of its bringing ; sympathy for those who were too many to share in it ; and, at top of all, hunger (eldest, strongest of the passions !) predominant, breaking down the stony fences of shame, and awkwardness, and a troubling over-consciousness.

I was a poor friendless boy. My parents, and

those who should care for me, were far away.
Those few acquaintances of theirs, which they
could reckon upon being kind to me in the great
city, after a little forced notice, which they had the
grace to take of me on my first arrival in town,
soon grew tired of my holiday visits. They seemed
to them to recur too often, though I thought them
few enough; and one after another, they all failed
me, and I felt myself alone among six hundred
playmates.

O the cruelty of separating a poor lad from his
early homestead! The yearnings which I used
to have towards it in those unfledged years!
How, in my dreams, would my native town (far
in the west) come back, with its church, and trees,
and faces! How I would wake weeping, and in
the anguish of my heart exclaim upon sweet Calne
in Wiltshire!

To this late hour of my life, I trace impressions
left by the recollection of those friendless holidays.
The long warm days of summer never return but
they bring with them a gloom from the haunting
memory of those *whole-day-leaves*, when, by some
strange arrangement, we were turned out, for the
live-long day, upon our own hands, whether we
had friends to go to, or none. I remember those
bathing-excursions to the New River, which L.
recalls with such relish, better, I think, than he
can—for he was a home-seeking lad, and did
not much care for such water-pastimes:—How
merrily we would sally forth into the fields; and
strip under the first warmth of the sun; and
wanton like young dace in the streams; getting
us appetites for noon, which those of us that were
penniless (our scanty morning crust long since

exhausted) had not the means of allaying, while the cattle, and the birds, and the fishes, were at feed about us, and we had nothing to satisfy our cravings—the very beauty of the day, and the exercise of the pastime, and the sense of liberty, setting a keener edge upon them! How faint and languid, finally, we would return, towards nightfall, to our desired morsel, half-rejoicing, half-reluctant, that the hours of our uneasy liberty had expired!

It was worse in the days of winter, to go prowling about the streets objectless—shivering at cold windows of print-shops, to extract a little amusement; or haply, as a last resort, in the hope of a little novelty, to pay a fifty-times repeated visit (where our individual faces should be as well known to the warden as those of his own charges) to the Lions in the Tower—to whose levée, by courtesy immemorial, we had a prescriptive title to admission.

L.'s governor (so we called the patron who presented us to the foundation) lived in a manner under his paternal roof. Any complaint which he had to make was sure of being attended to. This was understood at Christ's, and was an effectual screen to him against the severity of masters, or worse tyranny of the monitors. The oppressions of these young brutes are heart-sickening to call to recollection. I have been called out of my bed, and *waked for the purpose*, in the coldest winter nights—and this not once, but night after night—in my shirt, to receive the discipline of a leathern thong, with eleven other sufferers, because it pleased my callow overseer, when there has been any talking heard after we were gone to bed, to make the six last beds in the dormitory, where the youngest children of us slept, answerable for an offence they neither dared to commit, nor had the power to hinder.—The same execrable tyranny drove the younger part of us from the fires, when our feet were perishing with snow ; and, under the cruelest penalties, forbad the indulgence of a drink of water, when we lay in sleepless summer nights, fevered with the season, and the day's sports. . . .

I was a hypochondriac lad ; and the sight of a boy in fetters, upon the day of my first putting on the blue clothes, was not exactly fitted to assuage the natural terrors of initiation. I was of tender years, barely turned of seven ; and had only read of such things in books, or seen them but in dreams. I was told he had *run away*. This was the punishment for the first offence.— As a novice I was soon after taken to see the dungeons. These were little, square, Bedlam cells, where a boy could just lie at his length upon straw and a blanket—a mattress, I think, was afterwards substituted—with a peep of light, let in askance, from a prison-orifice at top, barely enough to read by. Here the poor boy was locked in by himself all day, without sight of any but the porter who brought him his bread and water—who *might not speak to him* ; or of the beadle, who came twice a week to call him out to receive his periodical chastisement, which was almost welcome, because it separated him for a brief interval from solitude : and here he was shut up by himself *of nights*, out of the reach of any sound, to suffer whatever horrors the weak nerves, and superstition incident to his time of life, might subject him to. This was the penalty for the second offence. Wouldst

thou like, reader, to see what became of him in
the next degree ?

The culprit, who had been a third time an
offender, and whose expulsion was at this time
deemed irreversible, was brought forth, as at
some solemn *auto da fe*, arrayed in uncouth and
most appalling attire—all trace of his late ' watchet
weeds' carefully effaced, he was exposed in a jacket,
resembling those which London lamplighters
formerly delighted in, with a cap of the same.
The effect of this divestiture was such as the
ingenious devisers of it could have anticipated.
With his pale and frighted features, it was as if
some of those disfigurements in Dante had seized
upon him. In this disguisement he was brought
into the hall (*L.'s favourite state-room*), where
awaited him the whole number of his schoolfellows, whose joint lessons and sports he was
thenceforth to share no more ; the awful presence
of the steward, to be seen for the last time ; of
the executioner beadle, clad in his state robe for
the occasion ; and of two faces more, of direr
import, because never but in these extremities
visible. These were governors ; two of whom,
by choice, or charter, were always accustomed to
officiate at these *Ultima Supplicia* ; not to
mitigate (so at least we understood it), but to
enforce the uttermost stripe. Old Bamber
Gascoigne, and Peter Aubert, I remember, were
colleagues on one occasion, when the beadle
turning rather pale, a glass of brandy was ordered
to prepare him for the mysteries. The scourging
was, after the old Roman fashion, long and stately.
The lictor accompanied the criminal quite round
the hall. We were generally too faint with

attending to the previous disgusting circumstances, to make accurate report with our eyes of the degree of corporal suffering inflicted. Report, of course, gave out the back knotty and livid. After scourging, he was made over, in his *San Benito*, to his friends, if he had any (but commonly such poor runagates were friendless), or to his parish officer, who, to enhance the effect of the scene, had his station allotted to him on the outside of the hall gate.

The Essays of Elia. 1823.

MY FIRST PLAY

At the north end of Cross Court there yet stands a portal, of some architectural pretensions, though reduced to humble use, serving at present for an entrance to a printing-office. This old door-way, if you are young, reader, you may not know was the identical pit entrance to Old Drury—Garrick's Drury—all of it that is left. I never pass it without shaking some forty years from off my shoulders, recurring to the evening when I passed through it to see *my first play*. The afternoon had been wet, and the condition of our going (the elder folks and myself) was, that the rain should cease. With what a beating heart did I watch from the window the puddles, from the stillness of which I was taught to prognosticate the desired cessation! I seem to remember the last spurt, and the glee with which I ran to announce it.

We went with orders, which my godfather F. had sent us. He kept the oil shop (now Davies's) at the corner of Featherstone-building, in Holborn.

F. was a tall grave person, lofty in speech, and had pretensions above his rank. He associated in those days with John Palmer, the comedian, whose gait and bearing he seemed to copy; if John (which is quite as likely) did not rather borrow somewhat of his manner from my godfather. He was also known to, and visited by, Sheridan. It was to his house in Holborn that young Brinsley brought his first wife on her elopement with him from a boarding school at Bath—the beautiful Maria Linley. My parents were present (over a quadrille table) when he arrived in the evening with his harmonious charge.—From either of these connexions it may be inferred that my godfather could command an order for the then Drury-lane theatre at pleasure—and, indeed, a pretty liberal issue of those cheap billets, in Brinsley's autograph, I have heard him say was the sole remuneration which he had received for many years' nightly illumination of the orchestra and various avenues of that theatre—and he was content it should be so. The honour of Sheridan's familiarity—or supposed familiarity—was better to my godfather than money.

F. was the most gentlemanly of oilmen; grandiloquent, yet courteous. His delivery of the commonest matters of fact was Ciceronian. He had two Latin words almost constantly in his mouth (how odd sounds Latin from an oilman's lips!), which my better knowledge since has enabled me to correct. In strict pronunciation they should have been sounded *vice versa*—but in those young years they impressed me with more awe than they would now do, read aright from Seneca or Varro—in his own peculiar pronunciation, monosyllabically elaborated, or Anglicized, into something like *verse verse*. By an imposing manner, and the help of these distorted syllables, he climbed (but that was little) to the highest parochial honours which St. Andrew's has to bestow.

He is dead—and thus much I thought due to his memory, both for my first orders (little wondrous talismans !—slight keys, and insignificant to outward sight, but opening to me more than Arabian paradises !) and moreover, that by his testamentary beneficence I came into possession of the only landed property which I could ever call my own —situate near the road-way village of pleasant Puckeridge, in Hertfordshire. When I journeyed down to take possession, and planted foot on my own ground, the stately habits of the donor descended upon me, and I strode (shall I confess the vanity ?) with larger paces over my allotment of three-quarters of an acre, with its commodious mansion in the midst, with the feeling of an English freeholder that all betwixt sky and centre was my own. The estate has passed into more prudent hands, and nothing but an agrarian can restore it.

In those days were pit orders. Beshrew the uncomfortable manager who abolished them !— with one of these we went. I remember the waiting at the door—not that which is left—but between that and an inner door in shelter—O when shall I be such an expectant again !—with the cry of nonpareils, an indispensable play-house accompaniment in those days. As near as I can recollect, the fashionable pronunciation of the theatrical fruiteresses then was, ' Chase some oranges, chase some numparels, chase a bill of the play ; '—chase

pro chuse. But when we got in, and I beheld the
green curtain that veiled a heaven to my imagination, which was soon to be disclosed—the breathless
anticipations I endured! I had seen something
like it in the plate prefixed to 'Troilus and Cressida',
in Rowe's *Shakspeare*—the tent scene with
Diomede—and a sight of that plate can always
bring back in a measure the feeling of that evening.
—The boxes at that time, full of well-dressed
women of quality, projected over the pit; and
the pilasters reaching down were adorned with
a glistering substance (I know not what) under
glass (as it seemed), resembling—a homely fancy
—but I judged it to be sugar-candy—yet, to my
raised imagination, divested of its homelier
qualities, it appeared a glorified candy!—The
orchestra lights at length rose, those 'fair Auroras!'
Once the bell sounded. It was to ring out yet once
again—and, incapable of the anticipation, I reposed
my shut eyes in a sort of resignation upon the
maternal lap. It rang the second time. The
curtain drew up—I was not past six years old—
and the play was *Artaxerxes*!

I had dabbled a little in the *Universal History*
—the ancient part of it—and here was the court
of Persia. It was being admitted to a sight to
the past. I took no proper interest in the action
going on, for I understood not its import—but
I heard the word Darius, and I was in the midst
of Daniel. All feeling was absorbed in vision.
Gorgeous vests, gardens, palaces, princesses, passed
before me. I knew not players. I was in Persepolis
for the time; and the burning idol of their devotion
almost converted me into a worshipper. I was
awe-struck, and believed those significations to

be something more than elemental fires. It was all enchantment and a dream. No such pleasure has since visited me but in dreams.—Harlequin's Invasion followed; where, I remember, the transformation of the magistrates into reverend beldams seemed to me a piece of grave historic justice, and the tailor carrying his own head, to be as sober a verity as the legend of St. Denys.

The next play to which I was taken was the *Lady of the Manor*, of which, with the exception of some scenery, very faint traces are left in my memory. It was followed by a pantomine, called *Lun's Ghost*—a satiric touch, I apprehend, upon Rich, not long since dead—but to my apprehension (too sincere for satire), Lun was as remote a piece of antiquity as Lud—the father of a line of Harlequins—transmitting his dagger of lath (the wooden sceptre) through countless ages. I saw the primeval Motley come from his silent tomb in a ghastly vest of white patch-work, like the apparition of a dead rainbow. So Harlequins (thought I) look when they are dead.

My third play followed in quick succession. It was the *Way of the World*. I think I must have sat at it as grave as a judge; for, I remember, the hysteric affections of good Lady Wishfort affected me like some solemn tragic passion. *Robinson Crusoe* followed; in which Crusoe, man Friday, and the parrot, were as good and authentic as in the story.—The clownery and pantaloonery of these pantomimes have clean passed out of my head 'I believe, I no more laughed at them, than at the same age I should have been disposed to laugh at the grotesque Gothic heads (seeming to me then replete with devout meaning) that gape, and grin, in stone around the inside of the old Round Church (my church) of the Templars.

I saw these plays in the season 1781-2, when I was from six to seven years old. After the intervention of six or seven other years (for at school all play-going was inhibited) I again entered the doors of a theatre. That old *Artaxerxes* evening had never done ringing in my fancy. I expected the same feelings to come again with the same occasion. But we differ from ourselves less at sixty and sixteen, than the latter does from six. In that interval what had I not lost! At the first period I knew nothing, understood nothing, discriminated nothing. I felt all, loved all, wondered all—

> Was nourished, I could not tell how—

I had left the temple a devotee, and was returned a rationalist. The same things were there materially; but the emblem, the reference, was gone!—The green curtain was no longer a veil, drawn between two worlds, the unfolding of which was to bring back past ages, to present a 'royal ghost',—but a certain quantity of green baize, which was to separate the audience for a given time from certain of their fellow-men who were to come forward and pretend those parts. The lights—the orchestra lights—came up a clumsy machinery. The first ring, and the second ring, was now but a trick of the prompter's bell—which had been, like the note of the cuckoo, a phantom of a voice, no hand seen or guessed at which ministered to its warning. The actors were men and women painted. I thought the fault was in them; but it was in myself, and the alteration which those many centuries—of six

short twelve-months had wrought in me.—Perhaps
it was fortunate for me that the play of the evening
was but an indifferent comedy, as it gave me time
to crop some unreasonable expectations, which
might have interfered with the genuine emotions
with which I was soon after enabled to enter upon
the first appearance to me of Mrs. Siddons in
Isabella. Comparison and retrospection soon
yielded to the present attraction of the scene;
and the theatre became to me, upon a new stock,
the most delightful of recreations.

The Essays of Elia. 1823.

BARBARA S——

ON the noon of the 14th of November, 1743 or 4,
I forget which it was, just as the clock had struck
one, Barbara S——, with her accustomed punctuality, ascended the long rambling staircase, with
awkward interposed landing-places, which led to
the office, or rather a sort of box with a desk in it,
whereat sat the then Treasurer of (what few of our
readers may remember) the Old Bath Theatre.
All over the island it was the custom, and remains
so I believe to this day, for the players to receive
their weekly stipend on the Saturday. It was not
much that Barbara had to claim.

The little maid had just entered her eleventh
year; but her important station at the theatre,
as it seemed to her, with the benefits which she
felt to accrue from her pious application of her
small earnings, had given an air of womanhood
to her steps and to her behaviour. You would
have taken her to have been at least five years older.

Till latterly she had merely been employed in choruses, or where children were wanted to fill up the scene. But the manager, observing a diligence and adroitness in her above her age, had for some few months past entrusted to her the performance of whole parts. You may guess the self-consequence of the promoted Barbara. She had already drawn tears in young Arthur; had rallied Richard with infantine petulance in the Duke of York; and in her turn had rebuked that petulance when she was Prince of Wales. She would have done the elder child in Morton's pathetic after-piece to the life; but as yet the *Children in the Wood* was not.

Long after this little girl was grown an aged woman, I have seen some of these small parts, each making two or three pages at most, copied out in the rudest hand of the then prompter, who doubtless transcribed a little more carefully and fairly for the grown-up tragedy ladies of the establishment. But such as they were, blotted and scrawled, as for a child's use, she kept them all; and in the zenith of her after reputation it was a delightful sight to behold them bound up in costliest Morocco, each single—each small part making a *book*—with fine clasps, gilt-splashed, &c. She had conscientiously kept them as they had been delivered to her; not a blot had been effaced or tampered with. They were precious to her for their affecting remembrancings. They were her principia, her rudiments; the elementary atoms; the little steps by which she pressed forward to perfection. 'What', she would say, 'could Indian rubber, or a pumice stone, have done for these darlings?'

I am in no hurry to begin my story—indeed, I have little or none to tell—so I will just mention an observation of hers connected with that interesting time.

Not long before she died I had been discoursing with her on the quantity of real present emotion which a great tragic performer experiences during acting. I ventured to think, that though in the first instance such players must have possessed the feelings which they so powerfully called up in others, yet by frequent repetition those feelings must become deadened in great measure, and the performer trust to the memory of past emotion, rather than express a present one. She indignantly repelled the notion, that with a truly great tragedian the operation, by which such effects were produced upon an audience, could ever degrade itself into what was purely mechanical. With much delicacy, avoiding to instance in her *self*-experience, she told me, that so long ago as when she used to play the part of the Little Son to Mrs. Porter's Isabella (I think it was), when that impressive actress has been bending over her in some heart-rending colloquy, she has felt real hot tears come trickling from her, which (to use her powerful expression) have perfectly scalded her back.

I am not quite so sure that it was Mrs. Porter; but it was some great actress of that day. The name is indifferent; but the fact of the scalding tears I most distinctly remember.

I was always fond of the society of players, and am not sure that an impediment in my speech (which certainly kept me out of the pulpit) even more than certain personal disqualifications, which

are often got over in that profession, did not
prevent me at one time of life from adopting it.
I have had the honour (I must ever call it) once
to have been admitted to the tea-table of Miss
Kelly. I have played at serious whist with
Mr. Liston. I have chatted with ever good-
humoured Mrs. Charles Kemble. I have conversed
as friend to friend with her accomplished husband.
I have been indulged with a classical conference
with Macready; and with a sight of the Player-
picture gallery, at Mr. Matthew's, when the kind
owner, to remunerate me for my love of the old
actors (whom he loves so much) went over it with
me, supplying to his capital collection, what alone
the artist could not give them—voice; and their
living motion. Old tones, half-faded, of Dodd,
and Parsons, and Baddeley, have lived again for
me at his bidding. Only Edwin he could not restore
to me. I have supped with——; but I am growing
a coxcomb.

As I was about to say—at the desk of the then
treasurer of the old Bath theatre—not Diamond's
—presented herself the little Barbara S——.

The parents of Barbara had been in reputable
circumstances. The father had practised, I believe,
as an apothecary in the town. But his practice
from causes which I feel my own infirmity too
sensibly that way to arraign—or perhaps from
that pure infelicity which accompanies some
people in their walk through life, and which it is
impossible to lay at the door of imprudence—was
now reduced to nothing. They were in fact in the
very teeth of starvation, when the manager, who
knew and respected them in better days, took the
little Barbara into his company.

At the period I commenced with, her slender earnings were the sole support of the family, including two younger sisters. I must throw a veil over some mortifying circumstances. Enough to say, that her Saturday's pittance was the only chance of a Sunday's (generally their only) meal of meat.

One thing I will only mention, that in some child's part, where in her theatrical character she was to sup off a roast fowl (O joy to Barbara!) some comic actor, who was for the night caterer for this dainty—in the misguided humour of his part, threw over the dish such a quantity of salt (O grief and pain of heart to Barbara!) that when he crammed a portion of it into her mouth, she was obliged sputteringly to reject it; and what with shame of her ill-acted part, and pain of real appetite at missing such a dainty, her little heart sobbed almost to breaking, till a flood of tears, which the well-fed spectators were totally unable to comprehend, mercifully relieved her.

This was the little starved, meritorious maid, who stood before old Ravenscroft, the treasurer, for her Saturday's payment.

Ravenscroft was a man, I have heard many old theatrical people besides herself say, of all men least calculated for a treasurer. He had no head for accounts, paid away at random, kept scarce any books, and summing up at the week's end, if he found himself a pound or so deficient, blest himself that it was no worse.

Now Barbara's weekly stipend was a bare half guinea.—By mistake he popped into her hand a—whole one.

Barbara tripped away.

She was entirely unconscious at first of the mistake : God knows, Ravenscroft would never have discovered it.

But when she had got down to the first of those uncouth landing-places, she became sensible of an unusual weight of metal pressing her little hand.

Now mark the dilemma.

She was by nature a good child. From her parents and those about her she had imbibed no contrary influence. But then they had taught her nothing. Poor men's smoky cabins are not always porticoes of moral philosophy. This little maid had no instinct to evil, but then she might be said to have no fixed principle. She had heard honesty commended, but never dreamed of its application to herself. She thought of it as something which concerned grown-up people— men and women. She had never known temptation or thought of preparing resistance against it.

Her first impulse was to go back to the old treasurer, and explain to him his blunder. He was already so confused with age, besides a natural want of punctuality, that she would have had some difficulty in making him understand it. She saw *that* in an instant. And then it was such a bit of money ! and then the image of a larger allowance of butcher's meat on their table the next day came across her, till her little eyes glistened, and her mouth moistened. But then Mr. Ravenscroft had always been so good-natured, had stood her friend behind the scenes, and even recommended her promotion to some of her little parts. But again the old man was reputed to be worth a world of money. He was supposed to have fifty pounds a year clear of the

theatre. And then came staring upon her the
figure of her little stockingless and shoeless sisters.
And when she looked at her own neat white cotton
stockings, which her situation at the theatre had
made it indispensable for her mother to provide
for her, with hard straining and pinching from
the family stock, and thought how glad she should
be to cover their poor feet with the same—and
how then they could accompany her to rehearsals,
which they had hitherto been precluded from
doing, by reason of their unfashionable attire—
in these thoughts she reached the second landing-
place—the second, I mean, from the top—for
there was still another left to traverse.

Now virtue support Barbara!

And that never-failing friend did step in—for at
that moment a strength not her own, I have heard
her say, was revealed to her—a reason above
reasoning—and without her own agency, as it
seemed (for she never felt her feet to move), she
found herself transported back to the individual
desk she had just quitted, and her hand in the old
hand of Ravenscroft, who in silence took back the
refunded treasure, and who had been sitting (good
man) insensible to the lapse of minutes, which to
her were anxious ages; and from that moment
a deep peace fell upon her heart, and she knew the
quality of honesty.

A year or two's unrepining application to her
profession brightened up the feet, and the prospects,
of her little sisters, set the whole family upon their
legs again, and released her from the difficulty of
discussing moral dogmas upon a landing-place.

I have heard her say, that it was a surprise, not
much short of mortification to her, to see the

coolness with which the old man pocketed the difference, which had caused her such mortal throes.

This anecdote of herself I had in the year 1800, from the mouth of the late Mrs. Crawford,[1] then sixty-seven years of age (she died soon after) ; and to her struggles upon this childish occasion I have sometimes ventured to think her indebted for that power of rending the heart in the representation of conflicting emotions, for which in after years she was considered as little inferior (if at all so in the part of Lady Randolph) even to Mrs. Siddons.

Last Essays of Elia. 1833.

---

[1] The maiden name of this lady was Street, which she changed, by successive marriages, for those of Dancer, Barry, and Crawford. She was Mrs. Crawford, and a third time a widow, when I knew her.

WILLIAM HAZLITT

1778–1830

JOHN CAVANAGH

A SINGULAR instance of manual dexterity was shewn in the person of the late John Cavanagh, whom I have several times seen. His death was celebrated at the time in an article in the *Examiner* newspaper, (Feb. 7, 1819), written apparently between jest and earnest : but as it is *pat* to our purpose, and falls in with my own way of considering such subjects, I shall here take leave to quote it.

' Died at his house in Burbage-street, St. Giles's, John Cavanagh, the famous hand fives-player. When a person dies, who does any one thing better than any one else in the world, which so many others are trying to do well, it leaves a gap in society. It is not likely that any one will now see the game of fives played in its perfection for many years to come—for Cavanagh is dead, and has not left his peer behind him. It may be said that there are things of more importance than striking a ball against a wall—there are things indeed that make more noise and do as little good, such as making war and peace, making speeches and answering them, making verses and blotting them ; making money and throwing it away. But the game of fives is what no one despises who has ever played at it. It is the finest exercise for the body, and the best relaxation for the mind. The Roman poet said that "Care mounted behind the horseman and stuck to his skirts". But this remark would not have applied to the fives-player. He who takes to playing at fives is twice young. He feels neither the past nor future "in the instant". Debts, taxes, "domestic treason, foreign levy, nothing can touch him further." He has no other wish, no other thought, from the moment the game begins, but that of striking the ball, of placing it, of *making* it! This Cavanagh was sure to do. Whenever he touched the ball, there was an end of the chase. His eye was certain, his hand fatal, his presence of mind complete. He could do what he pleased, and he always knew exactly what to do. He saw the whole game, and played it; took instant advantage of his adversary's weakness, and recovered balls, as if by a miracle and from sudden thought, that every one gave for lost. He had equal power and skill, quickness, and judgement. He could either outwit his antagonist by finesse, or beat him by main strength. Sometimes, when he seemed preparing to send the ball with the full swing of his arm, he would by a slight turn of his wrist drop it within an inch of the line. In general, the ball came from his hand, as if from a racket, in a straight horizontal line; so that it was in vain to attempt to overtake or stop it. As it was said of a great orator that he never was at a loss for a word, and for the properest word, so Cavanagh always could tell the degree of force necessary to be given to a ball, and the precise direction in which it should be sent. He did his work with the greatest ease; never took more pains than was necessary; and while others were fagging them-

selves to death, was as cool and collected as if he
had just entered the court. His style of play was
as remarkable as his power of execution. He had
no affectation, no trifling. He did not throw away
the game to show off an attitude, or try an experiment. He was a fine, sensible, manly player, who
did what he could, but that was more than any one
else could even affect to do. His blows were not
undecided and ineffectual—lumbering like Mr.
Wordsworth's epic poetry, nor wavering like Mr.
Coleridge's lyric prose, nor short of the mark like
Mr. Brougham's speeches, nor wide of it like Mr.
Canning's wit, nor foul like the *Quarterly*, nor *let*
balls like the *Edinburgh Review*. Cobbett and
Junius together would have made a Cavanagh.
He was the best *up-hill* player in the world; even
when his adversary was fourteen, he would play on
the same or better; and as he never flung away the
game through carelessness and conceit, he never
gave it up through laziness or want of heart. The
only peculiarity of his play was that he never
volleyed, but let the balls hop; but if they rose an
inch from the ground he never missed having them.
There was not only nobody equal, but nobody
second to him. It is supposed that he could give
any other player half the game, or beat them with
his left hand. His service was tremendous. He
once played Woodward and Meredith together
(two of the best players in England) in the Fives-
court, St. Martin's-street, and made seven and
twenty aces following by services alone—a thing
unheard of. He another time played Peru, who
was considered a first-rate fives-player, a match of
the best out of five games, and in the three first
games, which of course decided the match, Peru

got only one ace. Cavanagh was an Irishman by birth, and a house-painter by profession. He had once laid aside his working-dress, and walked up, in his smartest clothes, to the Rosemary Branch to have an afternoon's pleasure. A person accosted him, and asked him if he would have a game. So they agreed to play for half a crown a game, and a bottle of cider. The first game began—it was seven, eight, ten, thirteen, fourteen, all. Cavanagh won it. The next was the same. They played on, and each game was hardly contested. "There," said the unconscious fives-player, "there was a stroke that Cavanagh could not take: I never played better in my life, and yet I can't win a game. I don't know how it is!" However, they played on, Cavanagh winning every game, and the by-standers drinking the cider and laughing all the time. In the twelfth game, when Cavanagh was only four, and the stranger thirteen, a person came in, and said, "What! are you here, Cavanagh?" The words were no sooner pronounced than the astonished player let the ball drop from his hand, and saying, "What! have I been breaking my heart all this time to beat Cavanagh?" refused to make another effort. "And yet, I give you my word," said Cavanagh, telling the story with some triumph, "I played all the while with my clenched fist."—He used frequently to play matches at Copenhagen House for wagers and dinners. The wall against which they play is the same that supports the kitchen-chimney, and when the wall resounded louder than usual, the cooks exclaimed, "Those are the Irishman's balls", and the joints trembled on the spit !—Goldsmith consoled himself that there were places where he too was admired :

and Cavanagh was the admiration of all the fives-courts, where he ever played. Mr. Powell, when he played matches in the court in St. Martin's-street, used to fill his gallery at half a crown a head, with amateurs and admirers of talent in whatever department it is shown. He could not have shown himself in any ground in England but he would have been immediately surrounded with inquisitive gazers, trying to find out in what part of his frame his unrivalled skill lay, as politicians wonder to see the balance of Europe suspended in Lord Castle-reagh's face, and admire the trophies of the British Navy lurking under Mr. Croker's hanging brow. Now Cavanagh was as good-looking a man as the Noble Lord, and much better looking than the Right Hon. Secretary. He had a clear, open countenance, and did not look sideways or down, like Mr. Murray the bookseller. He was a young fellow of sense, humour, and courage. He once had a quarrel with a waterman at Hungerford-stairs, and they say, served him out in great style. In a word, there are hundreds at this day, who cannot mention his name without admiration, as the best fives-player that perhaps ever lived (the greatest excellence of which they have any notion) —and the noisy shout of the ring happily stood him in stead of the unheard voice of posterity !— The only person who seems to have excelled as much in another way as Cavanagh did in his was the late John Davies, the racket-player. It was remarked of him that he did not seem to follow the ball, but the ball seemed to follow him. Give him a foot of wall, and he was sure to make the ball. The four best racket-players of that day were Jack Spines, Jem Harding, Armitage, and

Church. Davies could give any one of these two hands a time, that is, half the game, and each of these, at their best, could give the best player now in London the same odds. Such are the gradations in all exertions of human skill and art. He once played four capital players together, and beat them. He was also a first-rate tennis-player, and an excellent fives-player. In the Fleet or King's Bench, he would have stood against Powell, who was reckoned the best open-ground player of his time. This last-mentioned player is at present the keeper of the Fives-court, and we might recommend to him for a motto over his door—"Who enters here, forgets himself, his country, and his friends." And the best of it is, that by the calculation of the odds, none of the three are worth remembering! Cavanagh died from the bursting of a blood-vessel, which prevented him from playing for the last two or three years. This, he was often heard to say, he thought hard upon him. He was fast recovering, however, when he was suddenly carried off, to the regret of all who knew him. As Mr. Peel made it a qualification of the present Speaker, Mr. Manners Sutton, that he was an excellent moral character, so Jack Cavanagh was a zealous Catholic, and could not be persuaded to eat meat on a Friday, the day on which he died. We have paid this willing tribute to his memory.

> Let no rude hand deface it,
> And his forlorn *Hic Jacet.*'

Table Talk. 1821.

GOING TO SEE A FIGHT

—The *fight*, the *fight's* the thing,
Wherein I'll catch the conscience of the King.

Where there's a will, there's a way.—I said so
to myself, as I walked down Chancery-lane, about
half-past six o'clock on Monday the 10th of
December, to inquire at Jack Randall's where the
fight the next day was to be; and I found 'the
proverb' nothing 'musty' in the present instance.
I was determined to see this fight, come what
would, and see it I did, in great style. It was my
first fight, yet it more than answered my expectations. Ladies! it is to you I dedicate this description; nor let it seem out of character for
the fair to notice the exploits of the brave. Courage and modesty are the old English virtues; and
may they never look cold and askance on one
another! Think, ye fairest of the fair, loveliest of
the lovely kind, ye practisers of soft enchantment, how many more ye kill with poisoned baits
than ever fell in the ring; and listen with subdued
air and without shuddering, to a tale tragic only
in appearance, and sacred to the FANCY!

I was going down Chancery-lane, thinking to ask
at Jack Randall's where the fight was to be, when
looking through the glass-door of the *Hole in the
Wall*, I heard a gentleman asking the same question
at Mrs. Randall, as the author of *Waverley* would
express it. Now Mrs. Randall stood answering
the gentleman's question, with the authenticity of
the lady of the Champion of the Light Weights.
Thinks I, I'll wait till this person comes out, and

learn from him how it is. .... I waited at the door,
when, who should issue forth but my friend Jo
Toms, and turning suddenly up Chancery-lane with
that quick jerk and impatient stride which dis-
tinguishes a lover of the FANCY, I said, ' I'll be
hanged if that fellow is not going to the fight, and
is on his way to get me to go with him.' So it
proved in effect, and we agreed to adjourn to my
lodgings to discuss measures with that cordiality
which makes old friends like new, and new friends
like old, on great occasions. We are cold to others
only when we are dull in ourselves, and have
neither thoughts nor feelings to impart to them.
Give a man a topic in his head, a throb of pleasure
in his heart, and he will be glad to share it with the
first person he meets. Toms and I, though we
seldom meet, were an *alter idem* on this memorable
occasion, and had not an idea that we did not
candidly impart ; and ' so carelessly did we fleet
the time ', that I wish no better, when there is
another fight, than to have him for a companion
on my journey down, and to return with my friend
Jack Pigott, talking of what was to happen or of
what did happen, with a noble subject always at
hand, and liberty to digress to others whenever
they offered. Indeed, on my repeating the lines
from Spenser in an involuntary fit of enthusiasm—

> What more felicity can fall to creature,
> Than to enjoy delight with liberty ?

my last-named ingenious friend stopped me by
saying that this, translated into the vulgate,
meant *Going to see a fight*.

Jo Toms and I could not settle about the method
of going down. He said there was a caravan, he

understood, to start from Tom Belcher's at two, which would go there *right out* and back again the next day. Now I never travel all night, and said I should get a cast to Newbury by one of the mails. Jo swore the thing was impossible, and I could only answer that I had made up my mind to it. In short, he seemed to me to waver, said he only came to see if I was going, had letters to write, a cause coming on the day after, and faintly said at parting (for I was bent on setting out that moment)—' Well, we meet at Philippi ! ' I made the best of my way to Piccadilly. The mail coach stand was bare. ' They are all gone,' said I— ' this is always the way with me—in the instant I lose the future—if I had not stayed to pour out that last cup of tea, I should have been just in time '—and, cursing my folly and ill-luck together, without inquiring at the coach-office whether the mails were gone or not, I walked on in despite, and to punish my own dilatoriness and want of determination. At any rate, I would not turn back : I might get to Hounslow, or perhaps farther, to be on my road the next morning. I passed Hyde Park Corner (my Rubicon), and trusted to fortune. Suddenly I heard the clattering of a Brentford stage, and the fight rushed full upon my fancy. I argued (not unwisely) that even a Brentford coachman was better company than my own thoughts (such as they were just then), and at his invitation mounted the box with him. I immediately stated my case to him—namely, my quarrel with myself for missing the Bath or Bristol mail, and my determination to get on in consequence as well as I could, without any disparagement or insulting comparison between

longer or shorter stages. It is a maxim with me
that stage-coaches, and consequently stage-coach-
men, are respectable in proportion to the distance
they have to travel: so I said nothing on that
subject to my Brentford friend. Any incipient
tendency to an abstract proposition, or (as he
might have construed it) to a personal reflection
of this kind, was however nipped in the bud; for
I had no sooner declared indignantly that I had
missed the mails, than he flatly denied that they
were gone along, and lo! at the instant three of
them drove by in rapid, provoking, orderly succession, as if they would devour the ground before
them. Here again I seemed in the contradictory
situation of the man in Dryden who exclaims,

I follow Fate, which does too hard pursue !

If I had stopped to inquire at the White Horse
Cellar, which would not have taken me a minute,
I should now have been driving down the road in
all the dignified unconcern and *ideal* perfection of
mechanical conveyance. The Bath mail I had set
my mind upon, and I had missed it, as I had missed
everything else, by my own absurdity, in putting
the will for the deed, and aiming at ends without
employing means. ' Sir,' said he of the Brentford,
' the Bath mail will be up presently, my brother-in-
law drives it, and I will engage to stop him if there
is a place empty.' I almost doubted my good
genius; but, sure enough, up it drove like lightning, and stopped directly at the call of the Brentford Jehu. I would not have believed this possible,
but the brother-in-law of a mail-coach driver is
himself no mean man. I was transferred without
loss of time from the top of one coach to that of

the other, desired the guard to pay my fare to the
Brentford coachman for me as I had no change,
was accommodated with a great coat, put up my
umbrella to keep off a drizzling mist, and we
began to cut through the air like an arrow. The
mile-stones disappeared one after another, the
rain kept off; Tom Turtle, the trainer, sat before
me on the coach-box, with whom I exchanged
civilities as a gentleman going to the fight; the
passion that had transported me an hour before
was subdued to pensive regret and conjectural
musing on the next day's battle; I was promised
a place inside at Reading, and upon the whole,
I thought myself a lucky fellow. Such is the force
of imagination! On the outside of any other
coach on the 10th of December with a Scotch mist
drizzling through the cloudy moonlight air, I should
have been cold, comfortless, impatient, and, no
doubt, wet through; but seated on the Royal
mail, I felt warm and comfortable, the air did me
good, the ride did me good, I was pleased with the
progress we had made, and confident that all would
go well through the journey. When I got inside
at Reading, I found Turtle and a stout valetu-
dinarian, whose costume bespoke him one of the
Fancy, and who had risen from a three months'
sick bed to get into the mail to see the fight. They
were intimate, and we fell into a lively discourse.
My friend the trainer was confined in his topics to
fighting dogs and men, to bears and badgers;
beyond this he was ' quite chap-fallen ', had not
a word to throw at a dog, or indeed very wisely fell
asleep, when any other game was started. The
whole art of training (I, however, learnt from him)
consists in two things, exercise and abstinence,

abstinence and exercise, repeatedly, alternately, and without end. A yolk of an egg with a spoonful of rum in it is the first thing in a morning, and then a walk of six miles till breakfast. This meal consists of a plentiful supply of tea and toast and beefsteaks. Then another six or seven miles till dinnertime, and another supply of solid beef or mutton with a pint of porter, and perhaps, at the utmost, a couple of glasses of sherry. Martin trains on water, but this increases his infirmity on another very dangerous side. The Gas-man takes now and then a chirping glass (under the rose) to console him, during a six weeks' probation, for the absence of Mrs. Hickman—an agreeable woman, with (I understand) a pretty fortune of two hundred pounds. How matter presses on me! What stubborn things are facts! How inexhaustible is nature and art! ' It is well,' as I once heard Mr. Richmond observe, ' to see a variety.' He was speaking of cock-fighting as an edifying spectacle. I cannot deny but that one learns more of what *is* (I do not say of what *ought to be*) in this desultory mode of practical study, than from reading the same book twice over, even though it should be a moral treatise. Where was I ? I was sitting at dinner with the candidate for the honours of the ring, ' where good digestion waits on appetite, and health on both.' Then follows an hour of social chat and native glee ; and afterwards, to another breathing over heathy hill or dale. Back to supper and then to bed, and up by six again—our hero

Follows so the ever-running sun,
With profitable *ardour*—

to the day that brings him victory or defeat in the

green fairy circle. Is not this life more sweet than
mine? I was going to say; but I will not libel any
life by comparing it to mine, which is (at the
date of these presents) bitter as coloquintida and
the dregs of aconitum!

The invalid in the Bath mail soared a pitch above
the trainer, and did not sleep so sound, because he
had 'more figures and more fantasies'. We
talked the hours away merrily. He had faith in
surgery, for he had had three ribs set right, that had
been broken in a *turn-up* at Belcher's, but thought
physicians old women, for they had no antidote in
their catalogue for brandy. An indigestion is an excellent common-place for two people that never met
before. By way of ingratiating myself, I told him
the story of my doctor, who, on my earnestly
representing to him that I thought his regimen had
done me harm, assured me that the whole phar-
macopoeia contained nothing comparable to the
prescription he had given me; and, as a proof of
its undoubted efficacy, said, that ' he had had one
gentleman with my complaint under his hands for
the last fifteen years'. This anecdote made my
companion shake the rough sides of his three great-
coats with boisterous laughter; and Turtle, starting out of his sleep, swore he knew how the fight
would go, for he had had a dream about it. Sure
enough the rascal told us how the first three rounds
went off, but ' his dream', like others, ' denoted
a foregone conclusion'. He knew his men. The
moon now rose in silver state, and I ventured, with
some hesitation, to point out this object of placid
beauty, with the blue serene beyond, to the man
of science, to which his ear he ' seriously inclined ',
the more as it gave promise *d'un beau jour* for the

morrow, and showed the ring undrenched by envious
showers, arrayed in sunny smiles. Just then, all
going on well, I thought on my friend Toms, whom
I had left behind, and said innocently, ' There was
a blockhead of a fellow I left in town, who said
there was no possibility of getting down by the
mail, and talked of going by a caravan from
Belcher's at two in the morning, after he had
written some letters.' ' Why,' said he of the
lapels, ' I should not wonder if that was the very
person we saw running about like mad from one
coach-door to another, and asking if any one had
seen a friend of his, a gentleman going to the fight,
whom he had missed stupidly enough by staying to
write a note.' ' Pray, sir,' said my fellow-
traveller, ' had he a plaid-cloak on ? '—' Why, no,'
said I, ' not at the time I left him, but he very well
might afterwards, for he offered to lend me one.'
The plaid-cloak and the letter decided the thing.
Jo, sure enough, was in the Bristol mail, which
preceded us by about fifty yards. This was droll
enough. We had now but a few miles to our place
of destination, and the first thing I did on alighting
at Newbury, both coaches stopping at the same
time, was to call out, ' Pray, is there a gentleman
in that mail of the name of Toms ? ' ' No,' said
Jo, borrowing something of the vein of Gilpin,
' for I have just got out.' ' Well ! ' says he, ' this
is lucky ; but you don't know how vexed I was to
miss you ; for ', added he, lowering his voice, ' do
you know when I left you I went to Belcher's to
ask about the caravan, and Mrs. Belcher said very
obligingly, she couldn't tell about that, but there
were two gentlemen who had taken places by the
mail and were gone on in a landau, and she could

frank us. It's a pity I didn't meet with you; we could then have got down for nothing. But *mum's the word.*' It's the devil for any one to tell me a secret, for it is sure to come out in print. I do not care so much to gratify a friend, but the public ear is too great a temptation to me.

Our present business was to get beds and a supper at an inn; but this was no easy task. The public-houses were full, and where you saw a light at a private house, and people poking their heads out of the casement to see what was going on, they instantly put them in and shut the window, the moment you seemed advancing with a suspicious overture for accommodation. Our guard and coachman thundered away at the outer gate of the Crown for some time without effect—such was the greater noise within;—and when the doors were unbarred, and we got admittance, we found a party assembled in the kitchen round a good hospitable fire, some sleeping, others drinking, others talking on politics and on the fight. A tall English yeoman (something like Matthews in the face, and quite as great a wag)—

A lusty man to ben an abbot able,—

was making such a prodigious noise about rent and taxes, and the price of corn now and formerly, that he had prevented us from being heard at the gate. The first thing I heard him say was to a shuffling fellow who wanted to be off a bet for a shilling glass of brandy and water—' Confound it, man, don't be *insipid*!' Thinks I, that is a good phrase. It was a good omen. He kept it up so all night, nor flinched with the approach of morning. He was a fine fellow, with sense, wit, and spirit, a hearty

body and a joyous mind, free-spoken, frank, con-
vivial—one of that home English breed that went
with Harry the Fifth to the siege of Harfleur—
' standing like greyhounds on the slips,' &c. We
ordered tea and eggs (beds were soon found to be
out of the question), and this fellow's conversation
was *sauce piquante*. It did one's heart good to see
him brandish his oaken towel and to hear him talk.
He made mince-meat of a drunken, stupid, red-
faced, quarrelsome, *frowsy* farmer, whose nose ' he
moralized into a thousand similes ', making it out
a firebrand like Bardolph's. ' I'll tell you what,
my friend,' says he, ' the landlady has only to keep
you here to save fire and candle. If one was to
touch your nose, it would go off like a piece of
charcoal.' At this the other only grinned like an
idiot, the sole variety in his purple face being his
little peering grey eyes and yellow teeth ; called
for another glass, swore he would not stand it ;
and after many attempts to provoke his humorous
antagonist to single combat, which the other
turned off (after working him up to a ludicrous pitch
of choler) with great adroitness, he fell quietly
asleep with a glass of liquor in his hand, which he
could not lift to his head. His laughing persecutor
made a speech over him, and turning to the
opposite side of the room, where they were all sleeping in the midst of this ' loud and furious fun ',
said, ' There's a scene, by G—d, for Hogarth to
paint. I think he and Shakespeare were our two
best men at copying life ! ' This confirmed me
in my good opinion of him. Hogarth, Shakespeare, and Nature, were just enough for him (indeed for any man) to know. I said, ' You read
Cobbett, don't you ? At least,' says I, ' you talk

just as well as he writes.' He seemed to doubt this. But I said, ' We have an hour to spare : if you'll get pen, ink, and paper, and keep on talking, I'll write down what you say ; and if it doesn't make a capital Political Register, I'll forfeit my head. You have kept me alive to-night, however. I don't know what I should have done without you.' He did not dislike this view of the thing, nor my asking if he was not about the size of Jem Belcher; and told me soon afterwards, in the confidence of friendship, that ' the circumstance which had given him nearly the greatest concern in his life, was Cribb's beating Jem after he had lost his eye by racket playing.'—The morning dawns ; that dim but yet clear light appears, which weighs like solid bars of metal on the sleepless eyelids ; the guests drop down from their chambers one by one—but it was too late to think of going to bed now (the clock was on the stroke of seven), we had nothing for it but to find a barber's (the pole that glittered in the morning sun lighted us to his shop), and then a nine miles' march to Hungerford. The day was fine, the sky was blue, the mists were retiring from the marshy ground, the path was tolerably dry, the sitting-up all night had not done us much harm—at least the cause was good ; we talked of this and that with amicable difference, roving and sipping of many subjects, but still invariably we returned to the fight. At length, a mile to the left of Hungerford, on a gentle eminence, we saw the ring surrounded by covered carts, gigs, and carriages, of which hundreds had passed us on the road ; Toms gave a youthful shout, and we hastened down a narrow lane to the scene of action.

New Monthly Magazine. 1822.

THOMAS DE QUINCEY

1785-1859

THE TRIAL OF JOAN OF ARC

Now came her trial. This trial, moving of
course under English influence, was conducted in
chief by the Bishop of Beauvais. He was a
Frenchman, sold to English interests, and hoping,
by favour of the English leaders, to reach the
highest preferment. *Bishop that art, Archbishop
that shalt be, Cardinal that mayest be,* were the words
that sounded continually in his ear ; and doubtless
a whisper of visions still higher, of a triple crown,
and feet upon the necks of kings, sometimes stole
into his heart. M. Michelet is anxious to keep us
in mind that this bishop was but an agent of the
English. True. But it does not better the case
for his countryman—that, being an accomplice in
the crime, making himself the leader in the persecution against the helpless girl, he was willing to be
all this in the spirit, and with the conscious vileness
of a cat's-paw. Never from the foundations of
the earth was there such a trial as this, if it were
laid open in all its beauty of defence, and all its
hellishness of attack. Oh, child of France !
shepherdess, peasant girl ! trodden under foot by
all around thee, how I honour thy flashing intellect,
quick as God's lightning, and true as God's lightning to its mark, that ran before France and laggard

Europe by many a century, confounding the malice
of the ensnarer, and making dumb the oracles of
falsehood ! Is it not scandalous, is it not humiliating to civilization, that, even at this day, France
exhibits the horrid spectacle of judges examining
the prisoner against himself ; seducing him, by
fraud, into treacherous conclusions against his own
head ; using the terrors of their power for extorting
confessions from the frailty of hope ; nay (which
is worse), using the blandishments of condescension
and snaky kindness for thawing into compliances
of gratitude those whom they had failed to freeze
into terror ? Wicked judges ! Barbarian juris-
prudence ! that, sitting in your own conceit on the
summits of social wisdom, have yet failed to learn
the first principles of criminal justice ; sit ye humbly
and with docility at the feet of this girl from
Domrémy, that tore your webs of cruelty into
shreds and dust. ' Would you examine me as a
witness against myself ? ' was the question by
which many times she defied their arts. Continually she showed that their interrogations were
irrelevant to any business before the court, or that
entered into the ridiculous charges against her.
General questions were proposed to her on points
of casuistical divinity ; two-edged questions, which
not one of themselves could have answered, without,
on the one side, landing himself in heresy (as then
interpreted), or, on the other, in some presump-
tuous expression of self-esteem. Next came a
wretched Dominican, that pressed her with an
objection, which, if applied to the Bible, would tax
every one of its miracles with unsoundness. The
monk had the excuse of never having read the
Bible. M. Michelet has no such excuse ; and it

makes one blush for him, as a philosopher, to find him describing such an argument as ' weighty ', whereas it is but a varied expression of rude Mahometan metaphysics. Her answer to this, if there were room to place the whole in a clear light, was as shattering as it was rapid. Another thought to entrap her by asking what language the angelic visitors of her solitude had talked ; as though heavenly counsels could want polyglot interpreters for every word, or that God needed language at all in whispering thoughts to a human heart. Then came a worse devil, who asked her whether the archangel Michael had appeared naked. Not comprehending the vile insinuation, Joanna, whose poverty suggested to her simplicity that it might be the *costliness* of suitable robes which caused the demur, asked them if they fancied God, who clothed the flowers of the valleys, unable to find raiment for his servants. The answer of Joanna moves a smile of tenderness, but the disappointment of her judges makes one laugh exultingly. Others succeeded by troops, who upbraided her with leaving her father ; as if that greater Father, whom she believed herself to have been serving, did not retain the power of dispensing with his own rules, or had not said, that for a less cause than martyrdom, man and woman should leave both father and mother.

On Easter Sunday, when the trial had been long proceeding, the poor girl fell so ill as to cause a belief that she had been poisoned. It was not poison. Nobody had any interest in hastening a death so certain. M. Michelet, whose sympathies with all feelings are so quick, that one would gladly see them always as justly directed, reads the case

most truly. Joanna had a twofold malady. She
was visited by a paroxysm of the complaint called
home-sickness; the cruel nature of her imprison-
ment, and its length, could not but point her solitary
thoughts, in darkness and in chains (for chained
she was), to Domrémy. And the season, which
was the most heavenly period of the spring, added
stings to this yearning. That was one of her
maladies—*nostalgia*, as medicine calls it; the
other was weariness and exhaustion from daily
combats with malice. She saw that everybody
hated her, and thirsted for her blood; nay, many
kind-hearted creatures that would have pitied her
profoundly, as regarded all political charges, had
their natural feelings warped by the belief that she
had dealings with fiendish powers. She knew she
was to die; that was *not* the misery: the misery
was, that this consummation could not be reached
without so much intermediate strife, as if she were
contending for some chance (where chance was
none) of happiness, or were dreaming for a moment
of escaping the inevitable. Why, then, *did* she
contend? Knowing that she would reap nothing
from answering her persecutors, why did she not
retire by silence from the superfluous contest?
It was because her quick and eager loyalty to truth
would not suffer her to see it darkened by frauds
which *she* could expose, but others, even of candid
listeners, perhaps, could not; it was through that
imperishable grandeur of soul, which taught her
to submit meekly and without a struggle to her
punishment, but taught her *not* to submit—no, not
for a moment—to calumny as to facts, or to mis-
construction as to motives. Besides, there were
secretaries all around the court taking down her

words.. That was meant for no good to *her*. But the end does not always correspond to the meaning. And Joanna might say to herself—these words that will be used against me to-morrow and the next day, perhaps in some nobler generation may rise again for my justification. Yes, Joanna, they *are* rising even now in Paris, and for more than justification.

Joan of Arc. 1847.

THE PASSAGE OF THE ANDES

THREE days our poor heroine followed the coast. Her horse was then almost unable to move ; and on *his* account she turned inland to a thicket, for grass and shelter. As she drew near to it, a voice challenged, 'Who goes there ?'—Kate answered, 'Spain.'—'What people ?'—'A friend.' It was two soldiers, deserters, and almost starving. Kate shared her provisions with these men : and, on hearing their plan, which was to go over the *cordilleras*, she agreed to join the party. *Their* object was the wild one of seeking the river Dorado, whose waters rolled along golden sands, and whose pebbles were emeralds. *Hers* was to throw herself upon a line the least liable to pursuit, and the readiest for a new chapter of life, in which oblivion might be found for the past. After a few days of incessant climbing and fatigue, they found themselves in the regions of perpetual snow. Summer came even hither ; but came as vainly to this kingdom of frost as to the grave of her brother. No fire, but the fire of human blood in youthful veins, could ever be kept burning in these aerial solitudes. Fuel was rarely to be found, and kindling a fire by interfriction of dry sticks was a secret almost exclusively Indian. However, our Kate can do everything; and she's the girl, if ever girl *did* such a thing, that I back at any odds for crossing the *cordilleras*. I would bet you something now, reader, if I thought you would deposit your stakes by return of post (as they play at chess through the post office), that Kate does the trick; that she gets down to the other side; that the soldiers do *not*; and that the horse, if preserved at all, is preserved in a way that will leave him very little to boast of.

The party had gathered wild berries and esculent roots at the foot of the mountains, and the horse was of very great use in carrying them. But this larder was soon emptied. There was nothing then to carry; so that the horse's value, as a beast of burden, fell cent. per cent. In fact, very soon he could not carry himself, and it became easy to calculate when he would reach the bottom on the wrong side the *cordilleras*. He took three steps back for one upwards. A council of war being held, the small army resolved to slaughter their horse. He, though a member of the expedition, had no vote; and, if he had, the votes would have stood three to one—majority, two against him. He was cut into quarters; a difficult fraction to distribute amongst a triad of claimants. No saltpetre or sugar could be had: but the frost was antiseptic. And the horse was preserved in as useful a sense as ever apricots were preserved or strawberries; and *that* was the kind of preservation which one page ago I promised to the horse.

On a fire, painfully devised out of broom and

withered leaves, a horse-steak was dressed; for drink, snow was allowed *à discretion*. This ought to have revived the party, and Kate, perhaps, it *did*. But the poor deserters were thinly clad, and they had not the boiling heart of Catalina. More and more they drooped. Kate did her best to cheer them. But the march was nearly at an end for *them*; and they were going in one half-hour to receive their last billet. Yet, before this consummation, they have a strange spectacle to see; such as few places could show but the upper chambers of the *cordilleras*. They had reached a billowy scene of rocky masses, large and small, looking shockingly black on their perpendicular sides as they rose out of the vast snowy expanse. Upon the highest of these that was accessible, Kate mounted to look around her, and she saw—oh, rapture at such an hour!—a man sitting on a shelf of rock, with a gun by his side. Joyously she shouted to her comrades, and ran down to communicate the good news. Here was a sportsman, watching, perhaps, for an eagle; and now they would have relief. One man's cheek kindled with the hectic of sudden joy, and he rose eagerly to march. The other was fast sinking under the fatal sleep that frost sends before herself as her merciful minister of death; but hearing in his dream the tidings of relief, and assisted by his friends, he also staggeringly arose. It could not be three minutes' walk, Kate thought, to the station of the sportsman. That thought supported them all. Under Kate's guidance, who had taken a sailor's glance at the bearings, they soon unthreaded the labyrinth of rocks so far as to bring the man within view. He had not left his resting--

place; their steps on the soundless snow, naturally, he could not hear; and, as their road brought them upon him from the rear, still less could he see them. Kate hailed him; but so keenly was he absorbed in some speculation, or in the object of his watching, that he took no notice of them, not even moving his head. Coming close behind him, Kate touched his shoulder, and said, 'My friend, are you sleeping?' Yes, he *was* sleeping; sleeping the sleep from which there is no awaking; and the slight touch of Kate having disturbed the equilibrium of the corpse, down it rolled on the snow: the frozen body rang like a hollow iron cylinder; the face uppermost and blue with mould, mouth open, teeth ghastly and bleaching in the frost, and a frightful grin upon the lips. This dreadful spectacle finished the struggles of the weaker man, who sank and died at once. The other made an effort with so much spirit, that, in Kate's opinion, horror had acted upon him beneficially as a stimulant. But it was not really so. It was simply a spasm of morbid strength. A collapse succeeded; his blood began to freeze; he sat down in spite of Kate, and *he* also died without further struggle. Yes, gone are the poor suffering deserters; stretched out and bleaching upon the snow; and insulted discipline is avenged. Great kings have long arms; and sycophants are ever at hand for the errand of the potent. What had frost and snow to do with the quarrel? Yet *they* made themselves sycophantic servants to the King of Spain; and *they* it was that dogged his deserters up to the summit of the *cordilleras*, more surely than any Spanish bloodhound, or any Spanish *tirailleur's* bullet.

Now is our Kate standing alone on the summit of the Andes ; and in solitude that is frightful, for she is alone with her own afflicted conscience. Twice before she had stood in solitude as deep upon the wild, wild waters of the Pacific ; but her conscience had been then untroubled. Now is there nobody left that can help ; her horse is dead—the soldiers are dead. There is nobody that she can speak to, except God ; and very soon you will find that she *does* speak to Him ; for already on these vast aerial deserts He has been whispering to *her*. The condition of Kate in some respects resembled that of Coleridge's *Ancient Mariner*. But possibly, reader, you may be amongst the many careless readers that have never fully understood what that condition was. Suffer me to enlighten you ; else you ruin the story of the mariner ; and by losing all its pathos, lose half its beauty.

There are three readers of the *Ancient Mariner*. The first is gross enough to fancy all the imagery of the mariner's visions delivered by the poet for actual facts of experience ; which being impossible, the whole pulverizes, for that reader, into a baseless fairy tale. The second reader is wiser than *that* ; he knows that the imagery is the imagery of febrile delirium ; really seen, but not seen as an external reality. The mariner had caught the pestilential fever, which carried off all his mates ; he only had survived—the delirium had vanished ; but the visions that had haunted the delirium remained. Yes,' says the third reader, ' they remained ; naturally they did, being scorched by fever into his brain ; but how did they happen to remain on his belief as gospel truths ? The delirium had

vanished : why had not the painted scenery of
the delirium vanished, except as visionary memo-
rials of a sorrow that was cancelled ? Why was it
that craziness settled upon this mariner's brain,
driving him, as if he were a Cain, or another
Wandering Jew, to "pass like night from land to
land "; and, at uncertain intervals, wrenching him
until he made rehearsal of his errors, even at the
difficult cost of " holding children from their play,
and old men from the chimney corner " ? ' That
craziness, as the *third* reader deciphers, rose out
of a deeper soil than any bodily affection. It had
its root in penitential sorrow. Oh, bitter is the
sorrow to a conscientious heart, when, too late, it
discovers the depth of a love that has been trampled
under foot ! This mariner had slain the creature
that, on all the earth, loved him best. In the
darkness of his cruel superstition he had done it,
to save his human brothers from a fancied incon-
venience ; and yet, by that very act of cruelty,
he had himself called destruction upon their heads.
The Nemesis that followed punished *him* through
them—him that wronged, through those that
wrongfully he sought to benefit. That spirit who
watches over the sanctities of love is a strong angel
—is a jealous angel ; and this angel it was

> That loved the bird, that loved the man
> That shot him with his bow.

He it was that followed the cruel archer into silent
and slumbering seas :—

> Nine fathom deep he had follow'd him,
> Through the realms of mist and snow.

This jealous angel it was that pursued the man into
noonday darkness, and the vision of dying oceans,

into delirium, and finally (when recovered from disease), into an unsettled mind.

Not altogether unlike, though free from the criminal intention of the mariner, had been the offence of Kate ; not unlike, also, was the punishment that now is dogging her steps. She, like the mariner, had slain the one sole creature that loved her upon the whole wide earth ; she, like the mariner, for this offence, had been hunted into frost and snow—very soon will be hunted into delirium ; and from *that* (if she escapes with life), will be hunted into the trouble of a heart that cannot rest. There was the excuse of one darkness, physical darkness, for *her* ; there was the excuse of another darkness, the darkness of superstition, for the mariner. But, with all the excuses that earth, and the darkness of earth, can furnish, bitter it would be for any of us, reader, through every hour of life, waking or dreaming, to look back upon one fatal moment when we had pierced the heart that would have died for *us*. In this only the darkness had been merciful to Kate—that it had hidden for ever from her victim the hand that slew him. But now, in such utter solitude, her thoughts ran back to their earliest interview. She remembered with anguish, how, on touching the shores of America, almost the first word that met her ear had been from *him*, the brother whom she had killed, about the Pussy of times long past ; how the gallant young man had hung upon her words, as in her native Basque she described her own mischievous little self, of twelve years back ; how his colour went and came, whilst his loving memory of the little sister was revived by her own descriptive traits, giving back, as in a mirror, the fawn-like grace, the squirrel-like restlessness, that once had kindled his own delighted laughter ; how he would take no denial, but showed on the spot, that simply to have touched—to have kissed—to have played with the little wild thing, that glorified, by her innocence, the gloom of St. Sebastian's cloisters, gave a *right* to his hospitality ; how, through *him* only, she had found a welcome in camps ; how, through *him*, she had found the avenue to honour and distinction. And yet this brother, so loving and generous, who, without knowing, had cherished and protected her, and all from pure holy love for herself as the innocent plaything of St. Sebastian's, *him* in a moment she had dismissed from life. She paused ; she turned round, as if looking back for his grave; she saw the dreadful wildernesses of snow which already she had traversed.   Silent they were at this season, even as in the panting heats of noon the Saharas of the torrid zone are oftentimes silent. Dreadful was the silence; it was the nearest thing to the silence of the grave. Graves were at the foot of the Andes, *that* she knew too well ; graves were at the summit of the Andes, *that* she saw too well.   And, as she gazed, a sudden thought flashed upon her, when her eyes settled upon the corpses of the poor deserters—Could she, like *them*, have been all this while unconsciously executing judgement upon herself ? Running from a wrath that was doubtful, into the very jaws of a wrath that was inexorable ? Flying in panic—and behold ! there was no man that pursued ? For the first time in her life, Kate trembled. *Not* for the first time, Kate wept. Far less for the first time was it, that Kate bent her knee—that Kate clasped her hands—that Kate prayed. But it *was* the first

time that she prayed as *they* pray, for whom no
more hope is left but in prayer.

Here let me pause a moment, for the sake of
making somebody angry. A Frenchman, who
sadly misjudges Kate, looking at her through a Par-
isian opera-glass, gives it as *his* opinion—that, because Kate first *records* her prayer on this occasion,
therefore now first of all she prayed. *I* think not
so. *I* love this Kate, blood-stained as she is ; and
I could not love a woman that never bent her knee
in thankfulness or in supplication. However, we
have all a right to our own little opinion ; and it is
not *you*, ' *mon cher* ', you Frenchman, that I am
angry with, but somebody else that stands behind
you. You, Frenchman, and your compatriots,
I love oftentimes for your festal gaiety of heart ;
and I quarrel only with your levity, and that
eternal worldliness that freezes too fiercely—that
absolutely blisters with its frost, like the upper air
of the Andes. *You* speak of Kate only as too
readily you speak of all women ; the instinct of
a natural scepticism being to scoff at all hidden
depths of truth. Else you are civil enough to Kate;
and your '*hommage*' (such as it may happen to be)
is always at the service of a woman on the shortest
notice. But behind *you* I see a worse fellow—
a gloomy fanatic, a religious sycophant, that seeks
to propitiate his circle by bitterness against the
offences that are most unlike his own. And
against him, I must say one word for Kate to the
too hasty reader. This villain opens his fire on our
Kate under shelter of a lie. For there is a standing
lie in the very constitution of civil society—a
necessity of error, misleading us as to the proportions
of crime. Mere necessity obliges man to create

many acts into felonies, and to punish them as the heaviest offences, which his better sense teaches him secretly to regard as perhaps among the lightest. Those poor mutineers or deserters, for instance, were they necessarily without excuse? They might have been oppressively used; but, in critical times of war, no matter for the individual palliations, the mutineer *must* be shot: there is no help for it: as, in extremities of general famine, we shoot the man (alas! we are *obliged* to shoot him) that is found robbing the common stores, in order to feed his own perishing children, though the offence is hardly visible in the sight of God. Only blockheads adjust their scale of guilt to the scale of human punishments. Now, our wicked friend the fanatic, who calumniates Kate, abuses the advantage which, for such a purpose, he derives from the exaggerated social estimate of all violence. Personal security being so main an object of social union, we are obliged to frown upon all modes of violence, as hostile to the central principle of that union. We are *obliged* to rate it, according to the universal results towards which it tends, and scarcely at all according to the special condition of circumstances in which it may originate. Hence a horror arises for that class of offences, which is (philosophically speaking) exaggerated; and by daily use, the ethics of a police-office translate themselves, insensibly, into the ethics even of religious people. But I tell that sycophantish fanatic—not this only, viz., that he abuses unfairly, against Kate, the advantage which he has from the *inevitably* distorted bias of society; but also I tell him this second little thing, that, upon turning away the glass from that one obvious aspect of

Kate's character, her too fiery disposition to vindicate all rights by violence, and viewing her in relation to *general* religious capacities, she was a thousand times more promisingly endowed than himself. It is impossible to be noble in many things, without having many points of contact with true religion. If you deny *that*, you it is that calumniate religion. Kate *was* noble in many things. Her worst errors never took a shape of self-interest or deceit. She was brave, she was generous, she was forgiving, she bore no malice, she was full of truth —qualities that God loves either in man or woman. She hated sycophants and dissemblers. *I* hate them; and more than ever at this moment on her behalf. I wish she were but here, to give a punch on the head to that fellow who traduces her. And, coming round again to the occasion from which this short digression has started—viz., the question raised by the Frenchman, whether Kate were a person likely to *pray* under other circumstances than those of extreme danger—I offer it as *my* opinion, that she was. Violent people are not always such from choice, but perhaps from situation. And, though the circumstances of Kate's position allowed her little means for realizing her own wishes, it is certain that those wishes pointed continually to peace and an unworldly happiness, if *that* were possible. The stormy clouds that enveloped her in camps, opened overhead at intervals, showing her a far-distant blue serene. She yearned, at many times, for the rest which is not in camps or armies; and it is certain, that she ever combined with any plans or day-dreams of tranquillity, as their most essential ally, some aid derived from that dove-like religion which, at

St. Sebastian's, from her infant days she had been taught so profoundly to adore.

Now, let us rise from this discussion of Kate against libellers, as Kate herself is rising from prayer, and consider, in conjunction with *her*, the character and promise of that dreadful ground which lies immediately before her. What is to be thought of it? I could wish we had a theodolite here, and a spirit-level, and other instruments, for settling some important questions. Yet, no: on consideration, if one *had* a wish allowed by that kind fairy, without whose assistance it would be quite impossible to send even for the spirit-level, nobody would throw away the wish upon things so paltry. I would not put the fairy upon such an errand: I would order the good creature to bring no spirit-level, but a stiff glass of spirits for Kate; also, next after which I would request a palanquin, and relays of fifty stout bearers—all drunk, in order that they might not feel the cold. The main interest at this moment, and the main difficulty—indeed, the ' open question ' of the case—was, to ascertain whether the ascent were yet accomplished or not; and when would the descent commence? or had it, perhaps, long commenced? The character of the ground, in those immediate successions that could be connected by the eye, decided nothing; for the undulations of the level had been so continual for miles, as to perplex any eye, even an engineer's, in attempting to judge whether, upon the whole, the tendency were upwards or downwards. Possibly it was yet neither way; it is, indeed, probable, that Kate had been for some time travelling along a series of terraces, that traversed the whole breadth of the topmost area at that point of crossing the *cordilleras* ; and this area, perhaps, but not certainly, might compensate any casual tendencies downwards by corresponding re-ascents. Then came the question, how long would these terraces yet continue ? and had the ascending parts *really* balanced the descending ? Upon *that* seemed to rest the final chance for Kate. Because, unless she very soon reached a lower level, and a warmer atmosphere, mere weariness would oblige her to lie down, under a fierceness of cold that would not suffer her to rise after once losing the warmth of motion ; or, inversely, if she even continued in motion, continued extremity of cold would, of itself, speedily absorb the little surplus energy for moving which yet remained unexhausted by weariness; that is, in short, the excessive weariness would give a murderous advantage to the cold, or the excessive cold would give a corresponding advantage to the weariness.

At this stage of her progress, and whilst the agonizing question seemed yet as indeterminate as ever, Kate's struggle with despair, which had been greatly soothed by the fervour of her prayer, revolved upon her in deadlier blackness. All turned, she saw, upon a race against time, and the arrears of the road ; and she, poor thing ! how little qualified could *she* be, in such a condition, for a race of any kind ; and against two such obstinate brutes as Time and Space ! This hour of the progress, this noontide of Kate's struggle, must have been the very crisis of the whole. Despair was rapidly tending to ratify itself. Hope, in any degree, would be a cordial for sustaining her efforts But to flounder along a dreadful chaos of snow-drifts, or snow-chasms, towards a point of rock, which

being turned, should expose only another interminable succession of the same character—might
that be endured by ebbing spirits, by stiffening limbs,
by the ghastly darkness that was now beginning
to gather upon the inner eye ? And, if once despair became triumphant, all the little arrear of
physical strength would collapse at once.

Oh ! verdure of human fields, cottages of men
and women (that now suddenly, in the eyes of Kate,
seemed all brothers and sisters), cottages with
children around them at play, that are so far below
—oh ! spring and summer, blossoms and flowers,
to which, as to *his* symbols, God has given the
gorgeous privilege of rehearsing for ever upon earth
his most mysterious perfection—Life, and the
resurrections of Life—is it indeed true that poor
Kate must never see you more ? Mutteringly she
put that question to herself. But strange are the
caprices of ebb and flow in the deep fountains of
human sensibilities. At this very moment, when
the utter incapacitation of despair was gathering
fast at Kate's heart, a sudden lightening, as it
were, or flashing inspiration of hope, shot far into
her spirit, a reflux almost supernatural, from the
earliest effects of her prayer. Dimmed and confused had been the accuracy of her sensations for
hours ; but all at once a strong conviction came
over her—that more and more was the sense of
descent becoming steady and continuous. Turning round to measure backwards with her eye the
ground traversed through the last half-hour, she
identified, by a remarkable point of rock, the spot
near which the three corpses were lying. The
silence seemed deeper than ever. Neither was there
any phantom memorial of life for the eye or for the

ear, nor wing of bird, nor echo, nor green leaf, nor
creeping thing that moved or stirred, upon the
soundless waste. Oh, what a relief to this burden
of silence would be a human groan! Here seemed
a motive for still darker despair. And yet, at that
very moment, a pulse of joy began to thaw the
ice at her heart. It struck her, as she reviewed
the ground, from that point where the corpses lay,
that undoubtedly it had been for some time slowly
descending. Her senses were much dulled by
suffering; but this thought it was, suggested by
a sudden apprehension of a continued descending
movement, which had caused her to turn round.
Sight had confirmed the suggestion first derived
from her own steps. The distance attained was
now sufficient to establish the tendency. Oh, yes,
yes, to a certainty she *was* descending—she *had*
been descending for some time. Frightful was the
spasm of joy which whispered that the worst was
over. It was as when the shadow of midnight,
that murderers had relied on, is passing away
from your beleaguered shelter, and dawn will soon
be manifest. It was as when a flood, that all day
long has raved against the walls of your house,
ceases (you suddenly think) to rise; yes! measured
by a golden plummet, it *is* sinking beyond a doubt,
and the darlings of your household are saved.
Kate faced round in agitation to her proper direction.
She saw, what previously, in her stunning confusion, she had *not* seen, that, hardly two stones'
throw in advance, lay a mass of rock, split as into
a gateway. Through that opening it now became
certain that the road was lying. Hurrying forward,
she passed within these natural gates. Gates of
paradise they were. Ah, what a vista did that

gateway expose before her dazzled eye! what
a revelation of heavenly promise! Full two miles
long, stretched a long narrow glen, everywhere
descending, and in many parts rapidly. All was
now placed beyond a doubt. She *was* descending;
for hours, perhaps, *had* been descending insensibly,
the mighty staircase. Yes, Kate is leaving behind
her the kingdom of frost and the victories of death.
Two miles farther, there may be rest, if there is not
shelter. And very soon, as the crest of her new-
born happiness, she distinguished at the other end
of that rocky vista a pavilion-shaped mass of dark
green foliage—a belt of trees, such as we see in the
lovely parks of England, but islanded by a screen
of thick bushy undergrowth. Oh, verdure of dark
olive foliage, offered suddenly to fainting eyes, as if
by some winged patriarchal herald of wrath relenting
—solitary Arab's tent, rising with saintly signals
of peace, in the dreadful desert, must Kate indeed
die even yet, whilst she sees but cannot reach you?
Outpost on the frontier of man's dominions, standing within life, but looking out upon everlasting
death, wilt thou hold up the anguish of thy mocking
invitation, only to betray? Never, perhaps, in
this world was the line so exquisitely grazed that
parts salvation and ruin. As the dove to her
dovecot from the swooping hawk; as the Christian
pinnace to the shelter of Christian batteries, from
the bloody Mohammedan corsair, so flew—so tried
to fly towards the anchoring thickets, that, alas!
could not weigh their anchors, and make sail to
meet her—the poor exhausted Kate from the vengeance of pursuing frost.

And she reached them; staggering, fainting,
reeling, she entered beneath the canopy of umbra-

geous trees. But as oftentimes the Hebrew fugitive
to a city of refuge, flying for his life before the
avenger of blood, was pressed so hotly, that, on
entering the archway of what seemed to *him* the
heavenly city gate, as he kneeled in deep thankfulness to kiss its holy merciful shadow, he could not
rise again, but sank instantly with infant weakness
into sleep—sometimes to wake no more ; so sank,
so collapsed upon the ground, without power to
choose her couch, and with little prospect of ever
rising again to her feet, the martial nun. She lay
as luck had ordered it, with her head screened by
the undergrowth of bushes from any gales that
might arise ; she lay exactly as she sank, with her
eyes up to heaven ; and thus it was that the nun
saw, before falling asleep, the two sights that upon
earth are fittest for the closing eyes of a nun,
whether destined to open again, or to close for ever.
She saw the interlacing of boughs overhead forming
a dome, that seemed like the dome of a cathedral.
She saw, through the fretwork of the foliage,
another dome, far beyond, the dome of an evening
sky, the dome of some heavenly cathedral, not
built with hands. She saw upon this upper dome
the vesper lights, all alive with pathetic grandeur
of colouring from a sunset that had just been
rolling down like a chorus. She had not, till now,
consciously observed the time of day ; whether
it were morning, or whether it were afternoon, in
the confusion of her misery, she had not distinctly
known. But now she whispered to herself, ' It is
evening ' : and what lurked half unconsciously in
these words might be, ' The sun, that rejoices, has
finished his daily toil ; man, that labours, has
finished *his* ; I, that suffer, have finished mine.'

That might be what she thought, but what she *said* was, ' It is evening ; and the hour is come when the Angelus is sounding through St. Sebastian.' What made her think of St. Sebastian, so far away in depths of space and time ? Her brain was wandering, now that her feet were *not* ; and, because her eyes had descended from the heavenly to the earthly dome, *that* made her think of earthly cathedrals, and of cathedral choirs, and of St. Sebastian's chapel, with its silvery bells that carried the echoing Angelus far into mountain recesses. Perhaps, as her wanderings increased, she thought herself back into childhood ; became Pussy once again ; fancied that all since then was a frightful dream ; that she was not upon the dreadful Andes, but still kneeling in the holy chapel at vespers ; still innocent as then ; loved as then she had been loved ; and that all men were liars, who said her hand was ever stained with blood. Little is mentioned of the delusions which possessed her ; but that little gives a key to the impulse which her palpitating heart obeyed, and which her rambling brain for ever reproduced in multiplying mirrors. Restlessness kept her in waking dreams for a brief half-hour. But then fever and delirium would wait no longer ; the killing exhaustion would no longer be refused ; the fever, the delirium, and the exhaustion, swept in together with power like an army with banners ; and the nun ceased through the gathering twilight any more to watch the cathedrals of earth, or the more solemn cathedrals that rose in the heavens above.

The Spanish Military Nun. 1847.

THOMAS CARLYLE

1795–1881

DEATH OF MARIE-ANTOINETTE

ON Monday the Fourteenth of October 1793, a Cause is pending in the Palais de Justice, in the new Revolutionary Court, such as these old stone-walls never witnessed : the Trial of Marie-Antoinette. The once brightest of Queens, now tarnished, defaced, forsaken, stands here at Fouquier-Tinville's Judgement-bar ; answering for her life. The Indictment was delivered her last night. To such changes of human fortune what words are adequate ? Silence alone is adequate.

There are few Printed things one meets with of such tragic, almost ghastly, significance as those bald Pages of the *Bulletin du Tribunal Révolutionnaire*, which bear title, *Trial of the Widow Capet*. Dim, dim, as if in disastrous eclipse ; like the pale kingdoms of Dis ! Plutonic Judges, Plutonic Tinville ; encircled, nine times, with Styx and Lethe, with Fire-Phlegethon and Cocytus named of Lamentation ! The very witnesses summoned are like Ghosts : exculpatory, inculpatory, they themselves are all hovering over death and doom ; they are known, in our imagination, as the prey of the Guillotine. Tall *ci-devant* Count d'Estaing, anxious to show himself Patriot, cannot escape ; nor Bailly, who, when asked If he knows the Accused, answers with a reverent inclination towards her,

'Ah, yes, I know Madame.' Ex-Patriots are here, sharply dealt with, as Procureur Manuel; Ex-Ministers, shorn of their splendour. We have cold Aristocratic impassivity, faithful to itself even in Tartarus; rabid stupidity, of Patriot Corporals, Patriot Washerwomen, who have much to say of Plots, Treasons, August Tenth, old Insurrection of Women. For all now has become a crime in her who has *lost*.

Marie-Antoinette, in this her utter abandonment, and hour of extreme need, is not wanting to herself, the imperial woman. Her look, they say, as that hideous Indictment was reading, continued calm; ' she was sometimes observed moving her fingers, as when one plays on the piano'. You discern, not without interest, across that dim Revolutionary Bulletin itself, how she bears herself queenlike. Her answers are prompt, clear, often of Laconic brevity; resolution, which has grown contemptuous without ceasing to be dignified, veils itself in calm words. ' You persist, then, in denial?'—' My plan is not denial: it is the truth I have said, and I persist in that.' Scandalous Hébert has borne his testimony as to many things: as to one thing, concerning Marie-Antoinette and her little Son,—wherewith Human Speech had better not farther be soiled. She has answered Hébert; a Juryman begs to observe that she has not answered as to *this*. ' I have not answered,' she exclaims with noble emotion, ' because Nature refuses to answer such a charge brought against a Mother. I appeal to all the Mothers that are here.' Robespierre, when he heard of it, broke out into something almost like swearing at the brutish blockheadism of this

Hébert; on whose foul head his foul lie has recoiled. At four o'clock on Wednesday morning, after two days and two nights of interrogating, jury-charging, and other darkening of counsel, the result comes out : sentence of Death. 'Have you anything to say?' The Accused shook her head, without speech. Night's candles are burning out; and with her too Time is finishing, and it will be Eternity and Day. This Hall of Tinville's is dark, ill-lighted except where she stands. Silently she withdraws from it, to die.

Two Processions, or Royal Progresses, three-and-twenty years apart, have often struck us with a strange feeling of contrast. The first is of a beautiful Archduchess and Dauphiness, quitting her Mother's City, at the age of Fifteen; towards hopes such as no other Daughter of Eve then had : 'On the morrow', says Weber an eye-witness, 'the Dauphiness left Vienna. The whole city crowded out; at first with a sorrow which was silent. She appeared: you saw her sunk back into her carriage; her face bathed in tears; hiding her eyes now with her handkerchief, now with her hands; several times putting out her head to see yet again this Palace of her Fathers, whither she was to return no more. She motioned her regret, her gratitude to the good Nation, which was crowding here to bid her farewell. Then arose not only tears; but piercing cries, on all sides. Men and women alike abandoned themselves to such expression of their sorrow. It was an audible sound of wail, in the streets and avenues of Vienna. The last Courier that followed her disappeared, and the crowd melted away.'

The young imperial Maiden of Fifteen has now

become a worn discrowned Widow of Thirty-eight; grey before her time : this is the last Procession : ' Few minutes after the Trial ended, the drums were beating to arms in all Sections ; at sunrise the armed force was on foot, cannons getting placed at the extremities of the Bridges, in the Squares, Crossways, all along from the Palais de Justice to the Place de la Révolution. By ten o'clock, numerous patrols were circulating in the Streets ; thirty thousand foot and horse drawn up under arms. At eleven, Marie-Antoinette was brought out. She had on an undress of *piqué blanc* : she was led to the place of execution, in the same manner as an ordinary criminal ; bound, on a Cart ; accompanied by a Constitutional Priest in Lay dress ; escorted by numerous detachments of infantry and cavalry. These, and the double row of troops all along her road, she appeared to regard with indifference. On her countenance there was visible neither abashment nor pride. To the cries of *Vive la République* and *Down with Tyranny*, which attended her all the way, she seemed to pay no heed. She spoke little to her Confessor. The tricolor Streamers on the housetops occupied her attention, in the Streets du Roule and Saint-Honoré ; she also noticed the Inscriptions on the house-fronts. On reaching the Place de la Révolution, her looks turned towards the *Jardin National*, whilom Tuileries ; her face at that moment gave signs of lively emotion. She mounted the Scaffold with courage enough ; at a quarter past Twelve, her head fell ; the Executioner showed it to the people, amid universal long-continued cries of *Vive la République*.'

History of the French Revolution. 1837.

THE ELECTION OF ABBOT SAMSON

ACCORDINGLY our Prior assembles us in Chapter;
and, we adjuring him before God to do justly,
nominates, not by our selection, yet with our
assent, Twelve Monks, moderately satisfactory.
Of whom are Hugo Third-Prior, Brother Dennis
a venerable man, Walter the *Medicus*, Samson
Subsacrista, and other esteemed characters,—
though Willelmus *Sacrista*, of the red nose, too is
one. These shall proceed straightway to Waltham;
and there elect the Abbot as they may and can.
Monks are sworn to obedience; must not speak
too loud, under penalty of foot-gyves, limbo, and
bread-and-water: yet monks too would know what
it is they are obeying. The St. Edmundsbury
Community has no hustings, ballot-box, indeed
no open voting: yet by various vague manipula-
tions, pulse-feelings, we struggle to ascertain what
its virtual aim is, and succeed better or worse.

This question, however, rises; alas, a quite pre-
liminary question: Will the *Dominus Rex* allow
us to choose freely? It is to be hoped! Well, if
so, we agree to choose one of our own Convent.
If not, if the *Dominus Rex* will force a stranger on
us, we decide on demurring, the Prior and his
Twelve shall demur: we can appeal, plead, remon-
strate; appeal even to the Pope, but trust it will
not be necessary. Then there is this other question,
raised by Brother Samson: What if the Thirteen
should not themselves be able to agree? Brother
Samson *Subsacrista*, one remarks, is ready oftenest
with some question, some suggestion, that has
wisdom in it. Though a servant of servants, and

saying little, his words all tell, having sense in
them ; it seems by his light mainly that we steer
ourselves in this great dimness.

What if the Thirteen should not themselves be
able to agree ? Speak, Samson, and advise.—
Could not, hints Samson, Six of our venerablest
elders be chosen by us, a kind of electoral committee, here and now : of these, ' with their hand
on the Gospels, with their eye on the *Sacrosancta*,'
we take oath that they will do faithfully ; let
these, in secret and as before God, agree on Three
whom they reckon fittest ; write their names in
a Paper, and deliver the same sealed, forthwith,
to the Thirteen : one of those Three the Thirteen
shall fix on, if permitted. If not permitted, that
is to say, if the *Dominus Rex* force us to demur,—
the Paper shall be brought back unopened, and
publicly burned, that no man's secret bring him
into trouble.

So Samson advises, so we act ; wisely, in this
and in other crises of the business. Our electoral
committee, its eye on the Sacrosancta, is soon
named, soon sworn ; and we, striking-up the Fifth
Psalm, ' *Verba mea*,

> ' Give ear unto my words, O Lord,
>   My meditation weigh,'

march out chanting, and leave the Six to their
work in the Chapter here. Their work, before
long, they announce as finished : they, with their
eye on the Sacrosancta, imprecating the Lord to
weigh and witness their meditation, have fixed
on Three Names, and written them in this Sealed
Paper. Let Samson Subsacrista, general servant
of the party, take charge of it. On the morrow

morning, our Prior and his Twelve will be ready
to get under way.

This then is the ballot-box and electoral winnowing-machine they have at St. Edmundsbury:
a mind fixed on the Thrice Holy, an appeal to God
on high to witness their meditation: by far the
best, and indeed the only good electoral winnowing-machine,—if men have souls in them. Totally
worthless, it is true, and even hideous and poison-
ous, if men have no souls. But without soul, alas,
what winnowing-machine in human elections can
be of avail? We cannot get along without soul;
we stick fast, the mournfullest spectacle; and salt
itself will not save us!

On the morrow morning, accordingly, our Thirteen set forth; or rather our Prior and Eleven;
for Samson, as general servant of the party, has
to linger, settling many things. At length he too
gets upon the road; and, 'carrying the sealed
Paper in a leather pouch hung round his neck;
and *froccum bajulans in ulnis*' (thanks to thee,
Bozzy Jocelin), 'his frock-skirts looped over his
elbow,' showing substantial stern-works, tramps
stoutly along. Away across the Heath, not yet
of Newmarket and horse-jockeying; across your
Fleam-dike and Devil's-dike, no longer useful as
a Mercian East-Anglian boundary or bulwark:
continually towards Waltham, and the Bishop of
Winchester's House there, for his Majesty is in
that. Brother Samson, as purse-bearer, has the
reckoning always, when there is one, to pay;
'delays are numerous,' progress none of the
swiftest.

But, in the solitude of the Convent, Destiny

thus big and in her birthtime, what gossiping, what babbling, what dreaming of dreams! The secret of the Three our electoral elders alone know : some Abbot we shall have to govern us ; but which Abbot, oh, which! One Monk discerns in a vision of the night-watches, that we shall get an Abbot of our own body, without needing to demur : a prophet appeared to him clad all in white, and said, ' Ye shall have one of yours, and he will rage among you like a wolf, *saeviet ut lupus*.' Verily ! —then which of ours ? Another Monk now dreams : he has seen clearly which ; a certain Figure taller by head and shoulders than the other two, dressed in alb and *pallium*, and with the attitude of one about to fight ;—which tall Figure a wise Editor would rather not name at this stage of the business ! Enough that the vision is true : that Saint Edmund himself, pale and awful, seemed to rise from his Shrine, with naked feet, and say audibly, ' He, *ille*, shall veil my feet ' ; which part of the vision also proves true. Such guessing, visioning, dim perscrutation of the momentous future : the very clothmakers, old women, all townsfolk speak of it, ' and more than once it is reported in St. Edmundsbury, This one is elected ; and then, This one, and That other.' Who knows ?

But now, sure enough, at Waltham ' on the Second Sunday of Quadragesima ', which Dryas-dust declares to mean the 22nd day of February, year 1182, Thirteen St. Edmundsbury Monks are, at last, seen processioning towards the Winchester Manorhouse ; and, in some high Presence-chamber, and Hall of State, get access to Henry II in all his glory. What a Hall,—not imaginary in the least, but entirely real and indisputable, though so extremely dim to us; sunk in the deep distances of Night! The Winchester Manorhouse has fled bodily, like a Dream of the old Night; not Dryasdust himself can show a wreck of it. House and people, royal and episcopal, lords and varlets, where are they? Why *there*, I say, Seven Centuries off; sunk *so* far in the Night, there they *are*; peep through the blankets of the old Night, and thou wilt see! King Henry himself is visibly there; a vivid, noble-looking man, with grizzled beard, in glittering uncertain costume; with earls round him, and bishops, and dignitaries, in the like. The Hall is large, and has for one thing an altar near it,—chapel and altar adjoining it; but what gilt seats, carved tables, carpeting of rush-cloth, what arras-hangings, and huge fire of logs:—alas, it has Human Life in it; and is not that the grand miracle, in what hangings or costume soever?—

The *Dominus Rex*, benignantly receiving our Thirteen with their obeisance, and graciously declaring that he will strive to act for God's honour and the Church's good, commands, ' by the Bishop of Winchester and Geoffrey the Chancellor,'—*Galfridus Cancellarius*, Henry's and the Fair Rosamond's authentic Son present here!—commands, ' That they, the said Thirteen, do now withdraw, and fix upon Three from their own Monastery.' A work soon done; the Three hanging ready round Samson's neck, in that leather pouch of his. Breaking the seal, we find the names,—what think *ye* of it, ye higher dignitaries, thou indolent Prior, thou Willelmus *Sacrista* with the red bottle-nose?— the names, in this order: of Samson *Subsacrista*, of Roger the distressed Cellarer, of Hugo *Tertius-Prior*.

The higher dignitaries, all omitted here, 'flush suddenly red in the face'; but have nothing to say. One curious fact and question certainly is, How Hugo Third-Prior, who was of the electoral committee, came to nominate *himself* as one of the Three? A curious fact, which Hugo Third-Prior has never yet entirely explained, that I know of!—However, we return, and report to the King our Three names; merely altering the order; putting Samson last, as lowest of all. The King, at recitation of our Three, asks us: 'Who are they? Were they born in my domain? Totally unknown to me! You must nominate three others.' Whereupon Willelmus Sacrista says, 'Our Prior must be named, *quia caput nostrum est*, being already our head.' And the Prior responds, Willelmus Sacrista is a fit man, *bonus vir est*,'— for all his red nose. Tickle me, Toby, and I'll tickle thee! Venerable Dennis too is named; none in his conscience can say nay. There are now Six on our List. 'Well', said the King, 'they have done it swiftly, they! *Deus est cum eis.*' The Monks withdraw again; and Majesty revolves, for a little, with his *Pares* and *Episcopi*, Lords or 'Law-wards' and Soul-Overseers, the thoughts of the royal breast. The Monks wait silent in an outer room.

In short while, they are next ordered, To add yet another three; but not from their own Convent; from other Convents, 'for the honour of my kingdom.' Here,—what is to be done here? We will demur, if need be! We do name three, however, for the nonce: the Prior of St. Faith's, a good Monk of St. Neot's, a good Monk of St. Alban's; good men all; all made abbots and dignitaries since, at this hour. There are now Nine upon our List. What the thoughts of the Dominus Rex may be farther ? The Dominus Rex, thanking graciously, sends out word that we shall now strike off three. The three strangers are instantly struck off. Willelmus Sacrista adds, that he will of his own accord decline,—a touch of grace and respect for the *Sacrosancta*, even in Willelmus ! The King then orders us to strike off a couple more ; then yet one more : Hugo Third-Prior goes, and Roger *Cellerarius*, and venerable Monk Dennis ;— and now there remain on our List two only, Samson Subsacrista and the Prior.

Which of these two ? It were hard to say,—by Monks who may get themselves foot-gyved and thrown into limbo for speaking ! We humbly request that the Bishop of Winchester and Geoffrey the Chancellor may again enter, and help us to decide. 'Which do you want ?' asks the Bishop. Venerable Dennis made a speech, 'commending the persons of the Prior and Samson ; but always in the corner of his discourse, *in angulo sui sermonis*, brought Samson in.' 'I see !' said the Bishop : 'We are to understand that your Prior is somewhat remiss ; that you want to have him you call Samson for Abbot.' 'Either of them is good,' said venerable Dennis, almost trembling ; 'but we would have the better, if it pleased God.' 'Which of the two *do* you want ?' inquires the Bishop pointedly. 'Samson !' answered Dennis ; 'Samson !' echoed all of the rest that durst speak or echo anything : and Samson is reported to the King accordingly. His Majesty, advising of it for a moment, orders that Samson be brought in with the other Twelve.

The King's Majesty, looking at us somewhat sternly, then says : ' You present to me Samson ; I do not know him : had it been your Prior, whom I do know, I should have accepted him : however, I will now do as you wish. But have a care of yourselves. By the true eyes of God, *per veros oculos Dei*, if you manage badly, I will be upon you ! ' Samson, therefore, steps forward, kisses the King's feet ; but swiftly rises erect again, swiftly turns towards the altar, uplifting with the other Twelve, in clear tenor-note, the Fifty-first Psalm, ' *Miserere mei Deus,*

> 'After thy loving-kindness, Lord,
> Have mercy upon *me* ; '

with firm voice, firm step and head, no change in his countenance whatever. ' By God's eyes,' said the King, ' that one, I think, will govern the Abbey well.' By the same oath (charged to your Majesty's account), I too am precisely of that opinion ! It is some while since I fell in with a likelier man anywhere than this new Abbot Samson. Long life to him, and may the Lord *have* mercy on him as Abbot !

Thus, then, have the St. Edmundsbury Monks, without express ballot-box or other good winnowing-machine, contrived to accomplish the most important social feat a body of men can do, to winnow-out the man that is to govern them: and truly one sees not that, by any winnowing-machine whatever, they could have done it better. O ye kind Heavens, there is in every Nation and Community a *fittest*, a wisest, bravest, best; whom could we find and make King over us, all were in very truth well;—the best that God and Nature had permitted *us* to make it! By what art discover him? Will the Heavens in their pity teach us no art; for our need of him is great!

Ballot-boxes, Reform Bills, winnowing-machines: all these are good, or are not so good;—alas, brethren, how *can* these, I say, be other than inadequate, be other than failures, melancholy to behold? Dim all souls of men to the divine, the high and awful meaning of Human Worth and Truth, we shall never, by all the machinery in Birmingham, discover the True and Worthy. It is written, 'if we are ourselves valets, there shall exist no hero for us; we shall not know the hero when we see him';—we shall take the quack for a hero; and cry, audibly through all ballot-boxes and machinery whatsoever, Thou art he; be thou King over us!

What boots it? Seek only deceitful Speciosity, money with gilt carriages, 'fame' with newspaper-paragraphs, whatever name it bear, you will find only deceitful Speciosity; godlike Reality will be forever far from you. The Quack shall be legitimate inevitable King of you; no earthly machinery able to exclude the Quack. Ye shall be born thralls of the Quack, and suffer under him; till your hearts are near broken, and no French Revolution or Manchester Insurrection, or partial or universal volcanic combustions and explosions, never so many, can do more than 'change the *figure* of your Quack'; the essence of him remaining, for a time and times.—'How long, O Prophet?' say some, with a rather melancholy sneer. Alas, ye *un*prophetic, ever till this come about: Till deep misery, if nothing softer will, have driven you out of your Speciosities *into* your Sincerities; and you find that there either is a Godlike in the world, or else ye are an unintelligible madness; that there is a God, as well as a Mammon and a Devil, and a Genius of Luxuries and canting Dilettantisms and Vain Shows! How long that will be, compute for yourselves. My unhappy brothers!—

Past and Present. 1843.

BATTLE OF DUNBAR

THE small Town of Dunbar stands, high and windy, looking down over its herring-boats, over its grim old Castle now much honey-combed,— on one of those projecting rock-promontories with which that shore of the Frith of Forth is niched and vandyked, as far as the eye can reach. A beautiful sea; good land too, now that the plougher understands his trade; a grim niched barrier of whinstone sheltering it from the chafings and tumblings of the big blue German Ocean. Seaward St. Abb's Head, of whinstone, bounds your horizon to the east, not very far off; west, close by, is the deep bay, and fishy little village of Belhaven: the gloomy Bass and other rock-islets, and farther the Hills of Fife, and fore-shadows of the Highlands, are visible as you look seaward. From the bottom of Belhaven bay to that of the next seabight St. Abb's-ward, the Town and its environs form a peninsula. Along the base of which peninsula, ' not much above a mile and a half from sea to sea,' Oliver Cromwell's

Army, on Monday 2nd of September 1650, stands
ranked, with its tents and Town behind it,—in
very forlorn circumstances. This now is all the
ground that Oliver is lord of in Scotland. His
Ships lie in the offing, with biscuit and transport
for him; but visible elsewhere in the Earth no help.

Landward as you look from the Town of Dunbar
there rises, some short mile off, a dusky continent
of barren heath Hills; the Lammermoor, where
only mountain-sheep can be at home. The crossing of *which*, by any of its boggy passes, and
brawling stream-courses, no Army, hardly a solitary
Scotch Packman could attempt, in such weather.
To the edge of these Lammermoor Heights, David
Lesley has betaken himself; lies now along the
outmost spur of them,—a long Hill of considerable
height, which the Dunbar people call the Dun,
Doon, or sometimes for fashion's sake the Down,
adding to it the Teutonic *Hill* likewise, though
Dun itself in old Celtic signifies Hill. On this
Doon Hill lies David Lesley with the victorious
Scotch Army, upwards of Twenty-thousand strong;
with the Committees of Kirk and Estates, the chief
Dignitaries of the Country, and in fact the flower
of what the pure Covenant in this the Twelfth
year of its existence can still bring forth. There
lies he since Sunday night, on the top and slope
of this Doon Hill, with the impassable heath-
continents behind him; embraces, as within out-
spread tiger-claws, the base-line of Oliver's Dunbar
peninsula; waiting what Oliver will do. Cock-
burnspath with its ravines has been seized on
Oliver's left, and made impassable; behind
Oliver is the sea; in front of him Lesley, Doon
Hill, and the heath-continent of Lammermoor.

Lesley's force is of Three-and-twenty-thousand, in
spirits as of men chasing, Oliver's about half as
many, in spirits as of men chased. What is to
become of Oliver ? . . .

The base of Oliver's 'Dunbar Peninsula', as we
have called it (or Dunbar Pinfold where he is now
hemmed in, upon 'an entanglement very difficult'),
extends from Belhaven Bay on his right, to
Brocksmouth House on his left ; 'about a mile
and a half from sea to sea.' Brocksmouth House,
the Earl (now Duke) of Roxburgh's mansion,
which still stands there, his soldiers now occupy
as their extreme post on the left. As its name
indicates, it is the *mouth* or issue of a small Rivulet,
or *Burn*, called *Brock*, *Brocksburn* ; which, springing from the Lammermoor, and skirting David
Lesley's Doon Hill, finds its egress here into the
sea. The reader who would form an image to
himself of the great Tuesday 3rd of September
1650, at Dunbar, must note well this little *Burn*.
It runs in a deep grassy glen, which the South-
country Officers in those old Pamphlets describe
as a ' deep *ditch*, forty feet in depth, and about as
many in width ',—ditch dug out by the little
Brook itself, and carpeted with greensward, in the
course of long thousands of years. It runs pretty
close by the foot of Doon Hill ; forms, from this
point to the sea, the boundary of Oliver's position :
his force is arranged in battle-order along the left
bank of this Brocksburn, and its grassy glen ;
he is busied all Monday, he and his Officers, in
ranking them there. ' Before sunrise on Monday '
Lesley sent down his horse from the Hill-top, to
occupy the other side of this Brook ; ' about four
in the afternoon ' his train came down, his whole

Army gradually came down; and they now are
ranking themselves on the opposite side of Brocksburn,—on rather narrow ground; cornfields, but
swiftly sloping upwards to the steep of Doon Hill.
This goes on, in the wild showers and winds of
Monday 2nd September 1650, on both sides of the
Rivulet of Brock. Whoever will begin the attack,
must get across this Brook and its glen first;
a thing of much disadvantage.

Behind Oliver's ranks, between him and Dunbar,
stand his tents; sprinkled up and down, by
battalions, over the face of this 'Peninsula';
which is a low though very uneven tract of ground;
now in our time all yellow with wheat and barley
in the autumn season, but at that date only
partially tilled,—describable by Yorkshire Hodgson as a place of plashes and rough bent-grass;
terribly beaten by showery winds that day, so
that your tent will hardly stand. There was then
but one Farm-house on this tract, where now are
not a few: thither were Oliver's Cannon sent this
morning; they had at first been lodged 'in the
Church', an edifice standing then as now somewhat apart, 'at the south end of Dunbar.' We
have notice of only one other 'small house',
belike some poor shepherd's homestead, in Oliver's
tract of ground: it stands close by the Brock
Rivulet itself, and in the bottom of the little glen;
at a place where the banks of it flatten themselves
out into a slope passable for carts: this of course,
as the one 'pass' in that quarter, it is highly
important to seize. Pride and Lambert lodged
'six horse and fifteen foot' in this poor hut early
in the morning: Lesley's horse came across, and
drove them out; killing some and 'taking three

prisoners ' ;—and so got possession of this pass and hut ; but did not keep it. Among the three prisoners was one musketeer, 'a very stout man, though he has but a wooden arm,' and some iron hook at the end of it, poor fellow. He 'fired thrice', not without effect, with his wooden arm ; and was not taken without difficulty : a handfast stubborn man ; they carried him across to General Lesley to give some account of himself. In several of the old Pamphlets, which agree in all the details of it, this is what we read :

'General *David* Lesley (old Leven,' the other Lesley, ' being in the Castle of Edinburgh, as they relate[1]), asked this man, If the Enemy did intend to fight ? He replied, " What do you think we come here for ? We come for nothing else ! "— " Soldier," says Lesley, " how will you fight, when you have shipped half of your men, and all your great guns ? " The Soldier replied, " Sir, if you please to draw down your men, you shall find both men and great guns too ! " '—A most dogged handfast man, this with the wooden arm, and iron hook on it ! 'One of the Officers asked, How he durst answer the General so saucily ? He said, " I only answer the question put to me ! " ' Lesley sent him across, free again, by a trumpet : he made his way to Cromwell ; reported what had passed, and added doggedly, He for one had lost twenty shillings by the business,—plundered from him in this action. ' The Lord General gave him thereupon two pieces,' which I think are forty shillings ; and sent him away rejoicing.—This is

---

[1] Old Leven *is here*, if the Pamphlet knew ; but only as a volunteer and without command, though nominally still General-in-Chief.

the adventure at the ' pass ' by the shepherd's hut in the bottom of the glen, close by the Brocksburn itself.

And now farther, on the great scale, we are to remark very specially that there is just one other ' pass ' across the Brocksburn; and this is precisely where the London road now crosses it; about a mile east from the former pass, and perhaps two gunshots west from Brocksmouth House. There the great road then as now crosses the Burn of Brock; the steep grassy glen, or ' broad ditch forty feet deep ', flattening itself out here once more into a passable slope : passable, but still steep on the southern or Lesley side, still mounting up there, with considerable acclivity, into a high table-ground, out of which the Doon Hill, as outskirt of the Lammermoor, a short mile to your right, gradually gathers itself. There, at this ' pass ', on and about the present London road, as you discover after long dreary dim examining, took place the brunt or essential agony of the Battle of Dunbar long ago. Read in the extirct old Pamphlets, and ever again obstinately read, till some light rise in them, look even with unmilitary eyes at the ground as it now is, you do at last obtain small glimmerings of distinct features here and there,—which gradually coalesce into a kind of image for you ; and some spectrum of the Fact becomes visible, face to face, on you, grim and sad in the depths of the old dead Time. Yes, my travelling friends, vehiculating in gigs or otherwise over that piece of London road, you may say to yourselves, Here without monument is the grave of a valiant thing which was done under the Sun ; the footprint of a Hero, not yet quite undistinguishable, is here !—

'The Lord General about four o'clock,' say the old Pamphlets, 'went into the Town to take some refreshment,' a hasty late dinner, or early supper, whichever we may call it; 'and very soon returned back,'—having written Sir Arthur's Letter, I think, in the interim. Coursing about the field, with enough of things to order; walking at last with Lambert in the Park or Garden of Brocksmouth House, he discerns that Lesley is astir on the Hill-side; altering his position somewhat. That Lesley in fact is coming wholly down to the basis of the Hill, where his horse had been since sunrise: coming wholly down to the edge of the Brook and glen, among the sloping harvest-fields there; and also is bringing up his left wing of horse, most part of it, towards his right; edging himself, 'shogging,' as Oliver calls it, his whole line more and more to the right! His meaning is, to get hold of Brocksmouth House and the pass of the Brook there; after which it will be free to him to attack us when he will !— Lesley in fact considers, or at least the Committee of Estates and Kirk consider, that Oliver is lost; that, on the whole, he must not be left to retreat, but must be attacked and annihilated here. A vague story, due to Bishop Burnet, the watery source of many such, still circulates about the world, That it was the Kirk Committee who forced Lesley down against his will; that Oliver, at sight of it, exclaimed, 'The Lord hath delivered' &c. : which nobody is in the least bound to believe. It appears, from other quarters, that Lesley *was* advised or sanctioned in this attempt by the

Committee of Estates and Kirk, but also that he was by no means hard to advise; that, in fact, lying on the top of Doon Hill, shelterless in such weather, was no operation to spin out beyond necessity;—and that if anybody pressed too much upon him with advice to come down and fight, it was likeliest to be Royalist Civil Dignitaries, who had plagued him with their cavillings at his cunctations, at his 'secret fellow-feeling for the Sectarians and Regicides', ever since this War began. The poor Scotch Clergy have enough of their own to answer for in this business; let every back bear the burden that belongs to it. In a word, Lesley descends, has been descending all day, and 'shogs' himself to the right,—urged, I believe, by manifold counsel, and by the nature of the case; and, what is equally important for us, Oliver sees him, and sees through him, in this movement of his.

At sight of this movement, Oliver suggests to Lambert standing by him, Does it not give *us* an advantage, if we, instead of him, like to begin the attack? Here is the Enemy's right wing coming out to the open space, free to be attacked on any side; and the main-battle hampered in narrow sloping ground between Doon Hill and the Brook, has no room to manœuvre or assist: beat this right wing where it now stands; take it in flank and front with an overpowering force,—it is driven upon its own main-battle, the whole Army is beaten? Lambert eagerly assents, 'had meant to say the same thing.' Monk, who comes up at the moment, likewise assents; as the other Officers do, when the case is set before them. It is the plan resolved upon for battle. The attack shall begin to-morrow before dawn.

And so the soldiers stand to their arms, or lie
within instant reach of their arms, all night;
being upon an engagement very difficult indeed.
The night is wild and wet;—2nd of September
means 12th by our calendar: the Harvest Moon
wades deep among clouds of sleet and hail.
Whoever has a heart for prayer, let him pray now,
for the wrestle of death is at hand. Pray,—and
withal keep his powder dry! And be ready for
extremities, and quit himself like a man!—Thus
they pass the night; making that Dunbar Peninsula and Brock Rivulet long memorable to me.
We English have some tents; the Scots have
none. The hoarse sea moans bodeful, swinging
low and heavy against these whinstone bays;
the sea and the tempests are abroad, all else
asleep but we,—and there is One that rides on the
wings of the wind.

Towards three in the morning the Scotch foot,
by order of a Major-General say some, extinguish
their matches, all but two in a company; cower
under the corn-shocks, seeking some imperfect
shelter and sleep. Be wakeful, ye English; watch,
and pray, and keep your powder dry. About four
o'clock comes order to my puddingheaded York-
shire friend, that his regiment must mount and
march straightway; his and various other regi-
ments march, pouring swiftly to the left to
Brocksmouth House, to the Pass over the Brock.
With overpowering force let us storm the Scots
right wing there; beat that, and all is beaten
Major Hodgson riding along, heard, he says
'a Cornet praying in the night;' a company of
poor men, I think, making worship there, under
the void Heaven, before battle joined: Major

Hodgson, giving his charge to a brother Officer, turned aside to listen for a minute, and worship and pray along with them; haply his last prayer on this Earth, as it might prove to be. But no: this Cornet prayed with such effusion as was wonderful; and imparted strength to my York-shire friend, who strengthened his men by telling them of it. And the Heavens, in their mercy, I think, have opened us a way of deliverance!— The Moon gleams out, hard and blue, riding among hail-clouds; and over St. Abb's Head, a streak of dawn is rising.

And now is the hour when the attack should be, and no Lambert is yet here, he is ordering the line far to the right yet; and Oliver occasionally, in Hodgson's hearing, is impatient for him. The Scots too, on this wing, are awake; thinking to surprise us; there is their trumpet sounding, we heard it once; and Lambert, who was to lead the attack, is not here. The Lord General is impatient;—behold Lambert at last! The trum-pets peal, shattering with fierce clangour Night's silence; the cannons awaken along all the Line: ' The Lord of Hosts! The Lord of Hosts!' On, my brave ones, on!—

The dispute ' on this right wing was hot and stiff, for three quarters of an hour'. Plenty of fire, from fieldpieces, snaphances, matchlocks, entertains the Scotch main-battle across the Brock;—poor stiffened men, roused from the corn-shocks with their matches all out! But here on the right, their horse, ' with lancers in the front rank,' charge desperately; drive us back across the hollow of the Rivulet;—back a little; but the Lord gives us courage, and we storm home again, horse and foot, upon them, with a shock like tornado tempests; break them, beat them, drive them all adrift. 'Some fled towards Copperspath, but most across their own foot.' Their own poor foot, whose matches were hardly well alight yet! Poor men, it was a terrible awakening for them: fieldpieces and charge of foot across the Brocksburn; and now here is their own horse in mad panic trampling them to death. Above Three-thousand killed upon the place: 'I never saw such a charge of foot and horse,' says one; nor did I. Oliver was still near to Yorkshire Hodgson when the shock succeeded; Hodgson heard him say, 'They run! I profess they run!' And over St. Abb's Head and the German Ocean, just then, bursts the first gleam of the level Sun upon us, 'and I heard Nol say, in the words of the Psalmist, "Let God arise, let His enemies be scattered,"'—or in Rous's metre,

Let God arise, and scattered
Let all his enemies be;
And let all those that do him hate
Before his presence flee!

Even so. The Scotch Army is shivered to utter ruin; rushes in tumultuous wreck, hither, thither; to Belhaven, or, in their distraction, even to Dunbar; the chase goes as far as Haddington; led by Hacker. 'The Lord General made a halt,' says Hodgson, 'and sang the Hundred-and-seventeenth Psalm,' till our horse could gather for the chase. Hundred-and-seventeenth Psalm, at the foot of the Doon Hill; there we uplift it, to the tune of Bangor, or some still higher score, and roll it strong and great against the sky:

> O give ye praise unto the Lord,
>   All nati-ons that be ;
> Likewise ye people all, accord
>   His name to magnify !
>
> For great to-us-ward ever are
>   His lovingkindnesses ;
> His truth endures forevermore :
>   The Lord O do ye bless !

And now, to the chase again.

The Prisoners are Ten-thousand,—all the foot in a mass. Many Dignitaries are taken ; not a few are slain ; of whom see Printed Lists,—full of blunders. Provost Jaffray of Aberdeen, Member of the Scots Parliament, one of the Committee of Estates, was very nearly slain : a trooper's sword was in the air to sever him, but one cried, He is a man of consequence ; he can ransom himself !— and the trooper kept him prisoner. The first of the Scots Quakers, by and by ; and an official person much reconciled to Oliver. Ministers also of the Kirk Committee were slain ; two Ministers I find taken, poor Carstairs of Glasgow, poor Waugh of some other place,—of whom we shall transiently hear again.

General David Lesley, vigorous for flight as for other things, got to Edinburgh by nine o'clock ; poor old Leven, not so light of movement, did not get till two. Tragical enough. What a change since January 1644, when we marched out of this same Dunbar up to the knees in snow ! It was to help and save these very men that we then marched ; with the Covenant in all our hearts. We have stood by the letter of the Covenant ; fought for our Covenanted Stuart King as we could ;—they again, they stand by the substance of it, and have trampled us and the letter of it into this ruinous state!—Yes, my poor friends;— and now be wise, be taught! The letter of your Covenant, in fact, will never rally again in this world. The spirit and substance of it, please God, will never die in this or in any world!

Such is Dunbar Battle; which might also be called Dunbar Drove, for it was a frightful rout. Brought on by miscalculation; misunderstanding of the difference between substances and semblances;—by mismanagement, and the chance of war.

Letters and Speeches of Oliver Cromwell. 1845.

THOMAS BABINGTON, LORD MACAULAY

1800–1859

THE TRIAL OF WARREN HASTINGS

THE place was worthy of such a trial. It was the great hall of William Rufus, the hall which had resounded with acclamations at the inauguration of thirty kings, the hall which had witnessed the just sentence of Bacon and the just absolution of Somers, the hall where the eloquence of Strafford had for a moment awed and melted a victorious party inflamed with just resentment, the hall where Charles had confronted the High Court of Justice with the placid courage which has half redeemed his fame. Neither military nor civil pomp was wanting. The avenues were lined with grenadiers. The streets were kept clear by cavalry. The peers, robed in gold and ermine, were marshalled by the heralds under Garter King-at-arms. The judges in their vestments of state attended to give advice on points of law. Near a hundred and seventy lords, three-fourths of the Upper House as the Upper House then was, walked in solemn order from their usual place of assembling to the tribunal. The junior Baron present led the way, George Eliott, Lord Heath-field, recently ennobled for his memorable defence of Gibraltar against the fleets and armies of France and Spain. The long procession was closed by

the Duke of Norfolk, Earl Marshal of the realm,
by the great dignitaries, and by the brothers and
sons of the King. Last of all came the Prince of
Wales, conspicuous by his fine person and noble
bearing. The grey old walls were hung with
scarlet. The long galleries were crowded by an
audience such as has rarely excited the fears or
the emulation of an orator. There were gathered
together, from all parts of a great, free, enlightened,
and prosperous empire, grace and female loveliness,
wit and learning, the representatives of every
science and of every art. There were seated round
the Queen the fair-haired young daughters of the
house of Brunswick. There the Ambassadors of
great Kings and Commonwealths gazed with
admiration on a spectacle which no other country
in the world could present. There Siddons, in the
prime of her majestic beauty, looked with emotion
on a scene surpassing all the imitations of the
stage. There the historian of the Roman Empire
thought of the days when Cicero pleaded the cause
of Sicily against Verres, and when, before a senate
which still retained some show of freedom, Tacitus
thundered against the oppressor of Africa. There
were seen, side by side, the greatest painter and
the greatest scholar of the age. The spectacle had
allured Reynolds from that easel which has preserved to us the thoughtful foreheads of so many
writers and statesmen, and the sweet smiles of so
many noble matrons. It had induced Parr to
suspend his labours in that dark and profound
mine from which he had extracted a vast treasure
of erudition, a treasure too often buried in the
earth, too often paraded with injudicious and
inelegant ostentation, but still precious, massive,

and splendid. There appeared the voluptuous charms of her to whom the heir of the throne had in secret plighted his faith. There too was she, the beautiful mother of a beautiful race, the Saint Cecilia whose delicate features, lighted up by love and music, art has rescued from the common decay. There were the members of that brilliant society which quoted, criticized, and exchanged repartees, under the rich peacock hangings of Mrs. Montague. And there the ladies whose lips, more persuasive than those of Fox himself, had carried the Westminster election against palace and treasury, shone round Georgiana Duchess of Devonshire.

The Serjeants made proclamation. Hastings advanced to the bar, and bent his knee. The culprit was indeed not unworthy of that great presence. He had ruled an extensive and populous country, had made laws and treaties, had sent forth armies, had set up and pulled down princes. And in his high place he had so borne himself, that all had feared him, that most had loved him, and that hatred itself could deny him no title to glory, except virtue. He looked like a great man, and not like a bad man. A person small and emaciated, yet deriving dignity from a carriage which, while it indicated deference to the court, indicated also habitual self-possession and self-respect, a high and intellectual forehead, a brow pensive, but not gloomy, a mouth of inflexible decision, a face pale and worn, but serene, on which was written, as legibly as under the picture in the council-chamber at Calcutta, *Mens aequa in arduis* ; such was the aspect with which the great Proconsul presented himself to his judges.

His counsel accompanied him, men all of whom were afterwards raised by their talents and learning to the highest posts in their profession, the bold and strong-minded Law, afterwards Chief Justice of the King's Bench; the more humane and eloquent Dallas, afterwards Chief Justice of the Common Pleas; and Plomer who, near twenty years later, successfully conducted in the same high court the defence of Lord Melville, and subsequently became Vice-Chancellor and Master of the Rolls.

But neither the culprit nor his advocates attracted so much notice as the accusers. In the midst of the blaze of red drapery, a space had been fitted up with green benches and tables for the Commons. The managers, with Burke at their head, appeared in full dress. The collectors of gossip did not fail to remark that even Fox, generally so regardless of his appearance, had paid to the illustrious tribunal the compliment of wearing a bag and sword. Pitt had refused to be one of the conductors of the impeachment; and his commanding, copious, and sonorous eloquence was wanting to that great muster of various talents. Age and blindness had unfitted Lord North for the duties of a public prosecutor; and his friends were left without the help of his excellent sense, his tact and his urbanity. But in spite of the absence of these two distinguished members of the Lower House, the box in which the managers stood contained an array of speakers such as perhaps had not appeared together since the great age of Athenian eloquence. There were Fox and Sheridan, the English Demosthenes and the English Hyperides. There was Burke, ignorant, indeed, or negligent of the art of adapting his reasonings and his style to the capacity and taste of his hearers, but in amplitude of comprehension and richness of imagination superior to every orator, ancient or modern. There, with eyes reverentially fixed on Burke, appeared the finest gentleman of the age, his form developed by every manly exercise, his face beaming with intelligence and spirit, the ingenious, the chivalrous, the high-souled Windham. Nor, though surrounded by such men, did the youngest manager pass unnoticed. At an age when most of those who distinguish themselves in life are still contending for prizes and fellowships at college, he had won for himself a conspicuous place in Parliament. No advantage of fortune or connexion was wanting that could set off to the height his splendid talents and his unblemished honour. At twenty-three he had been thought worthy to be ranked with the veteran statesmen who appeared as the delegates of the British Commons, at the bar of the British nobility. All who stood at that bar, save him alone, are gone, culprit, advocates, accusers. To the generation which is now in the vigour of life, he is the sole representative of a great age which has passed away. But those who, within the last ten years, have listened with delight, till the morning sun shone on the tapestries of the House of Lords, to the lofty and animated eloquence of Charles Earl Grey, are able to form some estimate of the powers of a race of men among whom he was not the foremost.

Essay on Warren Hastings. 1841.

THE ACQUITTAL OF THE SEVEN BISHOPS

IT was dark before the jury retired to consider of their verdict. The night was a night of intense anxiety. Some letters are extant which were dispatched during that period of suspense, and which have therefore an interest of a peculiar kind. ' It is very late,' wrote the Papal Nuncio ; ' and the decision is not yet known. The Judges and the culprits have gone to their own homes. The jury remain together. To-morrow we shall learn the event of this great struggle.'

The solicitor for the Bishops sate up all night with a body of servants on the stairs leading to the room where the jury was consulting. It was absolutely necessary to watch the officers who watched the doors ; for those officers were supposed to be in the interest of the crown, and might, if not carefully observed, have furnished a courtly juryman with food, which would have enabled him to starve out the other eleven. Strict guard was therefore kept. Not even a candle to light a pipe was permitted to enter. Some basins of water for washing were suffered to pass at about four in the morning. The jurymen, raging with thirst, soon lapped up the whole. Great numbers of people walked the neighbouring streets till dawn. Every hour a messenger came from Whitehall to know what was passing. Voices, high in altercation, were repeatedly heard within the room : but nothing certain was known.

At first nine were for acquitting and three for convicting. Two of the minority soon gave way : but Arnold was obstinate. Thomas Austin, a country gentleman of great estate, who had paid close attention to the evidence and speeches, and had taken full notes, wished to argue the question. Arnold declined. He was not used, he doggedly said, to reasoning and debating. His conscience was not satisfied; and he should not acquit the Bishops. 'If you come to that,' said Austin, 'look at me. I am the largest and strongest of the twelve; and before I find such a petition as this a libel, here I will stay till I am no bigger than a tobacco pipe.' It was six in the morning before Arnold yielded. It was soon known that the jury were agreed: but what the verdict would be was still a secret.

At ten the Court again met. The crowd was greater than ever. The jury appeared in their box; and there was a breathless stillness.

Sir Samuel Astry spoke. 'Do you find the defendants, or any of them, guilty of the misdemeanour whereof they are impeached, or not guilty?' Sir Roger Langley answered, 'Not guilty.' As the words were uttered, Halifax sprang up and waved his hat. At that signal, benches and galleries raised a shout. In a moment ten thousand persons, who crowded the great hall, replied with a still louder shout, which made the old oaken roof crack; and in another moment the innumerable throng without set up a third huzza, which was heard at Temple Bar. The boats which covered the Thames gave an answering cheer. A peal of gunpowder was heard on the water, and another, and another; and so, in a few moments, the glad tidings went flying past the Savoy and the Friars to London Bridge, and to the forest of masts below. As the news spread, streets and squares, market places and coffee-houses, broke forth into acclamations. Yet were the acclamations less strange than the weeping. For the feelings of men had been wound up to such a point that at length the stern English nature, so little used to outward signs of emotion, gave way, and thousands sobbed aloud for very joy. Meanwhile, from the outskirts of the multitude, horsemen were spurring off to bear along all the great roads intelligence of the victory of our Church and nation. Yet not even that astounding explosion could awe the bitter and intrepid spirit of the Solicitor. Striving to make himself heard above the din, he called on the Judges to commit those who had violated, by clamour, the dignity of a court of justice. One of the rejoicing populace was seized. But the tribunal felt that it would be absurd to punish a single individual for an offence common to hundreds of thousands, and dismissed him with a gentle reprimand. . . .

That joyful day was followed by a not less joyful evening. The Bishops, and some of their most respectable friends, in vain exerted themselves to prevent tumultuous demonstrations of public feeling. Never within the memory of the oldest, not even on that night on which it was known through London that the army of Scotland had declared for a free Parliament, had the streets been in such a glare with bonfires. Round every bonfire crowds were drinking good health to the Bishops and confusion to the Papists. The windows were lighted with rows of candles. Each row consisted of seven; and the taper in the centre, which was taller than the rest, represented the Primate. The noise of rockets, squibs, and

firearms, was incessant. One huge pile of faggots
blazed right in front of the great gate of Whitehall.
Others were lighted before the doors of Roman
Catholic peers. Lord Arundell of Wardour wisely
quieted the mob with a little money: but at
Salisbury House in the Strand an attempt at
resistance was made. Lord Salisbury's servants
sallied out and fired: but they killed only the
unfortunate beadle of the parish, who had come
thither to put out the fire; and they were soon
routed and driven back into the house. None of
the spectacles of that night interested the common
people so much as one with which they had, a few
years before, been familiar, and which they now,
after a long interval, enjoyed once more, the
burning of the Pope. This once familiar pageant
is known to our generation only by descriptions
and engravings. A figure, by no means resembling
those rude representations of Guy Fawkes which
are still paraded on the fifth of November, but
made of wax with some skill, and adorned at no
small expense with robes and a tiara, was mounted
on a chair resembling that in which the Bishops
of Rome are still, on some great festivals, borne
through St. Peter's Church to the high altar. His
Holiness was generally accompanied by a train
of Cardinals and Jesuits. At his ear stood a
buffoon disguised as a devil with horns and tail.
No rich and zealous Protestant grudged his guinea
on such an occasion, and, if rumour could be
trusted, the cost of the procession was sometimes
not less than a thousand pounds. After the Pope
had been borne some time in state over the heads
of the multitude, he was committed to the flames
with loud acclamations. In the time of the

popularity of Oates and Shaftesbury, this show
was exhibited annually in Fleet Street before the
windows of the Whig Club on the anniversary of
the birth of Queen Elizabeth. Such was the
celebrity of these grotesque rites, that Barillon once
risked his life in order to peep at them from
a hiding-place. But, from the day when the
Rye House Plot was discovered, till the day of the
acquittal of the Bishops, the ceremony had been
disused. Now, however, several Popes made
their appearance in different parts of London.
The Nuncio was much shocked; and the King
was more hurt by this insult to his Church than by
all the other affronts which he had received. The
magistrates, however, could do nothing. The
Sunday had dawned, and the bells of the parish
churches were ringing for early prayers, before the
fires began to languish and the crowds to disperse.
A proclamation was speedily put forth against the
rioters. Many of them, mostly young apprentices,
were apprehended; but the bills were thrown out
at the Middlesex sessions. The magistrates, many
of whom were Roman Catholics, expostulated
with the grand jury and sent them three or four
times back, but to no purpose.

Meanwhile the glad tidings were flying to every
part of the kingdom, and were everywhere received
with rapture. Gloucester, Bedford, and Lichfield,
were among the places which were distinguished
by peculiar zeal: but Bristol and Norwich, which
stood nearest to London in population and wealth,
approached nearest to London in enthusiasm on
this joyful occasion.

History of England, vol. ii.   1849.

WILLIAM MAKEPEACE THACKERAY

1811–1863

RETURN OF RAWDON CRAWLEY FROM
THE SPUNGING-HOUSE

FRIEND Rawdon drove on then to Mr. Moss's mansion in Cursitor Street, and was duly inducted into that dismal place of hospitality. Morning was breaking over the cheerful house-tops of Chancery Lane as the rattling cab woke up the echoes there. A little pink-eyed Jew-boy, with a head as ruddy as the rising morn, let the party into the house, and Rawdon was welcomed to the ground-floor apartments by Mr. Moss, his travelling companion and host, who cheerfully asked him if he would like a glass of something warm after his drive.

The colonel was not so depressed as some mortals would be, who, quitting a palace and a *placens uxor*, find themselves barred into a spunging-house, for, if the truth must be told, he had been a lodger at Mr. Moss's establishment once or twice before. We have not thought it necessary in the previous course of this narrative to mention these trivial little domestic incidents : but the reader may be assured that they can't unfrequently occur in the life of a man who lives on nothing a year.

Upon his first visit to Mr. Moss, the colonel,

then a bachelor, had been liberated by the generosity of his aunt; on the second mishap, little Becky, with the greatest spirit and kindness, had borrowed a sum of money from Lord Southdown, and had coaxed her husband's creditor (who was her shawl, velvet-gown, lace pocket-handkerchief, trinket, and gimcrack purveyor, indeed) to take a portion of the sum claimed, and Rawdon's promissory note for the remainder: so on both these occasions the capture and release had been conducted with the utmost gallantry on all sides, and Moss and the colonel were therefore on the very best of terms.

'You'll find your old bed, colonel, and everything comfortable,' that gentleman said, 'as I may honestly say. You may be pretty sure its kep aired, and by the best of company, too. It was slep in the night afore last by the Honourable Capting Famish, of the Fiftieth Dragoons, whose mar took him out, after a fortnight, jest to punish him, she said. But, Law bless you, I promise you, he punished my champagne, and had a party ere every night—reglar tip-top swells, down from the clubs and the West End—Capting Ragg, the Honourable Deuceace, who lives in the Temple, and some fellers as knows a good glass of wine, I warrant you. I've got a Doctor of Diwinity upstairs, five gents in the coffee-room, and Mrs. Moss has a tably-dy-hoty at half-past five, and a little cards or music afterwards, when we shall be most happy to see you.'

'I'll ring, when I want anything,' said Rawdon, and went quietly to his bedroom. He was an old soldier, we have said, and not to be disturbed by any little shocks of fate. A weaker man would have sent off a letter to his wife on the instant of his capture. ' But what is the use of disturbing her night's rest ? ' thought Rawdon. ' She won't know whether I am in my room or not. It will be time enough to write to her when she has had her sleep out, and I have had mine. It's only a hundred-and-seventy, and the deuce is in it if we can't raise that.' And so, thinking about little Rawdon (whom he would not have know that he was in such a queer place), the colonel turned into the bed lately occupied by Captain Famish, and fell asleep. It was ten o'clock when he woke up, and the ruddy-headed youth brought him, with conscious pride, a fine silver dressing-case, wherewith he might perform the operation of shaving. Indeed Mr. Moss's house, though somewhat dirty, was splendid throughout. There were dirty trays, and wine-coolers *en permanence* on the sideboard, huge dirty gilt cornices, with dingy yellow satin hangings to the barred windows which looked into Cursitor Street—vast and dirty gilt picture-frames surrounding pieces sporting and sacred, all of which works were by the greatest masters ; and fetched the greatest prices, too, in the bill transactions, in the course of which they were sold and bought over and over again. The colonel's breakfast was served to him in the same dingy and gorgeous plated ware. Miss Moss, a dark-eyed maid in curl-papers appeared with the teapot, and, smiling, asked the colonel how he had slept ? and she brought him in the *Morning Post*, with the names of all the great people who had figured at Lord Steyne's entertainment the night before. It contained a brilliant account of the festivities, and of the beautiful and accomplished Mrs. Rawdon Crawley's admirable personifications.

After a lively chat with this lady (who sat on the edge of the breakfast-table in an easy attitude displaying the drapery of her stocking and an ex-white satin shoe, which was down at heel), Colonel Crawley called for pens and ink, and paper ; and being asked how many sheets, chose one which was brought to him between Miss Moss's own finger and thumb. Many a sheet had that dark-eyed damsel brought in; many a poor fellow had scrawled and blotted hurried lines of entreaty, and paced up and down that awful room until his messenger brought back the reply. Poor men always use messengers instead of the post. Who has not had their letters with the wafers wet, and the announcement that a person is waiting in the hall ?

Now on the score of his application, Rawdon had not many misgivings.

DEAR BECKY (Rawdon wrote), *I hope you slept well.* Don't be *frightened* if I don't bring you in your *coffy.* Last night as I was coming home smoking, I met with an *accadent.* I was *nabbed* by Moss of Cursitor Street—from whose *gilt and splendid parler* I write this—the same that had me this time two years. Miss Moss brought in my tea —she is grown very *fat,* and as usual, had *her stockens down at heal.*

It's Nathan's business—a hundred-and-fifty—with costs hundred-and-seventy. Please send me my desk and some *cloths*—I'm in pumps and a white tye (something like Miss M.'s stockings)—I've seventy in it. And as soon as you get this, Drive to Nathan's—offer him seventy-five down and ask *him to renew*—say I'll take wine—we may as well have some dinner sherry; but not *picturs,* they're too dear.

If he won't stand it. Take my ticker and such of your things as you can *spare,* and send them to Balls—we must, of coarse, have the sum to-night. It won't do to let it stand over, as to-morrow's Sunday ; the beds here are not very *clean,* and there may be other things out against me— I'm glad it an't Rawdon's Saturday for coming home. God bless you.   Yours in haste, R. C.

P.S.—Make haste and come.

This letter, sealed with a wafer, was dispatched by one of the messengers who are always hanging about Mr. Moss's establishment ; and Rawdon, having seen him depart, went out in the courtyard, and smoked his cigar with a tolerably easy mind— in spite of the bars overhead ; for Mr. Moss's courtyard is railed in like a cage, lest the gentlemen who are boarding with him should take a fancy to escape from his hospitality.

Three hours, he calculated, would be the utmost time required, before Becky should arrive and open his prison doors : and he passed these pretty cheerfully in smoking, in reading the paper, and in the coffee-room with an acquaintance, Captain Walker, who happened to be there, and with whom he cut for sixpences for some hours, with pretty equal luck on either side.

But the day passed away and no messenger returned,—no Becky. Mr. Moss's tably-de-hoty was served at the appointed hour of half-past five, when such of the gentlemen lodging in the house as could afford to pay for the banquet, came and partook of it in the splendid front parlour before described, and with which Mr. Crawley's tem- porary lodging communicated, when Miss M. (Miss Hem, as her papa called her) appeared without the curl-papers of the morning, and Mrs. Hem did the honours of a prime boiled leg of mutton and turnips, of which the colonel ate with a very faint appetite. Asked whether he would

' stand ' a bottle of champagne for the company,
he consented, and the ladies drank to his 'ealth,
and Mr. Moss, in the most polite manner, ' looked
towards him '.

In the midst of this repast, however, the door-
bell was heard,—young Moss of the ruddy hair,
rose up with the keys and answered the summons,
and coming back, told the colonel that the messenger had returned with a bag, a desk, and a letter,
which he gave him. ' No ceremony, colonel,
I beg,' said Mrs. Moss, with a wave of her hand,
and he opened the letter rather tremulously.—It
was a beautiful letter, highly scented, on a pink
paper, and with a light green seal.

MON PAUVRE CHER PETIT (Mrs. Crawley wrote), I could
not sleep *one wink* for thinking of what had become of
my odious old monstre : and only got to rest in the morning after sending for Mr. Blench (for I was in a fever),
who gave me a composing draught and left orders with
Finette that I should be disturbed *on no account.*   So that
my poor old man's messenger, who had *bien mauvaise mine,*
Finette says, and *sentait le Genièvre,* remained in the hall
for some hours waiting my bell.   You may fancy my state
when I read your poor dear old ill-spelt letter.

Ill as I was, I instantly called for the carriage, and as
soon as I was dressed (though I couldn't drink a drop of
chocolate—I assure you I couldn't without my *monstre*
to bring it to me), I drove *ventre à terre* to Nathan's.
I saw him—I wept—I cried—I fell at his odious knees.
Nothing would mollify the horrid man.   He would have
all the money, he said, or keep my poor *monstre* in prison.
I drove home with the intention of paying that *triste visite
chez mon oncle* (when every trinket I have should be at your
disposal though they would not fetch a hundred pounds,
for some, you know, are with *ce cher oncle* already), and
found Milor there with the Bulgarian old sheep-faced
monster, who had come to compliment me upon last night's
performances.   Paddington came in, too, drawling and lisp-
ing and twiddling his hair; so did Champignac, and his chef

—everybody with *foison* of compliments and pretty speeches
—plaguing poor me, who longed to be rid of them, and was
thinking *every moment of the time* of *mon pauvre prisonnier.*

When they were gone, I went down on my knees to
Milor; told him we were going to pawn everything, and
begged and prayed him to give me two hundred pounds.
He pish'd and psha'd in a fury—told me not to be such
a fool as to pawn—and said he would see whether he could
lend me the money. At last he went away, promising that
he would send it me in the morning: when I will bring it
to my poor old monster with a kiss from his affectionate

BECKY.

I am writing in bed. Oh, I have such a headache and
such a heartache!

When Rawdon read over this letter, he turned
so red and looked so savage that the company at
the table d'hôte easily perceived that bad news
had reached him. All his suspicions, which he
had been trying to banish, returned upon him.
She could not even go out and sell her trinkets to
free him. She could laugh and talk about compliments paid to her, whilst he was in prison.
Who had put him there? Wenham had walked
with him. Was there . . . He could hardly bear
to think of what he suspected. Leaving the room
hurriedly, he ran into his own—opened his desk,
wrote two hurried lines, which he directed to
Sir Pitt or Lady Crawley, and bade the messenger
carry them at once to Gaunt Street, bidding him
to take a cab, and promising him a guinea if he
was back in an hour.

In the note he besought his dear brother and
sister, for the sake of God; for the sake of his
dear child and his honour; to come to him and
relieve him from his difficulty. He was in prison:
he wanted a hundred pounds to set him free—he
entreated them to come to him.

He went back to the dining-room after dispatching his messenger, and called for more wine. He laughed and talked with a strange boisterousness, as the people thought. Sometimes he laughed madly at his own fears, and went on drinking for an hour; listening all the while for the carriage which was to bring his fate back.

At the expiration of that time, wheels were heard whirling up to the gate—the young janitor went out with his gate-keys. It was a lady whom he let in at the bailiff's door.

'Colonel Crawley,' she said, trembling very much. He with a knowing look, locked the outer door upon her—then unlocked and opened the inner one, and calling out, 'Colonel, you're wanted,' led her into the back parlour, which he occupied.

Rawdon came in from the dining-parlour where all those people were carousing, into his back-room; a flare of coarse light following him into the apartment where the lady stood, still very nervous.

'It is I, Rawdon,' she said, in a timid voice, which she strove to render cheerful. 'It is Jane.' Rawdon was quite overcome by that kind voice and presence. He ran up to her—caught her in his arms—gasped out some inarticulate words of thanks, and fairly sobbed on her shoulder. She did not know the cause of his emotion.

The bills of Mr. Moss were quickly settled, perhaps to the disappointment of that gentleman, who had counted on having the colonel as his guest over Sunday at least; and Jane, with beaming smiles and happiness in her eyes, carried away Rawdon from the bailiff's house, and they went homewards in the cab in which she had hastened to his release. ' Pitt was gone to a Parliamentary dinner,' she said, ' when Rawdon's note came, and so, dear Rawdon, I—I came myself ; ' and she put her kind hand in his. Perhaps it was well for Rawdon Crawley that Pitt was away at that dinner. Rawdon thanked his sister a hundred times, and with an ardour of gratitude which touched and almost alarmed that soft-hearted woman. ' Oh,' said he, in his rude, artless way, ' you—you don't know how I'm changed since I've known you, and—and little Rawdy. I—I'd like to change somehow. You see I want—I want—to be——.'—He did not finish the sentence, but she could interpret it. And that night after he left her, and as she sat by her own little boy's bed, she prayed humbly for that poor wayworn sinner.

Rawdon left her and walked home rapidly. It was nine o'clock at night. He ran across the streets, and the great squares of Vanity Fair, and at length came up breathless opposite his own house. He started back and fell against the railings, trembling as he looked up. The drawing-room windows were blazing with light. She had said that she was in bed and ill. He stood there for some time, the light from the rooms on his pale face.

He took out his door-key and let himself into the house. He could hear laughter in the upper rooms. He was in the ball-dress in which he had been captured the night before. He went silently up the stairs ; leaning against the banisters at the stair-head.—Nobody was stirring in the house besides—all the servants had been sent away. Rawdon heard laughter within—laughter and singing. Becky was singing a snatch of the song of the night before; a hoarse voice shouted, 'Brava! Brava!'—it was Lord Steyne's.

Rawdon opened the door and went in. A little table with a dinner was laid out—and wine and plate. Steyne was hanging over the sofa on which Becky sat. The wretched woman was in a brilliant full toilette, her arms and all her fingers sparkling with bracelets and rings; and the brilliants on her breast which Steyne had given her. He had her hand in his, and was bowing over it to kiss it, when Becky started up with a faint scream as she caught sight of Rawdon's white face. At the next instant she tried a smile, a horrid smile, as if to welcome her husband: and Steyne rose up, grinding his teeth, pale, and with fury in his looks.

He, too, attempted a laugh—and came forward holding out his hand. 'What, come back! How d'ye do, Crawley?' he said, the nerves of his mouth twitching as he tried to grin at the intruder.

There was that in Rawdon's face which caused Becky to fling herself before him. 'I am innocent, Rawdon,' she said; 'before God, I am innocent.' She clung hold of his coat, of his hands; her own were all covered with serpents, and rings, and baubles. 'I am innocent.—Say I am innocent,' she said to Lord Steyne.

He thought a trap had been laid for him, and was as furious with the wife as with the husband. 'You innocent! Damn you,' he screamed out. 'You innocent! Why, every trinket you have on your body is paid for by me. I have given you thousands of pounds which this fellow has spent, and for which he has sold you. Innocent, by

——! You're as innocent as your mother, the ballet-girl, and your husband the bully. Don't think to frighten me as you have done others. Make way, sir, and let me pass;' and Lord Steyne seized up his hat, and, with flame in his eyes, and looking his enemy fiercely in the face, marched upon him, never for a moment doubting that the other would give way.

But Rawdon Crawley springing out, seized him by the neckcloth, until Steyne, almost strangled, writhed, and bent under his arm. 'You lie, you dog!' said Rawdon. 'You lie, you coward and villain!' And he struck the peer twice over the face with his open hand, and flung him bleeding to the ground. It was all done before Rebecca could interpose. She stood there trembling before him. She admired her husband, strong, brave, and victorious.

'Come here,' he said.—She came up at once.

'Take off those things.'—She began, trembling, pulling the jewels from her arms, and the rings from her shaking fingers, and held them all in a heap, quivering and looking up at him. 'Throw them down,' he said, and she dropped them. He tore the diamond ornament out of her breast, and flung it at Lord Steyne. It cut him on his bald forehead. Steyne wore the scar to his dying day.

'Come upstairs,' Rawdon said to his wife. 'Don't kill me, Rawdon,' she said. He laughed savagely.—'I want to see if that man lies about the money as he has about me. Has he given you any?'

'No,' said Rebecca, 'that is——'

'Give me your keys,' Rawdon answered, and they went out together.

Rebecca gave him all the keys but one : and she was in hopes that he would not have remarked the absence of that. It belonged to the little desk which Amelia had given her in early days, and which she kept in a secret place. But Rawdon flung open boxes and wardrobes, throwing the multifarious trumpery of their contents here and there, and at last he found the desk. The woman was forced to open it. It contained papers, love-letters many years old—all sorts of small trinkets and woman's memoranda. And it contained a pocket-book with banknotes. Some of these were dated ten years back, too, and one was quite a fresh one—a note for a thousand pounds which Lord Steyne had given her.

' Did he give you this ? ' Rawdon said.

' Yes,' Rebecca answered.

' I'll send it to him to-day,' Rawdon said (for day had dawned again, and many hours had passed in this search), ' and I will pay Briggs, who was kind to the boy, and some of the debts. You will let me know where I shall send the rest to you. You might have spared me a hundred pounds, Becky, out of all this—I have always shared with you.'

' I am innocent,' said Becky. And he left her without another word.

Vanity Fair. 1848.

COLONEL ESMOND BREAKS HIS SWORD

As we were talking, Castlewood entered the
room with a disturbed air.

'What news, Frank?' says the colonel, 'is
Mr. George coming at last?'

'Damn him, look here!' says Castlewood,
holding out a paper. 'I found it in the book—the
what you call it, *Eikum Basilikum*,—that villain
Martin put it there—he said his young mistress
bade him. It was directed to me, but it was
meant for him I know, and I broke the seal and
read it.'

The whole assembly of officers seemed to swim
away before Esmond's eyes as he read the paper;
all that was written on it was :—'Beatrix Esmond
is sent away to prison, to Castlewood, where she
will pray for happier days.'

'Can you guess where he is?' says Castlewood.

'Yes,' says Colonel Esmond. He knew full
well; Frank knew full well: our instinct told
whither that traitor had fled.

He had courage to turn to the company and
say, 'Gentlemen, I fear very much that Mr.
George will not be here to-day; something hath
happened—and—and—I very much fear some
accident may befall him, which must keep him
out of the way. Having had your noon's draught,
you had best pay the reckoning and go home;
there can be no game where there is no one to
play it.'

Some of the gentlemen went away without a
word, others called to pay their duty to her
Majesty and ask for her health. The little army

disappeared into the darkness out of which it had been called; there had been no writings, no paper to implicate any man. Some few officers and members of Parliament had been invited over night to breakfast at the 'King's Arms', at Kensington; and they had called for their bill and gone home.

'Does my mistress know of this?' Esmond asked of Frank, as they walked along.

'My mother found the letter in the book, on the toilet-table. She had writ it ere she had left home,' Frank said. 'Mother met her on the stairs, with her hand upon the door, trying to enter, and never left her after that till she went away. He did not think of looking at it there, nor had Martin the chance of telling him. I believe the poor devil meant no harm, though I half killed him; he thought 'twas to Beatrix's brother he was bringing the letter.'

Frank never said a word of reproach to me, for having brought the villain amongst us. As we knocked at the door I said, 'When will the horses be ready?' Frank pointed with his cane, they were turning the street that moment.

We went up and bade adieu to our mistress; she was in a dreadful state of agitation by this time, and that bishop was with her whose company she was so fond of.

'Did you tell him, my lord,' says Esmond, 'that Beatrix was at Castlewood?' The bishop blushed and stammered: 'Well,' says he, 'I——'

'You served the villain right,' broke out Mr. Esmond, 'and he has lost a crown by what you told him.'

My mistress turned quite white, 'Henry, Henry,' says she, 'do not kill him!'

'It may not be too late,' says Esmond; 'he may not have gone to Castlewood; pray God, it is not too late.' The bishop was breaking out with some *banales* phrases about loyalty and the sacredness of the sovereign's person; but Esmond sternly bade him hold his tongue, burn all papers, and take care of Lady Castlewood; and in five minutes he and Frank were in the saddle, John Lockwood behind them, riding towards Castlewood at a rapid pace.

We were just got to Alton, when who should meet us but old Lockwood, the porter from Castlewood, John's father, walking by the side of the Hexham flying-coach, who slept the night at Alton. Lockwood said his young mistress had arrived at home on Wednesday night, and this morning, Friday, had dispatched him with a packet for my lady at Kensington, saying the letter was of great importance.

We took the freedom to break it, while Lockwood stared with wonder, and cried out his 'Lord bless me's,' and 'Who'd a thought it's', at the sight of his young lord, whom he had not seen these seven years.

The packet from Beatrix contained no news of importance at all. It was written in a jocular strain, affecting to make light of her captivity. She asked whether she might have leave to visit Mrs. Tusher, or to walk beyond the court and the garden-wall. She gave news of the peacocks, and a fawn she had there. She bade her mother send her certain gowns and smocks by old Lockwood; she sent her duty to a certain person, if certain

other persons permitted her to take such a freedom ; how that, as she was not able to play cards
with him, she hoped he would read good books,
such as Doctor Atterbury's sermons and *Eikon
Basilike* : she was going to read good books : she
thought her pretty mamma would like to know
she was not crying her eyes out.

'Who is in the house besides you, Lockwood ? '
says the colonel.

'There be the laundry-maid, and the kitchen-
maid, Madam Beatrix's maid, the man from
London, and that be all ; and he sleepeth in my
lodge away from the maids,' says old Lockwood.

Esmond scribbled a line with a pencil on the
note, giving it to the old man, and bidding him
go on to his lady. We knew why Beatrix had
been so dutiful on a sudden, and why she spoke of
Eikon Basilike. She writ this letter to put the
prince on the scent, and the porter out of the way.

'We have a fine moonlight night for riding on,'
says Esmond ; 'Frank, we may reach Castlewood
in time yet.' All the way along they made
inquiries at the post-houses, when a tall young
gentleman in a grey suit, with a light-brown
periwig, just the colour of my Lord's, had been
seen to pass. He had set off at six that morning,
and we at three in the afternoon. He rode almost
as quickly as we had done ; he was seven hours
ahead of us still when we reached the last stage.

We rode over Castlewood Downs before the
breaking of dawn. We passed the very spot
where the car was upset fourteen years since, and
Mohun lay. The village was not up yet, nor the
forge lighted, as we rode through it, passing by the
elms, where the rooks were still roosting, and by

the church, and over the bridge. We got off our horses at the bridge and walked up to the gate.

'If she is safe,' says Frank, trembling, and his honest eyes filling with tears, 'a silver statue to Our Lady!' He was going to rattle at the great iron knocker on the oak gate; but Esmond stopped his kinsman's hand. He had his own fears, his own hopes, his own despairs and griefs, too; but he spoke not a word of these to his companion, or showed any signs of emotion.

He went and tapped at the little window at the porter's lodge, gently, but repeatedly, until the man came to the bars.

'Who's there?' says he, looking out; it was the servant from Kensington.

'My Lord Castlewood and Colonel Esmond,' we said, from below. 'Open the gate and let us in without any noise.'

'My Lord Castlewood?' says the other; 'my lord's here, and in bed.'

'Open, d——n you,' says Castlewood, with a curse.

'I shall open to no one,' says the man, shutting the glass window as Frank drew a pistol. He would have fired at the porter, but Esmond again held his hand.

'There are more ways than one,' says he, 'of entering such a great house as this.' Frank grumbled that the west gate was half a mile round. 'But I know of a way that's not a hundred yards off,' says Mr. Esmond; and leading his kinsman close along the wall, and by the shrubs, which had now grown thick on what had been an old moat about the house, they came to the buttress, at the side of which the little window was, which was Father Holt's private door. Esmond climbed up to this easily, broke a pane that had been mended, and touched the spring inside, and the two gentlemen passed in that way, treading as lightly as they could; and so going through the passage into the court, over which the dawn was now reddening, and where the fountain plashed in the silence.

They sped instantly to the porter's lodge, where the fellow had not fastened his door that led into the court; and pistol in hand came upon the terrified wretch, and bade him be silent. Then they asked him (Esmond's head reeled, and he almost fell as he spoke) when Lord Castlewood had arrived? He said on the previous evening, about eight of the clock.—'And what then?'—His lordship supped with his sister.—'Did the man wait?'—Yes, he and my lady's maid both waited: the other servants made the supper; and there was no wine, and they could give his lordship but milk, at which they grumbled; and—and Madam Beatrix kept Miss Lucy always in the room with her. And there being a bed across the court in the chaplain's room, she had arranged my lord was to sleep there. Madam Beatrix had come downstairs laughing with the maids, and had locked herself in, and my lord had stood for a while talking to her through the door, and she laughing at him. And then he paced the court awhile, and she came again to the upper window; and my lord implored her to come down and walk in the room; but she would not, and laughed at him again, and shut the window; and so my lord, uttering what seemed curses, but in a foreign language, went to the chaplain's room to bed.

' Was this all ? '—' All,' the man swore upon his honour ; ' all as he hoped to be saved.—Stop, there was one thing more. My lord, on arriving, and once or twice during supper, did kiss his sister as was natural, and she kissed him.' At this Esmond ground his teeth with rage, and well-nigh throttled the amazed miscreant who was speaking, whereas Castlewood, seizing hold of his cousin's hand, burst into a great fit of laughter.

' If it amuses thee,' says Esmond in French, ' that your sister should be exchanging of kisses with a stranger, I fear poor Beatrix will give thee plenty of sport.'—Esmond darkly thought, how Hamilton, Ashburnham, had before been masters of those roses that the young prince's lips were now feeding on. He sickened at that notion. Her cheek was desecrated, her beauty tarnished ; shame and honour stood between it and him. The love was dead within him ; had she a crown to bring him with her love, he felt that both would degrade him.

But this wrath against Beatrix did not lessen the angry feelings of the colonel against the man who had been the occasion if not the cause of the evil. Frank sat down on a stone bench in the courtyard, and fairly fell asleep, while Esmond paced up and down the court, debating what should ensue. What mattered how much or how little had passed between the prince and the poor faithless girl ? They were arrived in time perhaps to rescue her person, but not her mind ; had she not instigated the young prince to come to her ; suborned servants, dismissed others, so that she might communicate with him ? The treacherous heart within her had surrendered, though the place

was safe ; and it was to win this that he had given
a life's struggle and devotion ; this, that she was
ready to give away for the bribe of a coronet or
a wink of the prince's eye.

When he had thought his thoughts out he
shook up poor Frank from his sleep, who rose
yawning, and said he had been dreaming of
Clotilda. 'You must back me,' says Esmond,
'in what I am going to do. I have been thinking
that yonder scoundrel may have been instructed
to tell that story, and that the whole of it may
be a lie ; if it be, we shall find it out from the
gentleman who is asleep yonder. See if the door
leading to my lady's rooms' (so we called the
rooms at the north-west angle of the house),
'see if the door is barred as he saith.' We tried ;
it was indeed as the lackey had said, closed within.

'It may have been open and shut afterwards,'
says poor Esmond ; 'the foundress of our family
let our ancestor in in that way.'

'What will you do, Harry, if—if what that
fellow saith should turn out untrue ?' The young
man looked scared and frightened into his kinsman's face ; I dare say it wore no very pleasant
expression.

'Let us first go see whether the two stories
agree,' says Esmond ; and went in at the passage
and opened the door into what had been his own
chamber now for wellnigh five-and-twenty years.
A candle was still burning, and the prince asleep
dressed on the bed—Esmond did not care for
making a noise. The prince started up in his
bed, seeing two men in his chamber : '*Qui est là?*'
says he, and took a pistol from under his pillow.

'It is the Marquis of Esmond,' says the colonel,

'come to welcome his Majesty to his house of
Castlewood, and to report of what hath happened
in London. Pursuant to the king's orders, I passed
the night before last, after leaving his Majesty, in
waiting upon the friends of the king. It is a pity
that his Majesty's desire to see the country and
to visit our poor house should have caused the
king to quit London without notice yesterday,
when the opportunity happened which in all
human probability may not occur again ; and had
the king not chosen to ride to Castlewood, the
Prince of Wales might have slept at St. James's.'

 ' 'Sdeath ! gentlemen,' says the prince, starting
off his bed, whereon he was lying in his clothes,
' the doctor was with me yesterday morning, and
after watching by my sister all night, told me
I might not hope to see the queen.'

 ' It would have been otherwise,' says Esmond,
with another bow ; ' as, by this time, the queen
may be dead in spite of the doctor. The Council
was met, a new treasurer was appointed, the troops
were devoted to the king's cause ; and fifty loyal
gentlemen of the greatest names of this kingdom
were assembled to accompany the Prince of Wales,
who might have been the acknowledged heir of
the throne, or the possessor of it by this time, had
your Majesty not chosen to take the air. We were
ready ; there was only one person that failed us,
your Majesty's gracious——'

 ' *Morbleu, monsieur*, you give me too much
Majesty,' said the prince ; who had now risen up
and seemed to be looking to one of us to help him
to his coat. But neither stirred.

 ' We shall take care ', says Esmond, ' not much
oftener to offend in that particular.'

'What mean you, my lord?' says the prince, and muttered something about a *guet-à-pens*, which Esmond caught up.

'The snare, sir,' said he, 'was not of our laying; it is not we that invited you. We came to avenge, and not to compass, the dishonour of our family.'

'Dishonour! *Morbleu!* there has been no dishonour,' says the prince, turning scarlet. 'only a little harmless playing.'

'That was meant to end seriously.'

'I swear,' the prince broke out impetuously, 'upon the honour of a gentleman, my lords——'

'That we arrived in time. No wrong hath been done, Frank,' says Colonel Esmond, turning round to young Castlewood, who stood at the door as the talk was going on. 'See! here is a paper whereon his Majesty hath deigned to commence some verses in honour, or dishonour, of Beatrix. Here is *madame* and *flamme*, *cruelle* and *rebelle*, and *amour* and *jour*, in the royal writing and spelling. Had the gracious lover been happy, he had not passed his time in sighing.' In fact, and actually as he was speaking, Esmond cast his eyes down towards the table, and saw a paper on which my young prince had been scrawling a madrigal, that was to finish his charmer on the morrow.

'Sir,' says the prince, burning with rage (he had assumed his royal coat unassisted by this time), 'did I come here to receive insults?'

'To confer them, may it please your Majesty,' says the colonel, with a very low bow, 'and the gentlemen of our family are come to thank you.'

'*Malédiction!*' says the young man, tears starting into his eyes with helpless rage and mortification. 'What will you with me, gentlemen?'

'If your Majesty will please to enter the next apartment,' says Esmond, preserving his grave tone, ' I have some papers there which I would gladly submit to you, and by your permission I will lead the way ; ' and, taking the taper up, and backing before the prince with very great ceremony, Mr. Esmond passed into the little chaplain's room, through which we had just entered into the house :—' Please to set a chair for his Majesty, Frank,' says the colonel to his companion, who wondered almost as much at this scene, and was as much puzzled by it, as the other actor in it. Then going to the crypt over the mantelpiece, the colonel opened it, and drew thence the papers which so long had lain there.

'Here, may it please your Majesty,' says he, ' is the patent of Marquis sent over by your royal father at St. Germains to Viscount Castlewood, my father : here is the witnessed certificate of my father's marriage to my mother, and of my birth and christening ; I was christened of that religion of which your sainted sire gave all through life so shining example. These are my titles, dear Frank, and this what I do with them : here go baptism and marriage, and here the marquisate and the august sign-manual, with which your predecessor was pleased to honour our race.' And as Esmond spoke he set the papers burning in the brazier. 'You will please, sir, to remember,' he continued, ' that our family hath ruined itself by fidelity to yours : that my grandfather spent his estate, and gave his blood and his son to die for your service ; that my dear lord's grandfather (for lord you are now, Frank, by right and title too) died for the same cause ; that my poor kinswoman, my father's second wife, after giving away her honour to your wicked perjured race, sent all her wealth to the king; and got in return that precious title that lies in ashes, and this inestimable yard of blue ribbon. I lay this at your feet and stamp upon it: I draw this sword, and break it and deny you; and, had you completed the wrong you designed us, by Heaven I would have driven it through your heart, and no more pardoned you than your father pardoned Monmouth. Frank will do the same, won't you, cousin?'

Frank, who had been looking on with a stupid air at the papers as they flamed in the old brazier, took out his sword and broke it, holding his head down:—'I go with my cousin,' says he, giving Esmond a grasp of the hand. 'Marquis or not, by ——, I stand by him any day. I beg your Majesty's pardon for swearing; that is—that is—I'm for the Elector of Hanover. It's all your Majesty's own fault. The queen's dead most likely by this time. And you might have been king if you hadn't come dangling after 'Trix.'

'Thus to lose a crown,' says the young prince, starting up, and speaking French in his eager way; 'to lose the loveliest woman in the world; to lose the loyalty of such hearts as yours, is not this, my lords, enough of humiliation?—Marquis, if I go on my knees will you pardon me?—No, I can't do that, but I can offer you reparation, that of honour, that of gentlemen. Favour me by crossing the sword with mine: yours is broke—see, yonder in the armoire are two;' and the prince took them out as eager as a boy, and held them towards Esmond:—'Ah! you will? *Merci, monsieur merci!*'

Extremely touched by this immense mark of condescension and repentance for wrong done, Colonel Esmond bowed down so low as almost to kiss the gracious young hand that conferred on him such an honour, and took his guard in silence. The swords were no sooner met, than Castlewood knocked up Esmond's with the blade of his own, which he had broke off short at the shell; and the Colonel falling back a step dropped his point with another very low bow, and declared himself perfectly satisfied.

'*Eh bien, vicomte!*' says the young prince, who was a boy, and a French boy, '*il ne nous reste qu'une chose à faire:*' he placed his sword upon the table, and the fingers of his two hands upon his breast:— 'We have one more thing to do,' says he; 'you do not divine it?' He stretched out his arms:— '*Embrassons nous!*'

The talk was scarce over when Beatrix entered the room:—What came she to seek there? She started and turned pale at the sight of her brother and kinsman, drawn swords, broken sword-blades, and papers yet smouldering in the brazier.

'Charming Beatrix,' says the prince, with a blush which became him very well, 'these lords have come a-horseback from London, where my sister lies in a despaired state, and where her successor makes himself desired. Pardon me for my escapade of last evening. I had been so long a prisoner, that I seized the occasion of a promenade on horseback, and my horse naturally bore me towards you. I found you a queen in your little court, where you deigned to entertain me. Present my homages to your maids of honour. I sighed as you slept, under the window of your chamber, and then retired to seek rest in my own. It was there that these gentlemen agreeably roused me. Yes, milords, for that is a happy day that makes a prince acquainted, at whatever cost to his vanity, with such a noble heart as that of the Marquis of Esmond. Mademoiselle, may we take your coach to town? I saw it in the hangar, and this poor marquis must be dropping with sleep.'

' Will it please the king to breakfast before he goes ? ' was all Beatrix could say. The roses had shuddered out of her cheeks ; her eyes were glaring; she looked quite old. She came up to Esmond and hissed out a word or two :—' If I did not love you before, cousin,' says she, ' think how I love you now.' If words could stab, no doubt she would have killed Esmond ; she looked at him as if she could.

But her keen words gave no wound to Mr. Esmond ; his heart was too hard. As he looked at her, he wondered that he could ever have loved her. His love of ten years was over ; it fell down dead on the spot, at the Kensington tavern, where Frank brought him the note out of *Eikon Basilike*. The prince blushed and bowed low, as she gazed at him, and quitted the chamber. I have never seen her from that day.

Esmond. 1852.

CHARLES DICKENS

1812-1870

A VALENTINE

To ladies and gentlemen who are not in the habit of devoting themselves practically to the science of penmanship, writing a letter is no very easy task; it being always considered necessary in such cases for the writer to recline his head on his left arm, so as to place his eyes as nearly as possible on a level with the paper, while glancing sideways at the letters he is constructing, to form with his tongue imaginary characters to correspond. These motions, although unquestionably of the greatest assistance to original composition, retard in some degree the progress of the writer; and Sam had unconsciously been a full hour and a half writing words in small text, smearing out wrong letters with his little finger, and putting in new ones which required going over very often to render them visible through the old blots, when he was roused by the opening of the door and the entrance of his parent.

'Vell, Sammy,' said the father.

'Vell, my Prooshan Blue,' responded the son, laying down his pen. 'What's the last bulletin about mother-in-law?'

'Mrs. Veller passed a wery good night, but is uncommon perwerse, and unpleasant this mornin'.

Signed upon oath, T. Veller, Esquire, Senior.
That's the last vun as was issued, Sammy,'
replied Mr. Weller, untying his shawl.

'No better yet?' inquired Sam.

'All the symptoms aggerawated,' replied Mr.
Weller, shaking his head. 'But wot's that you're
a doing of? Pursuit of knowledge under difficulties, Sammy?'

'I've done now,' said Sam with slight embarrass-
ment; 'I've been a writin',.'

'So I see,' replied Mr. Weller. 'Not to any
young 'ooman, I hope, Sammy?'

'Why it's no use a sayin' it ain't,' replied Sam.
'It's a walentine.'

'A what!' exclaimed Mr. Weller, apparently
horror-stricken by the word.

'A walentine,' replied Sam.

'Samivel, Samivel,' said Mr. Weller, in reproach-
ful accents, 'I didn't think you'd ha' done it.
Arter the warnin' you've had o' your father's
wicious propensities; arter all I've said to you
upon this here wery subject; arter activally
seein' and bein' in the company o' your own
mother-in-law, vich I should ha' thought wos a
moral lesson as no man could never ha' forgotten
to his dyin' day! I didn't think you'd ha' done it,
Sammy, I didn't think you'd ha' done it!' These
reflections were too much for the good old man.
He raised Sam's tumbler to his lips and drank off
its contents.

'Wot's the matter now?' said Sam.

'Nev'r mind, Sammy,' replied Mr. Weller, 'it'll
be a wery agonizin' trial to me at my time of life,
but I'm pretty tough, that's vun consolation, as
the wery old turkey remarked wen the farmer

said he was afeerd he should be obliged to kill him for the London market.'

'Wot'll be a trial?' inquired Sam.

'To see you married, Sammy—to see you a dilluded wictim, and thinkin' in your innocence that it's all wery capital,' replied Mr. Weller. 'It's a dreadful trial to a father's feelin's, that 'ere, Sammy.'

'Nonsense,' said Sam. 'I ain't a goin' to get married, don't you fret yourself about that; I know you're a judge of these things. Order in your pipe, and I'll read you the letter. There!'

We cannot distinctly say whether it was the prospect of the pipe, or the consolatory reflection that a fatal disposition to get married ran in the family and couldn't be helped, which calmed Mr. Weller's feelings, and caused his grief to subside. We should be rather disposed to say that the result was attained by combining the two sources of consolation, for he repeated the second in a low tone, very frequently; ringing the bell meanwhile, to order in the first. He then divested himself of his upper coat; and lighting the pipe and placing himself in front of the fire with his back towards it, so that he could feel its full heat, and recline against the mantelpiece at the same time, turned towards Sam, and, with a countenance greatly mollified by the softening influence of tobacco, requested him to 'fire away'.

Sam dipped his pen into the ink to be ready for any corrections, and began with a very theatrical air:

' "Lovely——." '

'Stop,' said Mr. Weller, ringing the bell. 'A double glass o' the inwariable, my dear.'

'Very well, sir,' replied the girl; who with

great quickness appeared, vanished, returned, and disappeared.

' They seem to know your ways here,' observed Sam.

' Yes,' replied his father, ' I've been here before, in my time. Go on, Sammy.'

' " Lovely creetur," ' repeated Sam.

' 'Tain't in poetry, is it ? ' interposed his father.

' No, no,' replied Sam.

' Werry glad to hear it,' said Mr. Weller. ' Poetry's unnat'ral; no man ever talked poetry 'cept a beadle on boxin' day, or Warren's blackin', or Rowland's oil, or some o' them low fellows ; never you let yourself down to talk poetry, my boy. Begin agin, Sammy.'

Mr. Weller resumed his pipe with critical solemnity, and Sam once more commenced, and read as follows :

' " Lovely creetur i feel myself a dammed "—.'

' That ain't proper,' said Mr. Weller, taking his pipe from his mouth.

' No; it ain't " dammed ",' observed Sam, holding the letter up to the light, ' it's " shamed ", there's a blot there—"I feel myself ashamed ".'

' Werry good,' said Mr. Weller. ' Go on.'

' " Feel myself ashamed, and completely cir—" I forget what this here word is,' said Sam, scratching his head with the pen, in vain attempts to remember.

' Why don't you look at it, then ? ' inquired Mr. Weller.

' So I *am* a lookin' at it,' replied Sam, ' but there's another blot. Here's a " c ", and a " i ", and a " d ".'

' Circumwented, p'raps,' suggested Mr. Weller.

'No, it ain't that,' said Sam, 'circumscribed;
that's it.'

'That ain't as good a word as circumwented,
Sammy,' said Mr. Weller, gravely.

'Think not?' said Sam.

'Nothin' like it,' replied his father.

'But don't you think it means more?' inquired
Sam.

'Vell p'raps it is a more tenderer word,' said
Mr. Weller, after a few moments' reflection. 'Go
on, Sammy.'

'"Feel myself ashamed and completely circumscribed in a dressin' of you, for you *are* a nice gal
and nothin' but it."'

'That's a werry pretty sentiment,' said the
elder Mr. Weller, removing his pipe to make way
for the remark.

'Yes, I think it is rayther good,' observed Sam,
highly flattered.

'Wot I like in that 'ere style of writin',' said
the elder Mr. Weller, 'is, that there ain't no callin'
names in it,—no Wenuses, nor nothin' o' that
kind. Wot's the good o' callin' a young 'ooman
a Wenus or a angel, Sammy?'

'Ah! what, indeed?' replied Sam.

'You might jist as well call her a griffin, or
a unicorn, or a king's arms at once, which is werry
well known to be a col-lection o' fabulous animals,'
added Mr. Weller.

'Just as well,' replied Sam.

'Drive on, Sammy,' said Mr. Weller.

Sam complied with the request, and proceeded
as follows; his father continuing to smoke, with
a mixed expression of wisdom and complacency,
which was particularly edifying.

' " Afore I see you, I thought all women was alike." '

' So they are,' observed the elder Mr. Weller, parenthetically.

' " But now," continued Sam, " now I find what a reg'lar soft-headed, inkred'lous turnip I must ha' been; for there ain't nobody like you, though *I* like you better than nothin' at all." I thought it best to make that rayther strong,' said Sam, looking up.

Mr. Weller nodded approvingly, and Sam resumed.

' " So I take the prividge of the day, Mary, my dear—as the gen'l'm'n in difficulties did, ven he walked out of a Sunday,—to tell you that the first and only time I see you, your likeness was took on my hart in much quicker time and brighter colours than ever a likeness was took by the profeel macheen (wich p'raps you may have heerd on Mary my dear) altho it *does* finish a portrait and put the frame and glass on complete, with a hook at the end to hang it up by, and all in two minutes and a quarter." '

' I am afeerd that werges on the poetical, Sammy,' said Mr. Weller, dubiously.

' No it don't,' replied Sam, reading on very quickly, to avoid contesting the point:

' " Except of me Mary my dear as your walentine and think over what I've said.—My dear Mary I will now conclude." That's all,' said Sam.

' That's rather a sudden pull up, ain't it, Sammy ? ' inquired Mr. Weller.

' Not a bit on it,' said Sam ; ' she'll vish there wos more, and that's the great art o' letter writin'.'

' Well,' said Mr. Weller, ' there's somethin' in

that ; and I wish your mother-in-law 'ud only
conduct her conwersation on the same gen-teel
principle. Ain't you a goin' to sign it ? '

' That 's the difficulty,' said Sam ; I don't know
what *to* sign it.'

' Sign it, Veller,' said the oldest surviving proprietor of that name.

' Won't do,' said Sam. ' Never sign a walentine
with your own name.'

' Sign it " Pickvick ", then,' said Mr. Weller ;
' it 's a werry good name, and a easy one to spell.'

' The wery thing,' said Sam. ' I *could* end with
a werse ; what do you think ? '

' I don't like it, Sam,' rejoined Mr. Weller.
' I never know'd a respectable coachman as wrote
poetry, 'cept one, as made an affectin' copy o'
werses the night afore he wos hung for a highway
robbery ; and *he* wos only a Cambervell man, so
even that 's no rule.'

But Sam was not to be dissuaded from the
poetical idea that had occurred to him, so he
signed the letter,

' Your love-sick
Pickwick.'

And having folded it, in a very intricate manner,
squeezed a down-hill direction in one corner :
' To Mary, Housemaid, at Mr. Nupkin's Mayor's,
Ipswich, Suffolk ; ' and put it into his pocket,
wafered, and ready for the General Post.

Pickwick Papers. 1837.

THE STORM AT YARMOUTH

'DON'T you think that', I asked the coachman, in the first stage out of London, ' a very remarkable sky ? I don't remember to have seen one like it.'

' Nor I—not equal to it,' he replied. ' That's wind, sir. There'll be mischief done at sea, I expect, before long.'

It was a murky confusion—here and there blotted with a colour like the colour of the smoke from damp fuel—of flying clouds tossed up into most remarkable heaps, suggesting greater heights in the clouds than there were depths below them to the bottom of the deepest hollows in the earth, through which the wild moon seemed to plunge headlong, as if, in a dread disturbance of the laws of nature, she had lost her way and were frightened. There had been a wind all day ; and it was rising then, with an extraordinary great sound. In another hour it had much increased, and the sky was more overcast, and blew hard.

But as the night advanced, the clouds closing in and densely overspreading the whole sky, then very dark, it came on to blow, harder and harder. It still increased, until our horses could scarcely face the wind. Many times, in the dark part of the night (it was then late in September, when the nights were not short), the leaders turned about, or came to a dead stop ; and we were often in serious apprehension that the coach would be blown over. Sweeping gusts of rain came up before this storm, like showers of steel ; and, at those times, when there was any shelter of trees or lee walls to be got, we were fain to stop, in a sheer impossibility of continuing the struggle.

When the day broke, it blew harder and harder. I had been in Yarmouth when the seamen said it blew great guns, but I had never known the like of this, or anything approaching to it. We came to Ipswich—very late, having had to fight every inch of ground since we were ten miles out of London; and found a cluster of people in the market-place, who had risen from their beds in the night, fearful of falling chimneys. Some of these, congregating about the inn-yard while we changed horses, told us of great sheets of lead having been ripped off a high church-tower, and flung into a by-street, which they then blocked up. Others had to tell of country people, coming in from neighbouring villages, who had seen great trees lying torn out of the earth, and whole ricks scattered about the roads and fields. Still there was no abatement in the storm, but it blew harder.

As we struggled on, nearer and nearer to the sea, from which this mighty wind was blowing dead on shore, its force became more and more terrific. Long before we saw the sea, its spray was on our lips, and showered salt rain upon us. The water was out, over miles and miles of the flat country adjacent to Yarmouth; and every sheet and puddle lashed its banks, and had its stress of little breakers setting heavily towards us. When we came within sight of the sea, the waves on the horizon, caught at intervals above the rolling abyss, were like glimpses of another shore with towers and buildings. When at last we got into the town, the people came out to their doors, all aslant, and with streaming hair, making a wonder of the mail that had come through such a night.

I put up at the old inn, and went down to look at the sea; staggering along the street, which was strewn with sand and seaweed, and with flying blotches of sea-foam; afraid of falling slates and tiles; and holding by people I met, at angry corners. Coming near the beach, I saw, not only the boatmen, but half the people of the town, lurking behind buildings; some, now and then braving the fury of the storm to look away to sea, and blown sheer out of their course in trying to get zigzag back.

Joining these groups, I found bewailing women whose husbands were away in herring or oyster boats, which there was too much reason to think might have foundered before they could run in anywhere for safety. Grizzled old sailors were among the people, shaking their heads, as they looked from water to sky, and muttering to one another; shipowners, excited and uneasy; children, huddling together, and peering into older faces; even stout mariners, disturbed and anxious, levelling their glasses at the sea from behind places of shelter, as if they were surveying an enemy.

The tremendous sea itself, when I could find sufficient pause to look at it, in the agitation of the blinding wind, the flying stones and sand, and the awful noise, confounded me. As the high watery walls came rolling in, and, at their highest, tumbled into surf, they looked as if the least would engulf the town. As the receding wave swept back with a hoarse roar, it seemed to scoop out deep caves in the beach, as if its purpose were to undermine the earth. When some white-headed billows thundered on, and dashed themselves to pieces before they reached the land, every fragment of the late whole seemed possessed by the full might of its wrath, rushing to be gathered to the composition of another monster. Undulating hills were changed to valleys, undulating valleys (with a solitary storm-bird sometimes skimming through them) were lifted up to hills; masses of water shivered and shook the beach with a booming sound; every shape tumultuously rolled on, as soon as made, to change its shape and place, and beat another shape and place away; the ideal shore on the horizon, with its towers and buildings, rose and fell; the clouds fell fast and thick; I seemed to see a rending and upheaving of all nature.

Not finding Ham among the people whom this memorable wind—for it is still remembered down there, as the greatest ever known to blow upon that coast—had brought together, I made my way to his house. It was shut; and as no one answered to my knocking, I went, by back ways and by-lanes, to the yard where he worked. I learned, there, that he had gone to Lowestoft, to meet some sudden exigency of ship-repairing in which his skill was required; but that he would be back to-morrow morning, in good time.

I went back to the inn; and when I had washed and dressed, and tried to sleep, but in vain, it was five o'clock in the afternoon. I had not sat five minutes by the coffee-room fire, when the waiter coming to stir it, as an excuse for talking, told me that two colliers had gone down, with all hands, a few miles away; and that some other ships had been seen labouring hard in the Roads, and trying, in great distress, to keep off shore. Mercy on them, and on all poor sailors, said he, if we had another night like the last !

I was very much depressed in spirits ; very solitary ; and felt an uneasiness in Ham's not being there, disproportionate to the occasion. I was seriously affected, without knowing how much, by late events ; and my long exposure to the fierce wind had confused me. There was that jumble in my thoughts and recollections, that I had lost the clear arrangement of time and distance. Thus, if I had gone out into the town, I should not have been surprised, I think, to encounter some one who I knew must be then in London. So to speak, there was in these respects a curious inattention in my mind. Yet it was busy, too, with all the remembrances the place naturally awakened ; and they were particularly distinct and vivid.

In this state, the waiter's dismal intelligence about the ships immediately connected itself, without any effort of my volition, with my uneasiness about Ham. I was persuaded that I had an apprehension of his returning from Lowestoft by sea, and being lost. This grew so strong with me, that I resolved to go back to the yard before I took my dinner, and ask the boat-builder if he thought his attempting to return by sea at all likely ? If he gave me the least reason to think so, I would go over to Lowestoft and prevent it by bringing him with me.

I hastily ordered my dinner, and went back to the yard   I was none too soon ; for the boat-builder, with a lantern in his hand, was locking the yard-gate. He quite laughed when I asked him the question, and said there was no fear; no man in his senses, or out of them, would put off in such a gale of wind, least of all Ham Peggotty, who had been born to seafaring.

So sensible of this, beforehand, that I had really felt ashamed of doing what I was nevertheless impelled to do, I went back to the inn. If such a wind could rise, I think it was rising. The howl and roar, the rattling of the doors and windows, the rumbling in the chimneys, the apparent rocking of the very house that sheltered me, and the prodigious tumult of the sea, were more fearful than in the morning. But there was now a great darkness besides; and that invested the storm with new terrors, real and fanciful.

I could not eat, I could not sit still, I could not continue steadfast to anything. Something within me, faintly answering to the storm without, tossed up the depths of my memory and made a tumult in them. Yet, in all the hurry of my thoughts, wild running with the thundering sea,—the storm and my uneasiness regarding Ham were always in the foreground.

My dinner went away almost untasted, and I tried to refresh myself with a glass or two of wine. In vain. I fell into a dull slumber before the fire, without losing my consciousness, either of the uproar out of doors, or of the place in which I was. Both became overshadowed by a new and indefinable horror; and when I awoke—or rather when I shook off the lethargy that bound me in my chair—my whole frame thrilled with objectless and unintelligible fear.

I walked to and fro, tried to read an old gazetteer,

listened to the awful noises; looked at faces, scenes, and figures in the fire. At length, the steady ticking of the undisturbed clock on the wall tormented me to that degree that I resolved to go to bed.

It was reassuring, on such a night, to be told that some of the inn-servants had agreed together to sit up until morning. I went to bed, exceedingly weary and heavy; but, on my lying down, all such sensations vanished, as if by magic, and I was broad awake, with every sense refined.

For hours I lay there, listening to the wind and water; imagining, now, that I heard shrieks out at sea; now, that I distinctly heard the firing of signal guns; and now, the fall of houses in the town. I got up several times, and looked out; but could see nothing, except the reflection in the window-panes of the faint candle I had left burning, and of my own haggard face looking in at me from the black void.

At length, my restlessness attained to such a pitch, that I hurried on my clothes, and went down-stairs. In the large kitchen, where I dimly saw bacon and ropes of onions hanging from the beams, the watchers were clustered together, in various attitudes, about the table, purposely moved away from the great chimney, and brought near the door. A pretty girl, who had her ears stopped with her apron, and her eyes upon the door, screamed when I appeared, supposing me to be a spirit; but the others had more presence of mind, and were glad of an addition to their company. One man, referring to the topic they had been discussing, asked me whether I thought the souls of the collier-crews who had gone down, were out in the storm?

I remained there, I dare say, two hours. Once, I opened the yard-gate, and looked into the empty street. The sand, the seaweed, and the flakes of foam, were driving by; and I was obliged to call for assistance before I could shut the gate again, and make it fast against the wind.

There was a dark gloom in my solitary chamber, when I at length returned to it; but I was tired now, and, getting into bed again, fell—off a tower and down a precipice—into the depths of sleep. I have an impression that for a long time, though I dreamed of being elsewhere and in a variety of scenes, it was always blowing in my dream. At length, I lost that feeble hold upon reality, and was engaged with two dear friends, but who they were I don't know, at the siege of some town in a roar of cannonading.

The thunder of the cannon was so loud and incessant, that I could not hear something I much desired to hear, until I made a great exertion and awoke. It was broad day—eight or nine o'clock; the storm raging, in lieu of the batteries; and some one knocking and calling at my door.

'What is the matter?' I cried.

'A wreck! Close by!'

I sprung out of bed, and asked, what wreck?

'A schooner, from Spain or Portugal, laden with fruit and wine. Make haste, sir, if you want to see her! It's thought, down on the beach, she'll go to pieces every moment.'

The excited voice went clamouring along the staircase; and I wrapped myself in my clothes as quickly as I could, and ran into the street.

Numbers of people were there before me, all running in one direction to the beach. I ran the same way, outstripping a good many, and soon came facing the wild sea.

The wind might by this time have lulled a little, though not more sensibly than if the cannonading I had dreamed of had been diminished by the silencing of half-a-dozen guns out of hundreds. But the sea having upon it the additional agitation of the whole night, was infinitely more terrific than when I had seen it last. Every appearance it had then presented, bore the expression of being *swelled*; and the height to which the breakers rose, and, looking over one another, bore one another down, and rolled in, in interminable hosts, was most appalling.

In the difficulty of hearing anything but wind and waves, and in the crowd, and the unspeakable confusion, and my first breathless efforts to stand against the weather, I was so confused that I looked out to sea for the wreck, and saw nothing but the foaming heads of the great waves. A half-dressed boatman, standing next me, pointed with his bare arm (a tattoo'd arrow on it, pointing in the same direction) to the left. Then, O great Heaven, I saw it, close in upon us!

One mast was broken short off, six or eight feet from the deck, and lay over the side, entangled in a maze of sail and rigging; and all that ruin, as the ship rolled and beat—which she did without a moment's pause, and with a violence quite inconceivable—beat the side as if it would stave it in. Some efforts were even then being made, to cut this portion of the wreck away; for as the ship, which was broadside on, turned towards us in her rolling, I plainly descried her people at work with axes, especially one active figure with long curling hair, conspicuous among the rest. But a great cry, which was audible even above the wind and water, rose from the shore at this moment; the sea, sweeping over the rolling wreck, made a clean breach, and carried men, spars, casks, planks, bulwarks, heaps of such toys, into the boiling surge.

The second mast was yet standing, with the rags of a rent sail, and a wild confusion of broken cordage flapping to and fro. The ship had struck once, the same boatman hoarsely said in my ear, and then lifted in and struck again. I understood him to add that she was parting amidships, and I could readily suppose so, for the rolling and beating were too tremendous for any human work to suffer long. As he spoke, there was another great cry of pity from the beach; four men arose with the wreck out of the deep, clinging to the rigging of the remaining mast; uppermost, the active figure with the curling hair.

There was a bell on board; and as the ship rolled and dashed, like a desperate creature driven mad, now showing us the whole sweep of her deck as she turned on her beam-ends towards the shore, now nothing but her keel, as she sprung wildly over and turned towards the sea, the bell rang; and its sound, the knell of those unhappy men, was borne towards us on the wind. Again we lost her, and again she rose. Two men were gone. The agony on shore increased. Men groaned, and clasped their hands; women shrieked, and turned away their faces. Some ran wildly up and down along the beach, crying for help where no help could be. I found myself one of these, frantically imploring a knot of sailors whom I knew, not to let those two lost creatures perish before our eyes.

They were making out to me, in an agitated way—I don't know how, for the little I could hear I was scarcely composed enough to understand—that the lifeboat had been bravely manned an hour ago, and could do nothing; and that as no man would be so desperate as to attempt to wade off with a rope, and establish a communication with the shore, there was nothing left to try; when I noticed that some new sensation moved the people on the beach, and saw them part, and Ham come breaking through them to the front.

I ran to him—as well as I know—to repeat my appeal for help. But, distracted though I was by a sight so new to me and terrible, the determination in his face, and his look out to sea—exactly the same look as I remembered in connexion with the morning after Emily's flight—awoke me to a knowledge of his danger. I held him back with both arms; and implored the men with whom I had been speaking, not to listen to him, not to do murder, not to let him stir from off that sand!

Another cry arose on shore; and looking to the wreck, we saw the cruel sail, with blow on blow, beat off the lower of the two men, and fly up in triumph round the active figure left alone upon the mast.

Against such a sight, and against such determination as that of the calmly desperate man who was already accustomed to lead half the people present, I might as hopefully have entreated the wind. ' Mas'r Davy,' he said, cheerily grasping me by both hands, ' if my time is come, 'tis come. If 'tan't, I'll bide it. Lord above bless you, and bless all! Mates, make me ready! I'm a-going off!'

I was swept away, but not unkindly, to some distance, where the people around me made me stay ; urging, as I confusedly perceived, that he was bent on going, with help or without, and that I should endanger the precautions for his safety by troubling those with whom they rested. I don't know what I answered, or what they rejoined ; but I saw hurry on the beach, and men running with ropes from a capstan that was there, and penetrating into a circle of figures that hid him from me. Then, I saw him standing alone, in a seaman's frock and trowsers : a rope in his hand, or slung to his wrist : another round his body : and several of the best men holding, at a little distance, to the latter, which he laid out himself, slack upon the shore, at his feet.

The wreck, even to my unpractised eye, was breaking up. I saw that she was parting in the middle, and that the life of the solitary man upon the mast hung by a thread. Still, he clung to it. He had a singular red cap on,—not like a sailor's cap, but of a finer colour ; and as the few yielding planks between him and destruction rolled and bulged, and his anticipative death-knell rung, he was seen by all of us to wave it. I saw him do it now, and thought I was going distracted, when his action brought an old remembrance to my mind of a once dear friend.

Ham watched the sea, standing alone, with the silence of suspended breath behind him, and the storm before, until there was a great retiring wave, when, with a backward glance at those who held the rope which was made fast round his body, he dashed in after it, and in a moment was buffeting with the water ; rising with the hills, falling with

the valleys, lost beneath the foam ; then drawn
again to land. They hauled in hastily.

He was hurt. I saw blood on his face, from
where I stood ; but he took no thought of that.
He seemed hurriedly to give them some directions for leaving him more free—or so I judged
from the motion of his arm—and was gone as
before.

And now he made for the wreck, rising with the
hills, falling with the valleys, lost beneath the
rugged foam, borne in towards the shore, borne
on towards the ship, striving hard and valiantly.
The distance was nothing, but the power of the
sea and wind made the strife deadly. At length
he neared the wreck. He was so near, that with
one more of his vigorous strokes he would be
clinging to it,—when a high, green, vast hill-side
of water, moving on shoreward, from beyond the
ship, he seemed to leap up into it with a mighty
bound, and the ship was gone !

Some eddying fragments I saw in the sea, as if
a mere cask had been broken, in running to the
spot where they were hauling in. Consternation
was in every face. They drew him to my very feet
—insensible—dead. He was carried to the nearest
house ; and, no one preventing me now, I remained
near him, busy, while every means of restoration
were tried ; but he had been beaten to death by
the great wave, and his generous heart was stilled
for ever.

As I sat beside the bed, when hope was abandoned
and all was done, a fisherman, who had known me
when Emily and I were children, and ever since,
whispered my name at the door.

' Sir,' said he, with tears starting to his weather-beaten face, which, with his trembling lips, was ashy pale, ' will you come over yonder ? '

The old remembrance that had been recalled to me, was in his look. I asked him, terror-stricken, leaning on the arm he held out to support me :

' Has a body come ashore ? '

He said, ' Yes.'

' Do I know it ? ' I asked then.

He answered nothing.

But he led me to the shore. And on that part of it where she and I had looked for shells, two children—on that part of it where some lighter fragments of the old boat, blown down last night, had been scattered by the wind—among the ruins of the home he had wronged—I saw him lying with his head upon his arm, as I had often seen him lie at school.

David Copperfield.   1849–1850.

MR. WOPSLE'S HAMLET

ON our arrival in Denmark, we found the king and queen of that country elevated in two arm-chairs on a kitchen-table, holding a Court. The whole of the Danish nobility were in attendance ; consisting of a noble boy in the wash-leather boots of a gigantic ancestor, a venerable Peer with a dirty face, who seemed to have risen from the people late in life, and the Danish chivalry with a comb in its hair and a pair of white silk legs, and presenting on the whole a feminine appearance. My gifted townsman stood gloomily apart, with folded arms, and I could have wished that his curls and forehead had been more probable.

Several curious little circumstances transpired

as the action proceeded. The late king of the country not only appeared to have been troubled with a cough at the time of his decease, but to have taken it with him to the tomb, and to have brought it back. The royal phantom also carried a ghostly manuscript round its truncheon, to which it had the appearance of occasionally referring, and that, too, with an air of anxiety and a tendency to lose the place of reference which were suggestive of a state of mortality. It was this, I conceive, which led to the Shade's being advised by the gallery to ' turn over ! '—a recommendation which it took extremely ill. It was likewise to be noted of this majestic spirit that whereas it always appeared with an air of having been out a long time and walked an immense distance, it perceptibly came from a closely contiguous wall. This occasioned its terrors to be received derisively. The Queen of Denmark, a very buxom lady, though no doubt historically brazen, was considered by the public to have too much brass about her ; her chin being attached to her diadem by a broad band of that metal (as if she had a gorgeous toothache), her waist being encircled by another, and each of her arms by another, so that she was openly mentioned as ' the kettledrum '. The noble boy in the ancestral boots, was inconsistent ; representing himself, as it were in one breath, as an able seaman, a strolling actor, a gravedigger, a clergyman, and a person of the utmost importance at a Court fencing-match, on the authority of whose practised eye and nice discrimination the finest strokes were judged. This gradually led to a want of toleration for him, and even—on his being detected in holy orders, and declining to perform the funeral service—to the general indignation taking the form of nuts. Lastly, Ophelia was a prey to such slow musical madness, that when, in course of time, she had taken off her white muslin scarf, folded it up, and buried it, a sulky man who had been long cooling his impatient nose against an iron bar in the front row of the gallery, growled, 'Now the baby's put to bed, let's have supper!' Which, to say the least of it, was out of keeping.

Upon my unfortunate townsman all these incidents accumulated with playful effect. Whenever that undecided Prince had to ask a question or state a doubt, the public helped him out with it. As for example; on the question whether 'twas nobler in the mind to suffer, some roared yes, and some no, and some inclining to both opinions said 'toss up for it;' and quite a Debating Society arose. When he asked what should such fellows as he do crawling between earth and heaven, he was encouraged with loud cries of 'Hear, hear!' When he appeared with his stocking disordered (its disorder expressed, according to usage, by one very neat fold in the top, which I suppose to be always got up with a flat iron), a conversation took place in the gallery respecting the paleness of his leg, and whether it was occasioned by the turn the ghost had given him On his taking the recorders—very like a little black flute that had just been played in the orchestra and handed out at the door—he was called upon unanimously for Rule Britannia. When he recommended the player not to saw the air thus, the sulky man said, 'And don't *you* do it, neither; you're a deal worse than *him*!' And I grieve to add that peals of laughter greeted Mr. Wopsle on every one of these occasions.

But his greatest trials were in the churchyard: which had the appearance of a primeval forest, with a kind of small ecclesiastical wash-house on one side, and a turnpike gate on the other. Mr. Wopsle, in a comprehensive black cloak, being descried entering at the turnpike, the gravedigger was admonished in a friendly way, ' Look out! Here's the undertaker a coming, to see how you're a getting on with your work ! ' I believe it is well known in a constitutional country that Mr. Wopsle could not possibly have returned the skull, after moralizing over it, without dusting his fingers on a white napkin taken from his breast ; but even that innocent and indispensable action did not pass without the comment ' Wai-ter ! ' The arrival of the body for interment (in an empty black box with the lid tumbling open), was the signal for a general joy which was much enhanced by the discovery, among the bearers, of an individual obnoxious to identification. The joy attended Mr. Wopsle through his struggle with Laertes on the brink of the orchestra and the grave, and slackened no more until he had tumbled the king off the kitchen-table, and had died by inches from the ankles upward.

Great Expectations. 1861.

CHARLOTTE BRONTË

1816–1855

A STORM

MADAME BECK called me on Thursday afternoon, and asked whether I had any occupation to hinder me from going into town and executing some little commissions for her at the shops.

Being disengaged, and placing myself at her service, I was presently furnished with a list of the wools, silks, embroidering thread, etcetera, wanted in the pupils' work, and having equipped myself in a manner suiting the threatening aspect of a cloudy and sultry day, I was just drawing the spring-bolt of the street-door, in act to issue forth, when Madame's voice again summoned me to the salle-à-manger.

' Pardon, Meess Lucie ! ' cried she, in the seeming haste of an impromptu thought, ' I have just recollected one more errand for you, if your good nature will not deem itself overburdened ? '

Of course I ' confounded myself ' in asseverations to the contrary ; and Madame, running into the little salon, brought thence a pretty basket, filled with fine hothouse fruit, rosy, perfect, and tempting, reposing amongst the dark green, wax-like leaves, and pale yellow stars of, I know not what, exotic plant.

' There,' she said, ' it is not heavy, and will not shame your neat toilette, as if it were a household, servant-like detail. Do me the favour to leave this little basket at the house of Madame Walravens, with my felicitations on her fête. She lives down in the old town, Numéro 3, Rue des Mages. I fear you will find the walk rather long, but you have the whole afternoon before you, and do not hurry ; if you are not back in time for dinner, I will order a portion to be saved, or Goton, with whom you are a favourite, will have pleasure in tossing up some trifle, for your especial benefit. You shall not be forgotten, ma bonne Meess. And oh ! please ! ' (calling me back once more) ' be sure to insist on seeing Madame Walravens herself, and giving the basket into her own hands, in order that there may be no mistake, for she is rather a punctilious personage. Adieu ! Au revoir ! '

And at last I got away. The shop-commissions took some time to execute, that choosing and matching of silks and wools being always a tedious business, but at last I got through my list. The patterns for the slippers, the bell-ropes, the cabas were selected—the slides and tassels for the purses chosen—the whole 'tripotage' in short, was off my mind ; nothing but the fruit and the felicitations remained to be attended to.

I rather liked the prospect of a long walk, deep into the old and grim Basse-Ville ; and I liked it no worse because the evening sky, over the city, was settling into a mass of black-blue metal, heated at the rim, and inflaming slowly to a heavy red.

I fear a high wind, because storm demands that exertion of strength and use of action I always yield with pain ; but the sullen downfall, the thick snow descent, or dark rush of rain, ask only resignation—the quiet abandonment of garments and person to be drenched. In return, it sweeps a great capital clean before you ; it makes you a quiet path through broad, grand streets ; it petrifies a living city, as if by eastern enchantment ; it transforms a Villette into a Tadmor. Let, then, the rains fall, and the floods descend—only I must first get rid of this basket of fruit.

An unknown clock from an unknown tower (Jean Baptiste's voice was now too distant to be audible) was tolling the third quarter past five, when I reached that street and house whereof Madame Beck had given me the address. It was no street at all ; it seemed rather to be part of a square : it was quiet, grass grew between the broad grey flags, the houses were large and looked very old—behind them rose the appearance of trees, indicating gardens at the back. Antiquity brooded above this region, business was banished thence. Rich men had once possessed this quarter, and once grandeur had made her seat here. That church whose dark, half-ruinous turrets overlooked the square, was the venerable and formerly opulent shrine of the Magi. But wealth and greatness had long since stretched their gilded pinions and fled hence, leaving these their ancient nests, perhaps to house Penury for a time, or perhaps to stand cold and empty, mouldering untenanted in the course of winters.

As I crossed this deserted ' place ', on whose pavement drops almost as large as a five-franc piece were now slowly darkening, I saw, in its whole expanse, no symptom or evidence of life, except what was given in the figure of an infirm old priest, who went past, bending and propped on a staff— the type of eld and decay.

He had issued from the very house to which
I was directed ; and when I paused before the door
just closed after him, and rang the bell, he turned
to look at me. Nor did he soon avert his gaze ;
perhaps he thought me, with my basket of summer
fruit, and my lack of the dignity age confers, an
incongruous figure in such a scene. I know, had
a young ruddy-faced bonne opened the door to
admit me, I should have thought such a one little
in harmony with her dwelling ; but when I found
myself confronted by a very old woman, wearing
a very antique peasant costume, a cap alike hideous
and costly, with long flaps of native lace, a petticoat and jacket of cloth, and sabots more like little
boats than shoes, it seemed all right, and soothingly
in character.

The expression of her face was not quite so
soothing as the cut of her costume ; anything
more cantankerous I have seldom seen ; she would
scarcely reply to my inquiry after Madame Walravens ; I believe she would have snatched the
basket of fruit from my hand, had not the old
priest, hobbling up, checked her, and himself lent
an ear to the message with which I was charged.

His apparent deafness rendered it a little difficult
to make him fully understand that I must see
Madame Walravens, and consign the fruit into her
own hands. At last, however, he comprehended
the fact that such were my orders, and that duty
enjoined their literal fulfilment. Addressing the
aged bonne, not in French, but in the aboriginal
tongue of Labassecour, he persuaded her, at last,
to let me cross the inhospitable threshold, and
himself escorting me upstairs, I was ushered into
a sort of salon, and there left.

The room was large, and had a fine old ceiling, and almost church-like windows of coloured glass; but it was desolate, and in the shadow of a coming storm, looked strangely lowering. Within—opened a smaller room; there, however, the blind of the single casement was closed; through the deep gloom few details of furniture were apparent. These few I amused myself by puzzling to make out; and, in particular, I was attracted by the outline of a picture on the wall.

By-and-by the picture seemed to give way: to my bewilderment, it shook, it sunk, it rolled back into nothing; its vanishing left an opening arched, leading into an arched passage, with a mystic winding stair; both passage and stair were of cold stone, uncarpeted and unpainted. Down this donjon stair descended a tap, tap, like a stick; soon, there fell on the steps a shadow, and last of all, I was aware of a substance.

Yet, was it actual substance, this appearance approaching me? this obstruction, partially darkening the arch?

It drew near, and I saw it well. I began to comprehend where I was. Well might this old square be named quarter of the Magi—well might the three towers, overlooking it, own for godfathers three mystic sages of a dead and dark art. Hoar enchantment here prevailed; a spell had opened for me elf-land—that cell-like room, that vanishing picture, that arch and passage, and stair of stone, were all parts of a fairy tale. Distincter even than these scenic details stood the chief figure—Cunegonde, the sorceress! Malevola, the evil fairy. How was she?

She might be three feet high, but she had no

shape; her skinny hands rested upon each other, and pressed the gold knob of a wand-like ivory staff. Her face was large, set, not upon her shoulders, but before her breast; she seemed to have no neck; I should have said there were a hundred years in her features, and more perhaps in her eyes —her malign, unfriendly eyes, with thick grey brows above, and livid lids all round. How severely they viewed me, with a sort of dull displeasure!

This being wore a gown of brocade, dyed bright blue, full-tinted as the gentianella flower, and covered with satin foliage in a large pattern; over the gown a costly shawl, gorgeously bordered, and so large for her, that its many-coloured fringe swept the floor. But her chief points were her jewels: she had long, clear ear-rings, blazing with a lustre which could not be borrowed or false; she had rings on her skeleton hands, with thick gold hoops, and stones—purple, green and blood-red. Hunchbacked, dwarfish, and doting, she was adorned like a barbarian queen.

' Que me voulez-vous ? ' said she hoarsely, with the voice rather of male than of female old age; and, indeed, a silver beard bristled her chin.

I delivered my basket and my message.

' Is that all ? ' she demanded.

' It is all,' said I.

' Truly, it was well worth while,' she answered. ' Return to Madame Beck, and tell her I can buy fruit when I want it, et quant à ses félicitations, je m'en moque ! ' And this courteous dame turned her back.

Just as she turned, a peal of thunder broke, and a flash of lightning blazed broad over salon and boudoir. The tale of magic seemed to proceed with due accompaniment of the elements. The wanderer, decoyed into the enchanted castle, heard rising, outside, the spell-wakened tempest.

What, in all this, was I to think of Madame Beck? She owned strange acquaintance; she offered messages and gifts at an unique shrine, and inauspicious seemed the bearing of the uncouth thing she worshipped. There went that sullen Sidonia, tottering and trembling like palsy incarnate, tapping her ivory staff on the mosaic parquet, and muttering venomously as she vanished.

Down washed the rain, deep lowered the welkin; the clouds, ruddy a while ago, had now, through all their blackness, turned deadly pale, as if in terror. Notwithstanding my late boast about not fearing a shower, I hardly liked to go out under this waterspout. Then the gleams of lightning were very fierce, the thunder crashed very near; this storm had gathered immediately above Villette; it seemed to have burst at the zenith; it rushed down prone; the forked, slant bolts pierced athwart vertical torrents; red zig-zags interlaced a descent blanched as white metal: and all broke from a sky heavily black in its swollen abundance.

Leaving Madame Walravens' inhospitable salon, I betook myself to her cold staircase; there was a seat on the landing—there I waited. Somebody came gliding along the gallery just above; it was the old priest.

'Indeed Mademoiselle shall not sit there,' said he. 'It would displeasure our benefactor if he knew a stranger was so treated in this house.'

And he begged me so earnestly to return to the

salon, that, without discourtesy, I could not but comply. The smaller room was better furnished and more habitable than the larger; thither he introduced me. Partially withdrawing the blind, he disclosed what seemed more like an oratory than a boudoir, a very solemn little chamber, looking as if it were a place rather dedicated to relics and re-membrance, than designed for present use and comfort.

The good father sat down, as if to keep me company; but instead of conversing, he took out a book, fastened on the page his eyes, and employed his lips in whispering—what sounded like a prayer or litany. A yellow electric light from the sky gilded his bald head; his figure remained in shade—deep and purple; he sat still as sculpture; he seemed to forget me for his prayers; he only looked up when a fiercer bolt, or a harsher, closer rattle told of nearing danger; even then, it was not in fear, but in seeming awe, he raised his eyes. I too was awe-struck; being, however, under no pressure of slavish terror, my thoughts and observations were free.

To speak truth, I was beginning to fancy that the old priest resembled that Père Silas, before whom I had knelt in the church of the Béguinage. The idea was vague, for I had seen my confessor only in dusk and in profile, yet still I seemed to trace a likeness: I thought also I recognized the voice. While I watched him, he betrayed, by one lifted look, that he felt my scrutiny; I turned to note the room; that too had its half mystic interest.

Beside a cross of curiously carved old ivory, yellow with time, and sloped above a dark-red

prie-dieu, furnished duly with rich missal and ebon
rosary—hung the picture whose dim outline had
drawn my eyes before—the picture which moved,
fell away with the wall and let in phantoms. Imperfectly seen, I had taken it for a Madonna ; revealed by clearer light, it proved to be a woman's
portrait in a nun's dress. The face, though not
beautiful, was pleasing ; pale, young, and shaded
with the dejection of grief or ill-health. I say
again it was not beautiful ; it was not even intellectual ; its very amiability was the amiability of
a weak frame, inactive passions, acquiescent habits ;
yet I looked long at that picture, and could not
choose but look.

The old priest, who at first had seemed to me so
deaf and infirm, must yet have retained his faculties
in tolerable preservation ; absorbed in his book
as he appeared, without once lifting his head, or,
as far as I knew, turning his eyes, he perceived the
point towards which my attention was drawn, and,
in a slow distinct voice, dropped, concerning it,
these four observations.

' She was much beloved.

' She gave herself to God.

' She died young.

' She is still remembered, still wept.'

' By that aged lady, Madame Walravens ? '
I inquired, fancying that I had discovered in the
incurable grief of bereavement, a key to that same
aged lady's desperate ill-humour.

The father shook his head with half a smile.

' No, no,' said he ; ' a grand-dame's affection for
her children's children may be great, and her
sorrow for their loss, lively ; but it is only the
affianced lover, to whom Fate, Faith, and Death

have trebly denied the bliss of union, who mourns
what he has lost, as Justine Marie is still mourned.'

I thought the father rather wished to be questioned, and therefore I inquired who had lost and
who still mourned ' Justine Marie '. I got, in
reply, quite a little romantic narrative, told not un-
impressively, with the accompaniment of the now
subsiding storm. I am bound to say it might have
been made much more truly impressive, if there
had been less French, Rousseau-like sentimentaliz-
ing and wire-drawing; and rather more healthful
carelessness of effect. But the worthy father was
obviously a Frenchman born and bred (I became
more and more persuaded of his resemblance to my
confessor)—he was a true son of Rome; when he
did lift his eyes, he looked at me out of their corners,
with more and sharper subtlety than, one would
have thought, could survive the wear and tear of
seventy years. Yet, I believe, he was a good old
man.

The hero of his tale was some former pupil of
his, whom he now called his benefactor, and who,
it appears, had loved this pale Justine Marie, the
daughter of rich parents, at a time when his own
worldly prospects were such as to justify his aspir-
ing to a well-dowered hand. The pupil's father—
once a rich banker—had failed, died, and left
behind him only debts and destitution. The son
was then forbidden to think of Marie; especially
that old witch of a grand-dame I had seen, Madame
Walravens, opposed the match with all the violence of a temper which deformity made sometimes
demoniac. The mild Marie had neither the
treachery to be false, nor the force to be quite
staunch to her lover; she gave up her first suitor,

but, refusing to accept a second with a heavier
purse, withdrew to a convent, and there died in
her noviciate.

Lasting anguish, it seems, had taken possession
of the faithful heart which worshipped her, and the
truth of that love and grief had been shown in
a manner which touched even me, as I listened.

Some years after Justine Marie's death, ruin had
come on her house too; her father, by nominal
calling a jeweller, but who also dealt a good deal on
the Bourse, had been concerned in some financial
transactions which entailed exposure and ruinous
fines. He died of grief for the loss, and shame for
the infamy. His old hunchbacked mother and his
bereaved wife were left penniless, and might have
died too of want; but their lost daughter's once-
despised, yet most true-hearted suitor, hearing of
the condition of these ladies, came with singular
devotedness to the rescue. He took on their
insolent pride the revenge of the purest charity—
housing, caring for, befriending them, so as no son
could have done it more tenderly and efficiently.
The mother—on the whole a good woman—died
blessing him; the strange, godless, loveless, mis-
anthrope grandmother lived still, entirely supported by this self-sacrificing man. She, who had
been the bane of his life, blighting his hope, and
awarding him, for love and domestic happiness, long
mourning and cheerless solitude, he treated with
the respect a good son might offer a kind mother.
He had brought her to this house, ' and,' continued
the priest, while genuine tears rose to his eyes,
' here, too, he shelters me, his old tutor, and Agnes,
a superannuated servant of his father's family.
To our sustenance, and to other charities, I know

he devotes three parts of his income, keeping only
the fourth to provide himself with bread and the
most modest accommodations. By this arrangement he has rendered it impossible to himself ever
to marry : he has given himself to God and to his
angel-bride as much as if he were a priest, like me.'

The father had wiped away his tears before he
uttered these last words, and in pronouncing them,
he for one instant raised his eyes to mine. I caught
this glance, despite its veiled character ; the
momentary gleam shot a meaning which struck me.

These Romanists are strange beings. Such
a one among them—whom you know no more than
the last Inca of Peru, or the first Emperor of China
—knows you and all your concerns ; and has his
reasons for saying to you so and so, when you
simply thought the communication sprang impromptu from the instant's impulse : his plan in
bringing it about that you shall come on such a day,
to such a place, under such and such circumstances,
when the whole arrangement seems to your crude
apprehension the ordinance of chance, or the sequel
of exigency. Madame Beck's suddenly recollected
message and present, my artless embassy to the
Place of the Magi, the old priest accidentally
descending the steps and crossing the square, his
interposition on my behalf with the bonne who
would have sent me away, his reappearance on the
staircase, my introduction to this room, the
portrait, the narrative so affably volunteered—all
these little incidents, taken as they fell out, seemed
each independent of its successor ; a handful of
loose beads : but threaded through by that quick-
shot and crafty glance of a Jesuit-eye, they dropped
pendant in a long string, like that rosary on the

prie-dieu. Where lay the link of junction, where the little clasp of this monastic necklace ? I saw or felt union, but could not yet find the spot, or detect the means of connexion.

Perhaps the musing-fit into which I had by this time fallen, appeared somewhat suspicious in its abstraction ; he gently interrupted :

'Mademoiselle,' said he, ' I trust you have not far to go through these inundated streets ? '

'More than half a league.'

' You live—— ? '

' In the Rue Fossette.'

' Not ' (with animation), ' not at the pensionnat of Madame Beck ? '

' The same.'

' Donc ' (clapping his hands), ' donc, vous devez connaître mon noble élève, mon Paul ? '

' Monsieur Paul Emanuel, Professor of Literature ? '

' He, and none other.'

A brief silence fell. The spring of junction seemed suddenly to have become palpable ; I felt it yield to pressure.

' Was it of M. Paul you have been speaking ? ' I presently inquired. ' Was he your pupil and the benefactor of Madame Walravens ? '

' Yes, and of Agnes, the old servant : and moreover ' (with a certain emphasis), ' he was and *is* the lover, true, constant and eternal, of that saint in Heaven—Justine Marie.'

' And who, father, are *you* ? ' I continued ; and though I accentuated the question, its utterance was well-nigh superfluous ; I was ere this quite prepared for the answer which actually came.

' I, daughter, am Père Silas ; that unworthy son

of Holy Church whom you once honoured with
a noble and touching confidence, showing me the
core of a heart, and the inner shrine of a mind
whereof, in solemn truth, I coveted the direction,
in behalf of the only true faith. Nor have I for
a day lost sight of you, nor for an hour failed to
take in you a rooted interest. Passed under the
discipline of Rome, moulded by her high training,
inoculated with her salutary doctrines, inspired by
the zeal she alone gives—I realize what then might
be your spiritual rank, your practical value ; and
I envy Heresy her prey.'

This struck me as a special state of things—I
half-realized myself in that condition also; passed
under discipline, moulded, trained, inoculated,
and so on.   'Not so,' thought I, but I restrained
deprecation and sat quietly enough.

'I suppose M. Paul does not live here ?'
I resumed, pursuing a theme which I thought
more to the purpose than any wild renegade
dreams.

'No ; he only comes occasionally to worship his
beloved saint, to make his confession to me, and to
pay his respects to her he calls his mother. His own
lodging consists but of two rooms ; he has no
servant, and yet he will not suffer Madame Walravens to dispose of those splendid jewels with
which you see her adorned, and in which she takes
a puerile pride as the ornaments of her youth, and
the last relics of her son the jeweller's wealth.'

'How often', murmured I to myself, ' has this
man, this M. Emanuel, seemed to me to lack
magnanimity in trifles, yet how great he is in great
things ! '

I own I did not reckon amongst the proofs of his

greatness, either the act of confession, or the saint-
worship.

' How long is it since that lady died ? ' I inquired, looking at Justine Marie.

' Twenty years. She was somewhat older than
M. Emanuel; he was then very young, for he is
not much beyond forty.'

' Does he yet weep her ? '

' His heart will weep her always : the essence of
Emanuel's nature is—constancy.'

This was said with marked emphasis.

And now the sun broke out pallid and waterish ;
the rain yet fell, but there was no more tempest ;
that hot firmament had cloven and poured out its
lightnings. A longer delay would scarce leave
daylight for my return, so I rose, thanked the
father for his hospitality and his tale, was benignantly answered by a 'pax vobiscum', which I made
kindly welcome, because it seemed uttered with
a true benevolence ; but I liked less the mystic
phrase accompanying it :

' Daughter, you *shall* be what you *shall* be ! ' an
oracle that made me shrug my shoulders as soon as
I had got outside the door. Few of us know what
we are to come to certainly, but for all that had
happened yet, I had good hopes of living and dying
a sober-minded Protestant : there was a hollow-
ness within, and a flourish around ' Holy Church '
which tempted me but moderately. I went on my
way pondering many things. Whatever Romanism may be, there are good Romanists : this man,
Emanuel, seemed of the best; touched with superstition, influenced by priestcraft, yet wondrous
for fond faith, for pious devotion, for sacrifice of
self, for charity unbounded. It remained to see

how Rome, by her agents, handled such qualities; whether she cherished them for their own sake and for God's, or put them out to usury and made booty of the interest.

By the time I reached home, it was sundown. Goton had kindly saved me a portion of dinner, which indeed I needed. She called me into the little cabinet to partake of it, and there Madame Beck soon made her appearance, bringing me a glass of wine.

'Well,' began she, chuckling, 'and what sort of a reception did Madame Walravens give you? Elle est drôle, n'est-ce pas?'

I told her what had passed, delivering verbatim the courteous message with which I had been charged.

'Oh la singulière petite bossue!' laughed she: 'Et figurez-vous qu'elle me déteste, parcequ'elle me croit amoureuse de mon cousin Paul; ce petit dévot qui n'ose pas bouger, à moins que son confesseur ne lui donne la permission! Au reste' (she went on), 'if he wanted to marry ever so much—soit moi, soit une autre—he could not do it; he has too large a family already on his hands; Mère Walravens, Père Silas, Dame Agnes, and a whole troop of nameless paupers. There never was a man like him for laying on himself burdens greater than he can bear, voluntarily incurring needless responsibilities. Besides, he harbours a romantic idea about some pale-faced Marie Justine—personnage assez niaise à ce que je pense' (such was Madame's irreverent remark), 'who has been an angel in Heaven, or elsewhere, this score of years, and to whom he means to go, free from all earthly ties, pure comme un lis, à ce qu'il dit. Oh, you would laugh could you but know half M. Emanuel's crotchets and eccentricities! But I hinder you from taking refreshment, ma bonne meess, which you must need; eat your supper, drink your wine, oubliez les anges, les bossues, et surtout, les Professeurs—et bon soir!'

Villette. 1853.

EMILY BRONTË

1818–1848

HEATHCLIFF'S DEATH

I DISTINGUISHED Mr. Heathcliff's step, restlessly measuring the floor, and he frequently broke the silence by a deep inspiration, resembling a groan. He muttered detached words also; the only one I could catch was the name of Catherine, coupled with some wild term of endearment or suffering; and spoken as one would speak to a person present : low and earnest, and wrung from the depth of his soul. I had not courage to walk straight into the apartment; but I desired to divert him from his reverie, and therefore fell foul of the kitchen fire, stirred it, and began to scrape the cinders. It drew him forth sooner than I expected. He opened the door immediately and said—

'Nelly, come here—is it morning? Come in with your light.'

'It is striking four,' I answered. 'You want a candle to take upstairs : you might have lit one at this fire.'

'No, I don't wish to go upstairs,' he said. 'Come in, and kindle *me* a fire, and do anything there is to do about the room.'

'I must blow the coals red first before I can carry any,' I replied, getting a chair and the bellows.

He roamed to and fro, meantime, in a state approaching distraction; his heavy sighs succeeding each other so thick as to leave no space for common breathing between.

'When day breaks I'll send for Green,' he said; 'I wish to make some legal inquiries of him while I can bestow a thought on those matters, and while I can act calmly. I have not written my will yet; and how to leave my property I cannot determine. I wish I could annihilate it from the face of the earth.'

'I would not talk so, Mr. Heathcliff,' I interposed. 'Let your will be a while: you'll be spared to repent of your many injustices yet! I never expected that your nerves would be disordered: they are, at present, marvellously so, however; and almost entirely through your own fault. The way you've passed these three last days might knock up a Titan. Do take some food, and some repose. You need only look at yourself in a glass to see how you require both. Your cheeks are hollow, and your eyes bloodshot, like a person starving with hunger and going blind with loss of sleep.'

'It is not my fault, that I cannot eat or rest,' he replied. 'I assure you it is through no settled designs. I'll do both, as soon as I possibly can. But you might as well bid a man struggling in the water rest within arm's length of the shore! I must reach it first, and then I'll rest. Well, never mind Mr. Green: as to repenting of my injustices, I've done no injustice, and I repent of nothing. I'm too happy; and yet I'm not happy enough. My soul's bliss kills my body, but does not satisfy itself.'

'Happy, master?' I cried. 'Strange happiness! If you would hear me without being angry,

I might offer some advice that would make you happier.'

'What is that?' he asked. 'Give it.'

'You are aware, Mr. Heathcliff,' I said, 'that from the time you were thirteen years old, you have lived a selfish, unchristian life; and probably hardly had a Bible in your hands during all that period. You must have forgotten the contents of the book, and you may not have space to search it now. Could it be hurtful to send for some one—some minister of any denomination, it does not matter which—to explain it, and show you how very far you have erred from its precepts; and how unfit you will be for its heaven, unless a change takes place before you die?'

'I'm rather obliged than angry, Nelly,' he said, 'for you remind me of the manner in which I desire to be buried. It is to be carried to the churchyard in the evening. You and Hareton may, if you please, accompany me: and mind, particularly, to notice that the sexton obeys my directions concerning the two coffins! No minister need come; nor need anything be said over me.—I tell you, I have nearly attained *my* heaven; and that of others is altogether unvalued and uncoveted by me.'

'And supposing you persevered in your obstinate fast, and died by that means, and they refused to bury you in the precincts of the Kirk?' I said, shocked at his godless indifference. 'How would you like it?'

'They won't do that,' he replied: 'if they did, you must have me removed secretly; and if you neglect it, you shall prove, practically, that the dead are not annihilated!'

As soon as he heard the other members of the

family stirring he retired to his den, and I breathed freer. But in the afternoon, while Joseph and Hareton were at their work, he came into the kitchen again, and with a wild look, bid me come and sit in the house; he wanted somebody with him. I declined; telling him plainly that his strange talk and manner frightened me, and I had neither the nerve nor the will to be his companion alone.

' I believe you think me a fiend,' he said, with his dismal laugh : ' something too horrible to live under a decent roof.' Then turning to Catherine, who was there, and who drew behind me at his approach, he added, half sneeringly—' Will *you* come, chuck ? I'll not hurt you. No ! to you, I've made myself worse than the devil. Well, there is *one* who won't shrink from my company ! By God ! she 's relentless. Oh, damn it ! It 's unutterably too much for flesh and blood to bear— even mine.'

He solicited the society of no one more. At dusk, he went into his chamber. Through the whole night, and far into the morning, we heard him groaning and murmuring to himself. Hareton was anxious to enter; but I bid him fetch Mr. Kenneth, and he should go in and see him. When he came, and I requested admittance and tried to open the door, I found it locked ; and Heathcliff bid us be damned. He was better, and would be left alone ; so the doctor went away.

The following evening was very wet : indeed it poured down till day-dawn ; and, as I took my morning walk round the house, I observed the master's window swinging open, and the rain driving straight in. 'He cannot be in bed,' I thought : ' those showers would drench him through. He

must either be up or out. But I'll make no more
ado, I'll go boldly and look.'

Having succeeded in obtaining entrance with
another key, I ran to unclose the panels, for the
chamber was vacant; quickly pushing them aside,
I peeped in. Mr. Heathcliff was there—laid on his
back. His eyes met mine so keen and fierce, I
started; and then he seemed to smile. I could
not think him dead: but his face and throat were
washed with rain; the bed-clothes dripped, and he
was perfectly still. The lattice, flapping to and fro,
had grazed one hand that rested on the sill; no
blood trickled from the broken skin, and when
I put my fingers to it, I could doubt no more: he
was dead and stark!

I hasped the window; I combed his black long
hair from his forehead; I tried to close his eyes:
to extinguish, if possible, that frightful, life-like
gaze of exultation, before any one else beheld it.
They would not shut: they seemed to sneer at my
attempts; and his parted lips and sharp, white
teeth sneered too! Taken with another fit of
cowardice, I cried out for Joseph. Joseph shuffled
up and made a noise, but resolutely refused to
meddle with him.

' Th' divil's harried off his soul,' he cried, ' and
he may hev his carcass into t'bargin, for aught
I care! Ech! what a wicked un he looks girnning
at death!' and the old sinner grinned in mockery.
I thought he intended to cut a caper round the bed;
but suddenly composing himself, he fell on his
knees, and raised his hands, and returned thanks
that the lawful master and the ancient stock were
restored to their rights.

Wuthering Heights. 1848.

JAMES ANTHONY FROUDE

1818-1894

THE CORONATION OF ANNE BOLEYN
(1533)

In anticipation of the timely close of the proceedings at Dunstable, notice had been given in the city early in May, that preparations should be made for the coronation on the first of the following month. Queen Anne was at Greenwich, but, according to custom, the few preceding days were to be spent at the Tower; and on the 19th of May, she was conducted thither in state by the lord mayor and the city companies, with one of those splendid exhibitions upon the water which, in the days when the silver Thames deserved its name, and the sun could shine down upon it out of the blue summer sky, were spectacles scarcely rivalled in gorgeousness by the world-famous wedding of the Adriatic. The river was crowded with boats, the banks and the ships in the pool swarmed with people; and fifty great barges formed the procession, all blazing with gold and banners. The queen herself was in her own barge, close to that of the lord mayor; and in keeping with the fantastic genius of the time, she was preceded up the water by 'a foyst or wafter full of ordnance, in which was a great dragon continually moving and casting wildfire, and round about the foyst stood terrible monsters and wild men, casting fire and making hideous noise.' So, with trumpets blowing, cannon pealing, the Tower guns answering the guns of the ships, in a blaze of fireworks and splendour, Anne Boleyn was borne along to the great archway of the Tower, where the king was waiting on the stairs to receive her.

And now let us suppose eleven days to have elapsed, the welcome news to have arrived at length from Dunstable, and the fair summer morning of life dawning in treacherous beauty after the long night of expectation. No bridal ceremonial had been possible; the marriage had been huddled over like a stolen love-match, and the marriage feast had been eaten in vexation and disappointment. These past mortifications were to be atoned for by a coronation pageant which the art and the wealth of the richest city in Europe should be poured out in the most lavish profusion to adorn.

On the morning of the 31st of May, the families of the London citizens were stirring early in all houses. From Temple Bar to the Tower, the streets were fresh strewed with gravel, the footpaths were railed off along the whole distance, and occupied on one side by the guilds, their workmen, and apprentices, on the other by the city constables and officials in their gaudy uniforms, ' with their staves in hand to cause the people to keep good room and order.' Cornhill and Gracechurch-street had dressed their fronts in scarlet and crimson, in arras and tapestry, and the rich carpet-work from Persia and the East. Cheapside, to outshine her rivals, was draped even more splendidly in cloth of gold, and tissue, and velvet. The sheriffs were pacing up and down on their great Flemish horses, hung with liveries, and all the windows were

thronged with ladies crowding to see the procession
pass. At length the Tower guns opened, the grim
gates rolled back, and under the archway in the
bright May sunshine, the long column began slowly
to defile. Two states only permitted their representatives to grace the scene with their presence—
Venice and France. It was, perhaps, to make the
most of this isolated countenance, that the French
ambassador's train formed the van of the cavalcade.
Twelve French knights came riding foremost in
surcoats of blue velvet with sleeves of yellow silk,
their horses trapped in blue, with white crosses
powdered on their hangings. After them followed
a troop of English gentlemen, two and two, and
then the Knights of the Bath, 'in gowns of violet
with hoods purfled in miniver, like doctors.'
Next, perhaps at a little interval, the abbots passed
on, mitred in their robes; the barons followed
in crimson velvet, the bishops then, and then the
earls and marquises, the dresses of each order
increasing in elaborate gorgeousness. All these
rode on in pairs. Then came alone Audeley, lord
chancellor, and behind him the Venetian ambassador
and the Archbishop of York; the Archbishop of
Canterbury, and Du Bellay, Bishop of Bayonne
and of Paris, not now with bugle and hunting-
frock, but solemn with stole and crozier. Next,
the lord mayor, with the city mace in hand, and
Garter in his coat of arms; and then Lord William
Howard,—Belted Will Howard, of the Scottish
Border, Marshal of England. The officers of the
queen's household succeeded the marshal in scarlet
and gold, and the van of the procession was closed
by the Duke of Suffolk, as high constable, with his
silver wand. It is no easy matter to picture to

ourselves the blazing trail of splendour which in such a pageant must have drawn along the London streets,—those streets which now we know so black and smoke-grimed, themselves then radiant with masses of colour, gold, and crimson, and violet. Yet there it was, and there the sun could shine upon it, and tens of thousands of eyes were gazing on the scene out of the crowded lattices.

Glorious as the spectacle was, perhaps, however, it passed unheeded. Those eyes were watching all for another object, which now drew near. In an open space behind the constable there was seen approaching ' a white chariot ', drawn by two palfreys in white damask which swept the ground, a golden canopy borne above it making music with silver bells : and in the chariot sat the observed of all observers, the beautiful occasion of all this glittering homage ; fortune's plaything of the hour, the Queen of England—queen at last—borne along upon the waves of this sea of glory, breathing the perfumed incense of greatness which she had risked her fair name, her delicacy, her honour, her self-respect, to win ; and she had won it.

There she sat, dressed in white tissue robes, her fair hair flowing loose over her shoulders, and her temples circled with a light coronet of gold and diamonds—most beautiful—loveliest—most favoured perhaps, as she seemed at that hour, of all England's daughters.

. . . .

Three short years have yet to pass, and again, on a summer morning, Queen Anne Boleyn will leave the Tower of London—not radiant then with beauty on a gay errand of coronation, but a poor wandering ghost, on a sad tragic errand, from which she will never more return, passing away out of an earth where she may stay no longer, into a presence where, nevertheless, we know that all is well—for all of us—and therefore for her.

But let us not cloud her shortlived sunshine with the shadow of the future. She went on in her loveliness, the peeresses following in their carriages, with the royal guard in their rear. In Fenchurch-street she was met by the children of the city schools; and at the corner of Gracechurch-street a masterpiece had been prepared of the pseudo-classic art, then so fashionable, by the merchants of the Styll-yard. A Mount Parnassus had been constructed, and a Helicon fountain upon it playing into a basin with four jets of Rhenish wine. On the top of the mountain sat Apollo with Calliope at his feet, and on either side the remaining Muses, holding lutes or harps, and singing each of them some ' posy' or epigram in praise of the queen, which was presented, after it had been sung, written in letters of gold.

From Gracechurch-street the procession passed to Leadenhall, where there was a spectacle in better taste of the old English Catholic kind, quaint perhaps and forced, but truly and even beautifully emblematic. There was again a 'little mountain', which was hung with red and white roses; a gold ring was placed on the summit, on which, as the queen appeared, a white falcon was made to ' descend as out of the sky '—' and then incontinent came down an angel with great melody, and set a close crown of gold upon the falcon's head; and in the same pageant sat Saint Anne with all her issue beneath her; and Mary Cleophas with her four children, of the which children one made a goodly oration to the queen, of the fruitfulness of St. Anne, trusting that like fruit should come of her.'

With such 'pretty conceits', at that time the honest tokens of an English welcome, the new queen was received by the citizens of London. These scenes must be multiplied by the number of the streets, where some fresh fancy met her at every turn. To preserve the festivities from flagging, every fountain and conduit within the walls ran all day with wine; the bells of every steeple were ringing; children lay in wait with songs, and ladies with posies, in which all the resources of fantastic extravagance were exhausted; and thus in an unbroken triumph—and to outward appearance received with the warmest affection—she passed under Temple Bar, down the Strand by Charing Cross to Westminster Hall. The king was not with her throughout the day; nor did he intend to be with her in any part of the ceremony. She was to reign without a rival, the undisputed sovereign of the hour.

Saturday being passed in showing herself to the people, she retired for the night to ' the king's manor house at Westminster,' where she slept. On the following morning, between eight and nine o'clock, she returned to the hall, where the lord mayor, the city council, and the peers were again assembled, and took her place on the high dais at the top of the stairs under the cloth of state; while the bishops, the abbots, and the monks of the abbey formed in the area. A railed way had been laid with carpets across Palace Yard and the Sanctuary to the Abbey gates, and when all was ready, preceded by the peers in their robes of parliament, the Knights of the Garter in the dress of the order, she swept out under her canopy, the bishops and the monks ' solemnly singing '.   The train was borne by the old Duchess of Norfolk her aunt, the Bishops of London and Winchester on either side ' bearing up the lappets of her robe.' The Earl of Oxford carried the crown on its cushion immediately before her.   She was dressed in purple velvet furred with ermine, her hair escaping loose, as she usually wore it, under a wreath of diamonds.

On entering the Abbey, she was led to the coronation chair, where she sat while the train fell into their places, and the preliminaries of the ceremonial were dispatched.   Then she was conducted up to the high altar, and anointed Queen of England, and she received from the hands of Cranmer, fresh come in haste from Dunstable, with the last words of his sentence upon Catherine scarcely silent upon his lips, the golden sceptre, and St. Edward's crown.

Did any twinge of remorse, any pang of painful recollection, pierce at that moment the incense of glory which she was inhaling ?   Did any vision flit across her of a sad mourning figure which once had stood where she was standing, now desolate, neglected, sinking into the darkening twilight of a life cut short by sorrow ?   Who can tell ?   At such a time, that figure would have weighed heavily upon a noble mind, and a wise mind would have been taught by the thought of it, that although life be fleeting as a dream, it is long enough to experience strange vicissitudes of fortune   But Anne Boleyn was not noble and was not wise,—too probably she felt nothing but the delicious, all-absorbing, all-intoxicating present, and if that plain, suffering face presented itself to her memory at all, we may fear that it was rather as a foil to her own surpassing loveliness. Two years later, she was able to exult over Catherine's death; she is not likely to have thought of her with gentler feelings in the first glow and flush of triumph.

We may now leave these scenes. They concluded in the usual English style, with a banquet in the great hall, and with all outward signs of enjoyment and pleasure. There must have been but few persons present however who did not feel that the sunshine of such a day might not last for ever, and that over so dubious a marriage no Englishman could exult with more than half a heart. It is foolish to blame lightly actions which arise in the midst of circumstances which are and can be but imperfectly known; and there may have been political reasons which made so much pomp desirable. Anne Boleyn had been the subject of public conversation for seven years, and Henry, no doubt, desired to present his jewel to them in the rarest and choicest setting. Yet to our eyes, seeing, perhaps, by the light of what followed, a more modest introduction would have appeared more suited to the doubtful nature of her position.

History of England, vol. i. 1856.

JOHN RUSKIN

1819-1900

OF THE OPEN SKY

It is a strange thing how little in general people know about the sky. It is the part of creation in which Nature has done more for the sake of pleasing man, more for the sole and evident purpose of talking to him and teaching him, than in any other of her works, and it is just the part in which we least attend to her. There are not many of her other works in which some more material or essential purpose than the mere pleasing of man is not answered by every part of their organization; but every essential purpose of the sky might, so far as we know, be answered, if once in three days, or thereabouts, a great, ugly, black rain-cloud were brought up over the blue, and everything well watered, and so all left blue again till next time, with perhaps a film of morning and evening mist for dew. And instead of this, there is not a moment of any day of our lives, when nature is not producing scene after scene, picture after picture, glory after glory, and working still upon such exquisite and constant principles of the most perfect beauty, that it is quite certain it is all done for us, and intended for our perpetual pleasure. And every man, wherever placed, however far from other sources of interest or of beauty, has this doing for him constantly. The noblest scenes of the earth can be seen and known but by few : it is not

intended that man should live always in the midst
of them; he injures them by his presence, he
ceases to feel them if he be always with them: but
the sky is for all; bright as it is, it is not

> Too bright, nor good,
> For human nature's daily food;

it is fitted in all its functions for the perpetual
comfort and exalting of the heart, for the soothing
it and purifying it from its dross and dust. Sometimes gentle, sometimes capricious, sometimes
awful, never the same for two moments together;
almost human in its passions, almost spiritual in
its tenderness, almost divine in its infinity, its
appeal to what is immortal in us is as distinct, as
its ministry of chastisement or of blessing to what
is mortal is essential. And yet we never attend
to it, we never make it a subject of thought, but as
it has to do with our animal sensations; we look
upon all by which it speaks to us more clearly than
to brutes, upon all which bears witness to the
intention of the Supreme that we are to receive
more from the covering vault than the light and
the dew which we share with the weed and the
worm, only as a succession of meaningless and
monotonous accident, too common and too vain to
be worthy of a moment of watchfulness, or a glance
of admiration. If in our moments of utter idleness
and insipidity, we turn to the sky as a last resource,
which of its phenomena do we speak of? One says,
it has been wet; and another, it has been windy;
and another, it has been warm. Who, among the
whole chattering crowd, can tell me of the forms and
the precipices of the chain of tall white mountains
that girded the horizon at noon yesterday? Who
saw the narrow sunbeam that came out of the

south, and smote upon their summits until they melted and mouldered away in a dust of blue rain ? Who saw the dance of the dead clouds when the sunlight left them last night, and the west wind blew them before it like withered leaves ? All has passed, unregretted as unseen ; or if the apathy be ever shaken off, even for an instant, it is only by what is gross, or what is extraordinary ; and yet it is not in the broad and fierce manifestations of the elemental energies, not in the clash of the hail, nor the drift of the whirlwind, that the highest characters of the sublime are developed. God is not in the earthquake, nor in the fire, but in the still small voice. They are but the blunt and the low faculties of our nature, which can only be addressed through lampblack and lightning. It is in quiet and subdued passages of unobtrusive majesty, the deep, and the calm, and the perpetual ; that which must be sought ere it is seen, and loved ere it is understood ; things which the angels work out for us daily, and yet vary eternally ; which are never wanting and never repeated ; which are to be found always, yet each one found but once ; it is through these that the lesson of devotion is chiefly taught, and the blessing of beauty given.

Modern Painters, vol. i.   1843.

ST. MARK'S

I wish that the reader, before I bring him into St. Mark's Place, would imagine himself for a little time in a quiet English cathedral town, and walk with me to the west front of its cathedral. Let us go together up the more retired street, at the end of which we can see the pinnacles of one of the towers, and then through the low grey gateway,

with its battlemented top and small latticed
window in the centre, into the inner private-looking
road or close, where nothing goes in but the carts
of the tradesmen who supply the bishop and the
chapter, and where there are little shaven grass-
plots, fenced in by neat rails, before old-fashioned
groups of somewhat diminutive and excessively
trim houses, with little oriel and bay windows
jutting out here and there, and deep wooden
cornices and eaves painted cream colour and white,
and small porches to their doors in the shape of
cockle-shells, or little, crooked, thick, indescribable
wooden gables warped a little on one side ; and so
forward till we come to larger houses, also old-
fashioned, but of red brick, and with gardens
behind them, and fruit walls, which show here and
there, among the nectarines, the vestiges of an old
cloister arch or shaft, and looking in front on the
cathedral square itself, laid out in rigid divisions
of smooth grass and gravel walk, yet not uncheerful,
especially on the sunny side where the canons'
children are walking with their nursery-maids.
And so, taking care not to tread on the grass, we
will go along the straight walk to the west front,
and there stand for a time, looking up at its deep-
pointed porches and the dark places between their
pillars where there were statues once, and where
the fragments, here and there, of a stately figure
are still left, which has in it the likeness of a king,
perhaps indeed a king on earth, perhaps a saintly
king long ago in heaven ; and so higher and higher
up to the great mouldering wall of rugged sculpture
and confused arcades, shattered and grey, and
grisly with heads of dragons and mocking fiends,
worn by the rain and swirling winds into yet

unseemlier shape, and coloured on their stony
scales by the deep russet-orange lichen, melancholy
gold; and so, higher still, to the bleak towers, so far
above that the eye loses itself among the bosses of
their traceries, though they are rude and strong,
and only sees like a drift of eddying black points,
now closing, now scattering, and now settling
suddenly into invisible places among the bosses
and flowers, the crowd of restless birds that fill the
old square with that strange clangour of theirs, so
harsh and yet so soothing, like the cries of birds
on a solitary coast between the cliffs and the sea.

Think for a little while of that scene, and the
meaning of all its small formalisms, mixed with
its serene sublimity. Estimate its secluded, continuous, drowsy felicities, and its evidence of the
sense and steady performance of such kind of
duties as can be regulated by the cathedral clock ;
and weigh the influence of those dark towers on
all who have passed through the lonely square at
their feet for centuries, and on all who have seen
them rising far away over the wooded plain, or
catching on their square masses the last rays of
the sunset, when the city at their feet was indicated
only by the mist at the bend of the river. And
then let us quickly recollect that we are in Venice,
and land at the extremity of the Calla Lunga San
Moisè, which may be considered as there answering
to the secluded street that led us to our English
cathedral gateway.

We find ourselves in a paved alley, some seven
feet wide where it is widest, full of people, and
resonant with cries of itinerant salesmen,—a shriek
in their beginning, and dying away into a kind of
brazen ringing, all the worse for its confinement

between the high houses of the passage along which we have to make our way. Over head an inextricable confusion of rugged shutters, and iron balconies and chimney flues pushed out on brackets to save room, and arched windows with projecting sills of Istrian stone, and gleams of green leaves here and there where a fig-tree branch escapes over a lower wall from some inner cortile, leading the eye up to the narrow stream of blue sky high over all. On each side, a row of shops, as densely set as may be, occupying, in fact, intervals between the square stone shafts, about eight feet high, which carry the first floors : intervals of which one is narrow and serves as a door ; the other is, in the more respectable shops, wainscoted to the height of the counter and glazed above, but in those of the poorer tradesmen left open to the ground, and the wares laid on benches and tables in the open air, the light in all cases entering at the front only, and fading away in a few feet from the threshold into a gloom which the eye from without cannot penetrate, but which is generally broken by a ray or two from a feeble lamp at the back of the shop, suspended before a print of the Virgin. The less pious shopkeeper sometimes leaves his lamp unlighted, and is contented with a penny print ; the more religious one has his print coloured and set in a little shrine with a gilded or figured fringe, with perhaps a faded flower or two on each side, and his lamp burning brilliantly. Here at the fruiterer's, where the dark-green water-melons are heaped upon the counter like cannon-balls, the Madonna has a tabernacle of fresh laurel leaves ; but the pewterer next door has let his lamp out, and there is nothing to be seen in his shop but the

dull gleam of the studded patterns on the copper
pans, hanging from his roof in the darkness. Next
comes a ' Vendita Frittole e Liquori ', where the
Virgin, enthroned in a very humble manner beside
a tallow candle on a back shelf, presides over certain
ambrosial morsels of a nature too ambiguous to be
defined or enumerated. But a few steps farther on,
at the regular wine-shop of the calle, where we are
offered ' Vino Nostrani a Soldi 28·32 ', the Madonna
is in great glory, enthroned above ten or a dozen
large red casks of three-year-old vintage, and
flanked by goodly ranks of bottles of Maraschino,
and two crimson lamps ; and for the evening, when
the gondoliers will come to drink out, under her
auspices, the money they have gained during the
day, she will have a whole chandelier.

A yard or two farther, we pass the hostelry of the
Black Eagle, and, glancing as we pass through the
square door of marble, deeply moulded, in the
outer wall, we see the shadows of its pergola of
vines resting on an ancient well, with a pointed
shield carved on its side ; and so presently emerge
on the bridge and Campo San Moisè, whence to the
entrance into St. Mark's Place, called the Bocca di
Piazza (mouth of the square), the Venetian character is nearly destroyed, first by the frightful
façade of San Moisè, which we will pause at
another time to examine, and then by the moder-
nizing of the shops as they near the piazza, and the
mingling with the lower Venetian populace of
lounging groups of English and Austrians. We will
push fast through them into the shadow of the
pillars at the end of the ' Bocca di Piazza ', and
then we forget them all ; for between those pillars
there opens a great light, and, in the midst of it,

as we advance slowly, the vast tower of St. Mark seems to lift itself visibly forth from the level field of chequered stones ; and, on each side, the count-less arches prolong themselves into ranged sym-metry, as if the rugged and irregular houses that pressed together above us in the dark alley had been struck back into sudden obedience and lovely order, and all their rude casements and broken walls had been transformed into arches charged with goodly sculpture, and fluted shafts of delicate stone.

And well may they fall back, for beyond those troops of ordered arches there rises a vision out of the earth, and all the great square seems to have opened from it in a kind of awe, that we may see it far away ;—a multitude of pillars and white domes, clustered into a long low pyramid of coloured light ; a treasure-heap, it seems, partly of gold, and partly of opal and mother-of-pearl, hollowed beneath into five great vaulted porches, ceiled with fair mosaic, and beset with sculpture of alabaster, clear as amber and delicate as ivory,— sculpture fantastic and involved, of palm leaves and lilies, and grapes and pomegranates, and birds clinging and fluttering among the branches, all twined together into an endless network of buds and plumes ; and, in the midst of it, the solemn forms of angels, sceptred, and robed to the feet, and leaning to each other across the gates, their figures indistinct among the gleaming of the golden ground through the leaves beside them, interrupted and dim, like the morning light as it faded back among the branches of Eden, when first its gates were angel-guarded long ago. And round the walls of the porches there are set pillars of varie-gated stones, jasper and porphyry, and deep-green serpentine spotted with flakes of snow, and marbles, that half refuse and half yield to the sunshine, Cleopatra-like ' their bluest veins to kiss '—the shadow, as it steals back from them, revealing line after line of azure undulation, as a receding tide leaves the waved sand ; their capitals rich with interwoven tracery, rooted knots of herbage, and drifting leaves of acanthus and vine, and mystical signs, all beginning and ending in the Cross ; and above them, in the broad archivolts, a continuous chain of language and of life—angels, and the signs of heaven and the labours of men, each in its appointed season upon the earth ; and above these another range of glittering pinnacles, mixed with white arches edged with scarlet flowers,—a confusion of delight, amidst which the breasts of the Greek horses are seen blazing in their breadth of golden strength, and the St. Mark's Lion, lifted on a blue field covered with stars, until at last, as if in ecstasy, the crests of the arches break into a marble foam, and toss themselves far into the blue sky in flashes and wreaths of sculptured spray, as if the breakers on the Lido shore had been frost-bound before they fell, and the sea-nymphs had inlaid them with coral and amethyst.

Between that grim cathedral of England and this, what an interval ! There is a type of it in the very birds that haunt them ; for, instead of the restless crowd, hoarse-voiced and sable-winged, drifting on the bleak upper air, the St. Mark's porches are full of doves, that nestle among the marble foliage, and mingle the soft iridescence of their living plumes, changing at every motion, with the tints, hardly less lovely, that have stood unchanged for seven hundred years.

And what effect has this splendour on those who pass beneath it ? You may walk from sunrise to sunset, to and fro, before the gateway of St. Mark's, and you will not see an eye lifted to it, nor a countenance brightened by it. Priest and layman, soldier and civilian, rich and poor, pass by it alike regardlessly. Up to the very recesses of the porches, the meanest tradesmen of the city push their counters ; nay, the foundations of its pillars are themselves the seats—not 'of them that sell doves' for sacrifice, but of the venders of toys and caricatures. Round the whole square in front of the church there is almost a continuous line of cafés, where the idle Venetians of the middle classes lounge, and read empty journals ; in its centre the Austrian bands play during the time of vespers, their martial music jarring with the organ notes,—the march drowning the miserere, and the sullen crowd thickening round them,—a crowd, which, if it had its will, would stiletto every soldier that pipes to it. And in the recesses of the porches, all day long, knots of men of the lowest classes, unemployed and listless, lie basking in the sun like lizards ; and unregarded children,—every heavy glance of their young eyes full of desperation and stony depravity, and their throats hoarse with cursing,—gamble, and fight, and snarl, and sleep, hour after hour, clashing their bruised centesimi upon the marble ledges of the church porch. And the images of Christ and His angels look down upon it continually.

That we may not enter the church out of the midst of the horror of this, let us turn aside under the portico which looks towards the sea, and passing round within the two massive pillars brought from

St. Jean d'Acre, we shall find the gate of the Baptistery; let us enter there. The heavy door closes behind us instantly, and the light and the turbulence of the Piazetta are together shut out by it.

We are in a low vaulted room; vaulted, not with arches, but with small cupolas starred with gold, and chequered with gloomy figures: in the centre is a bronze font charged with rich bas-reliefs, a small figure of the Baptist standing above it in a single ray of light that glances across the narrow room, dying as it falls from a window high in the wall, and the first thing that it strikes, and the only thing that it strikes brightly, is a tomb. We hardly know if it be a tomb indeed; for it is like a narrow couch set beside the window, low-roofed and curtained, so that it might seem, but that it is some height above the pavement, to have been drawn towards the window, that the sleeper might be wakened early;—only there are two angels who have drawn the curtain back, and are looking down upon him. Let us look also, and thank that gentle light that rests upon his forehead for ever, and dies away upon his breast.

The face is of a man in middle life, but there are two deep furrows right across the forehead, dividing it like the foundations of a tower: the height of it above is bound by the fillet of the ducal cap. The rest of the features are singularly small and delicate, the lips sharp, perhaps the sharpness of death being added to that of the natural lines; but there is a sweet smile upon them, and a deep serenity upon the whole countenance. The roof of the canopy above has been blue, filled with stars; beneath, in the centre of the tomb on which the figure rests,

is a seated figure of the Virgin, and the border of it
all around is of flowers and soft leaves, growing rich
and deep, as if in a field in summer.

It is the Doge Andrea Dandolo, a man early
great among the great of Venice; and early lost.
She chose him for her king in his 36th year; he
died ten years later, leaving behind him that
history to which we owe half of what we know of
her former fortunes.

Look round at the room in which he lies. The
floor of it is of rich mosaic, encompassed by a low
seat of red marble, and its walls are of alabaster,
but worn and shattered, and darkly stained with
age, almost a ruin,—in places the slabs of marble
have fallen away altogether, and the rugged brick-
work is seen through the rents, but all beautiful;
the ravaging fissures fretting their way among the
islands and channelled zones of the alabaster, and
the time-stains on its translucent masses darkened
into fields of rich golden brown, like the colour of
seaweed when the sun strikes on it through deep
sea. The light fades away into the recess of the
chamber towards the altar, and the eye can hardly
trace the lines of the bas-relief behind it of the
baptism of Christ: but on the vaulting of the roof
the figures are distinct, and there are seen upon it
two great circles, one surrounded by the ' Princi-
palities and powers in heavenly places ', of which
Milton has expressed the ancient division in the
single massy line,

Thrones, Dominations, Princedoms, Virtues, Powers,

and around the other, the Apostles; Christ the
centre of both: and upon the walls, again and again
repeated, the gaunt figure of the Baptist, in every

circumstance of his life and death; and the streams of the Jordan running down between their cloven rocks; the axe laid to the root of a fruitless tree that springs upon their shore. 'Every tree that bringeth not forth good fruit shall be hewn down, and cast into the fire.' Yes, verily: to be baptized with fire, or to be cast therein; it is the choice set before all men. The march-notes still murmur through the grated window, and mingle with the sounding in our ears of the sentence of judgement, which the old Greek has written on that Baptistery wall. Venice has made her choice.

He who lies under that stony canopy would have taught her another choice, in his day, if she would have listened to him; but he and his counsels have long been forgotten by her, and the dust lies upon his lips.

Through the heavy door whose bronze network closes the place of his rest, let us enter the church itself. It is lost in still deeper twilight, to which the eye must be accustomed for some moments before the form of the building can be traced; and then there opens before us a vast cave, hewn out into the form of a Cross, and divided into shadowy aisles by many pillars. Round the domes of its roof the light enters only through narrow apertures like large stars; and here and there a ray or two from some far-away casement wanders into the darkness, and casts a narrow phosphoric stream upon the waves of marble that heave and fall in a thousand colours along the floor. What else there is of light is from torches, or silver lamps, burning ceaselessly in the recesses of the chapels; the roof sheeted with gold, and the polished walls covered with alabaster, give back, at every curve

and angle, some feeble gleaming to the flames ; and
the glories round the heads of the sculptured saints
flash out upon us as we pass them, and sink again
into the gloom. Under foot and over head, a continual succession of crowded imagery, one picture
passing into another, as in a dream; forms beautiful
and terrible mixed together ; dragons and serpents,
and ravening beasts of prey, and graceful birds that
in the midst of them drink from running fountains
and feed from vases of crystal ; the passions and
the pleasures of human life symbolized together,
and the mystery of its redemption ; for the mazes
of interwoven lines and changeful pictures lead
always at last to the Cross, lifted and carved in
every place and upon every stone ; sometimes with
the serpent of eternity wrapt round it, sometimes
with doves beneath its arms, and sweet herbage
growing forth from its feet ; but conspicuous most
of all on the great rood that crosses the church
before the altar, raised in bright blazonry against
the shadow of the apse. And although in the
recesses of the aisles and chapels, when the mist of
the incense hangs heavily, we may see continually
a figure traced in faint lines upon their marble,
a woman standing with her eyes raised to heaven,
and the inscription above her, ' Mother of God ',
she is not here the presiding deity. It is the Cross
that is first seen, and always, burning in the centre
of the temple ; and every dome and hollow of its
roof has the figure of Christ in the utmost height
of it, raised in power, or returning in judgement.

Nor is this interior without effect on the minds
of the people. At every hour of the day there are
groups collected before the various shrines, and
solitary worshippers scattered through the darker

places of the church, evidently in prayer both deep
and reverent, and, for the most part, profoundly
sorrowful. The devotees at the greater number of
the renowned shrines of Romanism may be seen
murmuring their appointed prayers with wandering eyes and unengaged gestures; but the step of
the stranger does not disturb those who kneel on
the pavement of St. Mark's; and hardly a moment
passes, from early morning to sunset, in which we
may not see some half-veiled figure enter beneath
the Arabian porch, cast itself into long abasement
on the floor of the temple, and then rising slowly
with more confirmed step, and with a passionate
kiss and clasp of the arms given to the feet of the
crucifix, by which the lamps burn always in the
northern aisle, leave the church, as if comforted.

But we must not hastily conclude from this that
the nobler characters of the building have at present
any influence in fostering a devotional spirit. There
is distress enough in Venice to bring many to their
knees, without excitement from external imagery;
and whatever there may be in the temper of the
worship offered in St. Mark's more than can be
accounted for by reference to the unhappy circumstances of the city, is assuredly not owing either
to the beauty of its architecture or to the im-
pressiveness of the Scripture histories embodied
in its mosaics. That it has a peculiar effect, however slight, on the popular mind, may perhaps be
safely conjectured from the number of worshippers
which it attracts, while the churches of St. Paul
and the Frari, larger in size and more central in
position, are left comparatively empty. But this
effect is altogether to be ascribed to its richer
assemblage of those sources of influence which

address themselves to the commonest instincts of
the human mind, and which, in all ages and
countries, have been more or less employed in the
support of superstition. Darkness and mystery;
confused recesses of building; artificial light employed in small quantity, but maintained with
a constancy which seems to give it a kind of
sacredness; preciousness of material easily comprehended by the vulgar eye; close air loaded with
a sweet and peculiar odour associated only with
religious services, solemn music, and tangible idols
or images having popular legends attached to
them,—these, the stage properties of superstition,
which have been from the beginning of the world,
and must be to the end of it, employed by all
nations, whether openly savage or nominally
civilized, to produce a false awe in minds incapable
of apprehending the true nature of the Deity, are
assembled in St. Mark's to a degree, as far as
I know, unexampled in any other European church.
The arts of the Magus and the Brahmin are exhausted in the animation of a paralyzed Christian-
ity; and the popular sentiment which these arts
excite is to be regarded by us with no more respect
than we should have considered ourselves justified
in rendering to the devotion of the worshippers at
Eleusis, Ellora, or Edfou.

Indeed, these inferior means of exciting religious
emotion were employed in the ancient Church as
they are at this day, but not employed alone.
Torchlight there was, as there is now; but the
torchlight illumined Scripture histories on the walls,
which every eye traced and every heart comprehended, but which, during my whole residence
in Venice, I never saw one Venetian regard for an

instant. I never heard from any one the most languid expression of interest in any feature of the church, or perceived the slightest evidence of their understanding the meaning of its architecture; and while, therefore, the English cathedral, though no longer dedicated to the kind of services for which it was intended by its builders, and much at variance in many of its characters with the temper of the people by whom it is now surrounded, retains yet so much of its religious influence that no prominent feature of its architecture can be said to exist altogether in vain, we have in St. Mark's a building apparently still employed in the ceremonies for which it was designed, and yet of which the impressive attributes have altogether ceased to be comprehended by its votaries. The beauty which it possesses is unfelt, the language it uses is forgotten; and in the midst of the city to whose service it has so long been consecrated, and still filled by crowds of the descendants of those to whom it owes its magnificence, it stands, in reality, more desolate than the ruins through which the sheep-walk passes unbroken in our English valleys; and the writing on its marble walls is less regarded and less powerful for the teaching of men, than the letters which the shepherd follows with his finger, where the moss is lightest on the tombs in the desecrated cloister.

The Stones of Venice, vol. ii. 1852.

'GEORGE ELIOT' (MARY ANN CROSS)

1819-1880

'IN THEIR DEATH THEY WERE NOT DIVIDED'

WHAT was happening to them at the Mill? The flood had once nearly destroyed it. They might be in danger—in distress: her mother and her brother, alone there, beyond reach of help! Her whole soul was strained now on that thought; and she saw the long-loved faces looking for help into the darkness, and finding none.

She was floating in smooth water now—perhaps far on the over-flooded fields. There was no sense of present danger to check the outgoing of her mind to the old home; and she strained her eyes against the curtain of gloom that she might seize the first sight of her whereabout—that she might catch some faint suggestion of the spot towards which all her anxieties tended.

O how welcome, the widening of that dismal watery level—the gradual uplifting of the cloudy firmament—the slowly defining blackness of objects above the glassy dark! Yes—she must be out on the fields—those were the tops of hedgerow trees. Which way did the river lie? Looking behind her, she saw the lines of black trees: looking before her, there were none: then, the river lay before her. She seized an oar and began to paddle the boat forward with the energy of wakening hope:

the dawning seemed to advance more swiftly, now she was in action; and she could soon see the poor dumb beasts crowding piteously on a mound where they had taken refuge. Onward she paddled and rowed by turns in the growing twilight: her wet clothes clung round her, and her streaming hair was dashed about by the wind, but she was hardly conscious of any bodily sensations—except a sensation of strength, inspired by mighty emotion. Along with the sense of danger and possible rescue for those long-remembered beings at the old home, there was an undefined sense of reconcilement with her brother: what quarrel, what harshness, what unbelief in each other can subsist in the presence of a great calamity, when all the artificial vesture of our life is gone, and we are all one with each other in primitive mortal needs? Vaguely, Maggie felt this;—in the strong resurgent love towards her brother that swept away all the later impressions of hard, cruel offence and misunderstanding, and left only the deep, underlying, unshakable memories of early union.

But now there was a large dark mass in the distance, and near to her Maggie could discern the current of the river. The dark mass must be—yes, it was—St. Ogg's. Ah, now she knew which way to look for the first glimpse of the well-known trees—the grey willows, the now yellowing chestnuts—and above them the old roof! But there was no colour, no shape yet: all was faint and dim. More and more strongly the energies seemed to come and put themselves forth, as if her life were a stored-up force that was being spent in this hour, unneeded for any future.

She must get her boat into the current of the

Floss, else she would never be able to pass the
Ripple and approach the house: this was the
thought that occurred to her, as she imagined with
more and more vividness the state of things round
the old home. But then she might be carried
very far down, and be unable to guide her boat
out of the current again. For the first time
distinct ideas of danger began to press upon her;
but there was no choice of courses, no room for
hesitation, and she floated into the current.
Swiftly she went now, without effort; more and
more clearly in the lessening distance and the
growing light she began to discern the objects
that she knew must be the well-known trees
and roofs; nay, she was not far off a rushing
muddy current that must be the strangely altered
Ripple.

Great God! there were floating masses in it,
that might dash against her boat as she passed,
and cause her to perish too soon. What were
those masses?

For the first time Maggie's heart began to beat
in an agony of dread. She sat helpless—dimly
conscious that she was being floated along—more
intensely conscious of the anticipated clash. But
the horror was transient: it passed away before
the oncoming warehouses of St. Ogg's: she had
passed the mouth of the Ripple, then: *now*, she
must use all her skill and power to manage the
boat and get it if possible out of the current. She
could see now that the bridge was broken down:
she could see the masts of a stranded vessel far out
over the watery field. But no boats were to be
seen moving on the river—such as had been laid
hands on were employed in the flooded streets.

With new resolution, Maggie seized her oar, and stood up again to paddle; but the now ebbing tide added to the swiftness of the river, and she was carried along beyond the bridge. She could hear shouts from the windows overlooking the river, as if the people there were calling to her. It was not till she had passed on nearly to Tofton that she could get the boat clear of the current. Then with one yearning look towards her uncle Deane's house that lay farther down the river, she took to both her oars and rowed with all her might across the watery fields, back towards the Mill. Colour was beginning to awake now, and as she approached the Dorlcote fields, she could discern the tints of the trees—could see the old Scotch firs far to the right, and the home chestnuts —Oh! how deep they lay in the water: deeper than the trees on this side the hill. And the roof of the Mill—where was it? Those heavy fragments hurrying down the Ripple—what had they meant? But it was not the house—the house stood firm; drowned up to the first story, but still firm—or was it broken in at the end towards the Mill?

With panting joy that she was there at last— joy that overcame all distress—Maggie neared the front of the house. At first she heard no sound: she saw no object moving. Her boat was on a level with the up-stairs windows. She called out in a loud piercing voice,

' Tom, where are you? Mother, where are you? Here is Maggie!'

Soon, from the window of the attic in the central gable, she heard Tom's voice:

' Who is it? Have you brought a boat?'

' It is I, Tom—Maggie. Where is mother?'

' She is not here : she went to Garum, the day before yesterday. I'll come down to the lower window.'

' Alone, Maggie ? ' said Tom, in a voice of deep astonishment, as he opened the middle window on a level with the boat.

' Yes, Tom : God has taken care of me, to bring me to you. Get in quickly. Is there no one else ? '

' No,' said Tom, stepping into the boat, ' I fear the man is drowned : he was carried down the Ripple, I think, when part of the Mill fell with the crash of trees and stones against it : I've shouted again and again, and there has been no answer. Give me the oars, Maggie.'

It was not till Tom had pushed off and they were on the wide water—he face to face with Maggie— that the full meaning of what had happened rushed upon his mind. It came with so overpowering a force—it was such a new revelation to his spirit, of the depths in life, that had lain beyond his vision which he had fancied so keen and clear—that he was unable to ask a question. They sat mutely gazing at each other : Maggie with eyes of intense life looking out from a weary, beaten face—Tom pale with a certain awe and humiliation. Thought was busy though the lips were silent : and though he could ask no question, he guessed a story of almost miraculous divinely-protected effort. But at last a mist gathered over the blue-grey eyes, and the lips found a word they could utter : the old childish—' Magsie ! '

Maggie could make no answer but a long deep sob of that mysterious wondrous happiness that is one with pain.

As soon as she could speak, she said, ' We will

go to Lucy, Tom : we'll go and see if she is safe, and then we can help the rest.'

Tom rowed with untired vigour, and with a different speed from poor Maggie's. The boat was soon in the current of the river again, and soon they would be at Tofton.

' Park House stands high up out of the flood,' said Maggie. ' Perhaps they have got Lucy there.'

Nothing else was said ; a new danger was being carried towards them by the river. Some wooden machinery had just given way on one of the wharves, and huge fragments were being floated along. The sun was rising now, and the wide area of watery desolation was spread out in dreadful clearness around them—in dreadful clearness floated onwards the hurrying, threatening masses. A large company in a boat that was working its way along under the Tofton houses, observed their danger, and shouted, ' Get out of the current ! '

But that could not be done at once, and Tom, looking before him, saw death rushing on them. Huge fragments, clinging together in fatal fellowship, made one wide mass across the stream.

' It is coming, Maggie ! ' Tom said, in a deep hoarse voice, loosing the oars, and clasping her.

The next instant the boat was no longer seen upon the water—and the huge mass was hurrying on in hideous triumph.

But soon the keel of the boat reappeared, a black speck on the golden water.

The boat reappeared—but brother and sister had gone down in an embrace never to be parted : living through again in one supreme moment the days when they had clasped their little hands in love, and roamed the daisied fields together.

The Mill on the Floss. 1860.

NANCY LAMMETER

SOME one opened the door at the other end of the room, and Nancy felt that it was her husband. She turned from the window with gladness in her eyes, for the wife's chief dread was stilled.

'Dear, I'm so thankful you're come,' she said, going towards him. 'I began to get . . .'

She paused abruptly, for Godfrey was laying down his hat with trembling hands, and turned towards her with a pale face and a strange unanswering glance, as if he saw her indeed, but saw her as part of a scene invisible to herself. She laid her hand on his arm, not daring to speak again; but he left the touch unnoticed, and threw himself into his chair.

Jane was already at the door with the hissing urn. 'Tell her to keep away, will you?' said Godfrey; and when the door was closed again he exerted himself to speak more distinctly.

'Sit down, Nancy—there,' he said, pointing to a chair opposite him. 'I came back as soon as I could, to hinder anybody's telling you but me. I've had a great shock—but I care most about the shock it'll be to you.'

'It isn't father and Priscilla?' said Nancy, with quivering lips, clasping her hands together tightly on her lap.

'No, it's nobody living,' said Godfrey, unequal to the considerate skill with which he would have wished to make his revelation, 'It's Dunstan—my brother Dunstan, that we lost sight of sixteen years ago. We've found him—found his body—his skeleton.'

The deep dread Godfrey's look had created in Nancy made her feel these words a relief. She sat in comparative calmness to hear what else he had to tell. He went on:

'The Stone-pit has gone dry suddenly—from the draining, I suppose; and there he lies—has lain for sixteen years, wedged between two great stones. There's his watch and seals, and there's my gold-handled hunting-whip, with my name on: he took it away, without my knowing, the day he went hunting on Wildfire, the last time he was seen.'

Godfrey paused: it was not so easy to say what came next. 'Do you think he drowned himself?' said Nancy, almost wondering that her husband should be so deeply shaken by what had happened all those years ago to an unloved brother, of whom worse things had been augured.

'No, he fell in', said Godfrey, in a low but distinct voice, as if he felt some deep meaning in the fact. Presently he added: 'Dunstan was the man that robbed Silas Marner.'

The blood rushed to Nancy's face and neck at this surprise and shame, for she had been bred up to regard even a distant kinship with crime as a dishonour.

'Oh, Godfrey!' she said, with compassion in her tone, for she had immediately reflected that the dishonour must be felt still more keenly by her husband.

'There was the money in the pit,' he continued— 'all the weaver's money. Everything's being gathered up, and they're taking the skeleton to the Rainbow. But I came back to tell you: there was no hindering it; you must know.'

He was silent, looking on the ground for two
long minutes. Nancy would have said some words
of comfort under this disgrace, but she refrained,
from an instinctive sense that there was something
behind—that Godfrey had something else to tell
her. Presently he lifted his eyes to her face, and
kept them fixed on her, as he said—

Everything comes to light, Nancy, sooner or
later. When God Almighty wills it, our secrets
are found out. I've lived with a secret on my mind,
but I'll keep it from you no longer. I wouldn't
have you know it by somebody else, and not by
me—I wouldn't have you find it out after I'm
dead. I'll tell you now. It 's been " I will " and
" I won't " with me all my life—I'll make sure of
myself now.'

Nancy's utmost dread had returned. The eyes
of the husband and wife met with awe in them, as
at a crisis which suspended affection.

' Nancy,' said Godfrey, slowly, ' when I married
you, I hid something from you—something I ought
to have told you. That woman Marner found dead
in the snow—Eppie's mother—that wretched
woman—was my wife : Eppie is my child.'

He paused, dreading the effect of his confession.
But Nancy sat quite still, only that her eyes
dropped and ceased to meet his. She was pale
and quiet as a meditative statue, clasping her
hands on her lap.

' You'll never think the same of me again,' said
Godfrey, after a little while, with some tremor in
his voice.

She was silent.

' I oughtn't to have left the child unowned :
I oughtn't to have kept it from you. But I couldn't

bear to give you up, Nancy. I was led away into marrying her—I suffered for it.'

Still Nancy was silent, looking down; and he almost expected that she would presently get up and say she would go to her father's. How could she have any mercy for faults that must seem so black to her, with her simple, severe notions?

But at last she lifted up her eyes to his again and spoke. There was no indignation in her voice —only deep regret.

'Godfrey, if you had but told me this six years ago, we could have done some of our duty by the child. Do you think I'd have refused to take her in, if I'd known she was yours?'

At that moment Godfrey felt all the bitterness of an error that was not simply futile, but had defeated its own end. He had not measured this wife with whom he had lived so long. But she spoke again, with more agitation.

'And—Oh, Godfrey—if we'd had her from the first, if you'd taken to her as you ought, she'd have loved me for her mother—and you'd have been happier with me: I could better have bore my little baby dying, and our life might have been more like what we used to think it 'ud be.'

The tears fell, and Nancy ceased to speak.

'But you wouldn't have married me then, Nancy, if I'd told you,' said Godfrey, urged, in the bitterness of his self-reproach, to prove to himself that his conduct had not been utter folly. 'You may think you would now, but you wouldn't then. With your pride and your father's, you'd have hated having anything to do with me after the talk there'd have been.'

'I can't say what I should have done about

that, Godfrey. I should never have married anybody else. But I wasn't worth doing wrong for—
nothing is in this world. Nothing is so good as it
seems beforehand—not even our marrying wasn't,
you see.' There was a faint sad smile on Nancy's
face as she said the last words.

' I'm a worse man than you thought I was,
Nancy', said Godfrey, rather tremulously. ' Can
you forgive me ever ? '

' The wrong to me is but little, Godfrey : you've
made it up to me—you've been good to me for
fifteen years. It's another you did the wrong to ;
and I doubt it can never be all made up for.'

' But we can take Eppie now', said Godfrey.
'I won't mind the world knowing at last. I'll be
plain and open for the rest o' my life.'

' It'll be different coming to us, now she's
grown up', said Nancy, shaking her head sadly.
' But it's your duty to acknowledge her and provide
for her ; and I'll do my part by her, and pray to
God Almighty to make her love me.'

' Then we'll go together to Silas Marner's this
very night, as soon as everything's quiet at the
Stone-pits.'

                                    Silas Marner. 1861.

GEORGE MEREDITH

1828-1909

FERDINAND AND MIRANDA

ABOVE green-flashing plunges of a weir, and shaken by the thunder below, lilies, golden and white, were swaying at anchor among the reeds. Meadowsweet hung from the banks thick with weed and trailing bramble, and there also hung a daughter of earth. Her face was shaded by a broad straw hat with a flexible brim that left her lips and chin in the sun, and, sometimes nodding, sent forth a light of promising eyes. Across her shoulders, and behind, flowed large loose curls, brown in shadow, almost golden where the ray touched them. She was simply dressed, befitting decency and the season. On a closer inspection you might see that her lips were stained. This blooming young person was regaling on dewberries. They grew between the bank and the water. Apparently she found the fruit abundant, for her hand was making pretty progress to her mouth. Fastidious youth, which revolts at woman plumping her exquisite proportions on bread-and-butter, and would (we must suppose) joyfully have her scraggy to have her poetical, can hardly object to dewberries. Indeed, the act of eating them is dainty and induces musing. The dewberry is a sister to the lotus, and an innocent sister. You eat: mouth, eye, and hand are

occupied, and the undrugged mind free to roam.
And so it was with the damsel who knelt there.
The little skylark went up above her, all song, to
the smooth southern cloud lying along the blue :
from a dewy copse dark over her nodding hat
the blackbird fluted, calling to her with thrice
mellow note : the kingfisher flashed emerald out
of green osiers : a bow-winged heron travelled
aloft, seeking solitude ; a boat slipped toward her,
containing a dreamy youth ; and still she plucked
the fruit, and ate, and mused, as if no fairy prince
were invading her territories, and as if she wished
not for one, or knew not her wishes. Surrounded
by the green shaven meadows, the pastoral
summer buzz, the weir-fall's thundering white,
amid the breath and beauty of wild flowers, she
was a bit of lovely human life in a fair setting ;
a terrible attraction. The Magnetic Youth leaned
round to note his proximity to the weir-piles, and
beheld the sweet vision. Stiller and stiller grew
nature, as at the meeting of two electric clouds.
Her posture was so graceful, that though he was
making straight for the weir, he dared not dip
a scull. Just then one enticing dewberry caught
her eyes. He was floating by unheeded, and saw
that her hand stretched low, and could not gather
what it sought. A stroke from his right brought
him beside her. The damsel glanced up dismayed,
and her whole shape trembled over the brink.
Richard sprang from his boat into the water.
Pressing a hand beneath her foot, which she had
thrust against the crumbling wet sides of the
bank to save herself, he enabled her to recover
her balance, and gain safe earth, whither he
followed her.

He had landed on an island of the still-vexed Bermoothes. The world lay wrecked behind him: Raynham hung in mists, remote, a phantom to the vivid reality of this white hand which had drawn him thither away thousands of leagues in an eye-twinkle. Hark, how Ariel sang overhead ! What splendour in the heavens ! What marvels of beauty about his enchanted brows ! And, O you wonder ! Fair Flame, by whose light the glories of being are now first seen. . . . Radiant Miranda ! Prince Ferdinand is at your feet.

Or is it Adam, his rib taken from his side in sleep, and thus transformed, to make him behold his Paradise, and lose it ? . . .

The youth looked on her with as glowing an eye. It was the first woman to him.

And she—mankind was all Caliban to her, saving this one princely youth.

So to each other said their changing eyes in the moment they stood together ; he pale, and she blushing.

The Ordeal of Richard Feverel. 1859.

THE DUEL IN THE PASS

She gave him a look of fire and passed him ; whereat, following her, he clapped hands, and affected to regard the movement as part of an operatic scena. 'It is now time to draw your dagger,' he said. 'You have one, I'm certain.'

'Anything but touch me !' cried Vittoria, turning on him. 'I know that I am safe. You shall teaze me, if it amuses you.'

'Am I not, now, the object of your detestation ?'

'You are near being so.'

'You see! You put on no disguise; why should I?'

This remark struck her with force.

'My temper is foolish,' she said softly. 'I have always been used to kindness.'

He vowed that she had no comprehension of kindness; otherwise would she continue defiant of him? She denied that she was defiant: upon which he accused the hand in her bosom of clutching a dagger. She cast the dagger at his feet. It was nobly done, and he was not insensible to the courage and inspiration of the act; for it checked a little example of a trial of strength that he had thought of exhibiting to an armed damsel.

'Shall I pick it up for you?' he said.

'You will oblige me,' was her answer; but she could not control a convulsion of her underlip that her defensive instinct told her was best hidden.

'Of course, you know you are safe,' he repeated her previous words, while examining the silver handle of the dagger. 'Safe? certainly! Here is C. A. to V . . . . A. neatly engraved: a gift; so that the young gentleman may be sure the young lady will defend herself from lions and tigers and wild boars, if ever she goes through forests and over mountain passes. I will not obtrude my curiosity, but who is V . . . . A.?'

The dagger was Carlo's gift to her; the engraver, by singular misadventure, had put a capital letter for the concluding letter of her name instead of little *a*; she remembered the blush on Carlo's face when she had drawn his attention to the error, and her own blush when she had guessed its meaning.

'It spells my name,' she said.

'Your assumed name of Vittoria. And who is C. A. ?'

'Those are the initials of Count Carlo Ammiani.'

'Another lover ?'

'He is my sole lover. He is my betrothed. Oh, good God !' she threw her eyes up to heaven ; 'how long am I to endure the torture of this man in my pathway ? Go, sir, or let me go on. You are intolerable. It's the spirit of a tiger. I have no fear of you.'

'Nay, nay,' said Weisspriess ; 'I asked the question because I am under an obligation to run Count Carlo Ammiani through the body, and felt at once that I should regret the necessity. As to your not fearing me, really, far from wishing to hurt you ——'

Vittoria had caught sight of a white face framed in the autumnal forest above her head. So keen was the glad expression of her face, that Weisspriess looked up.

'Come, Angelo, come to me,' she said confidently.

Weisspriess plucked his sword out, and called to him imperiously to descend.

Beckoned downward by white hand and flashing blade, Angelo steadied his feet and hands among drooping chestnut boughs, and bounded to Vittoria's side.

'Now march on,' Weisspriess waved his sword ; 'you are my prisoners.'

'You,' retorted Angelo ; 'I know you ; you are a man marked out for one of us. I bid you turn back, if you care for your body's safety.'

'Angelo Guidascarpi, I also know you. Assassin !

you double murderer! Defy me, and I slay you in the sight of your paramour.'

'Captain Weisspriess, what you have spoken merits death. I implore of my Maker that I may not have to kill you.'

'Fool! you are unarmed.'

Angelo took his stilet in his fist.

'I have warned you, Captain Weisspriess. Here I stand. I dare you to advance.'

'You pronounce my name abominably,' said the captain, dropping his sword's point. 'If you think of resisting me, let us have no women looking on.' He waved his left hand at Vittoria.

Angelo urged her to go. 'Step on for our Carlo's sake.' But it was asking too much of her.

'Can you fight this man?' she asked.

'I can fight him and kill him.'

'I will not step on,' she said. 'Must you fight him?'

'There is no choice.'

Vittoria walked to a distance at once.

Angelo directed the captain's eyes to where, lower in the pass, there was a level plot of meadow.

Weisspriess nodded. 'The odds are in my favour, so you shall choose the ground.'

All three went silently to the meadow.

It was a circle of green on a projecting shoulder of the mountain, bounded by woods that sank toward the now shadowy South-flowing Adige vale, whose Western heights were gathering red colour above a strongly-marked brown line. Vittoria stood at the border of the wood, leaving the two men to their work. She knew when speech was useless.

Captain Weisspriess paced behind Angelo until the latter stopped short, saying, 'Here!'

'Wherever you please,' Weisspriess responded.
'The ground is of more importance to you than
to me.'

They faced mutually; one felt the point of his
stilet, the other the temper of his sword.

'Killing you, Angelo Guidascarpi, is the killing
of a dog. But there are such things as mad dogs.
This is not a duel. It is a righteous execution,
since you force me to it: I shall deserve your
thanks for saving you from the hangman. I think
you have heard that I can use my weapon. There's
death on this point for you. Make your peace
with your Maker.'

Weisspriess spoke sternly. He delayed the lifting
of his sword that the bloody soul might pray.

Angelo said, 'You are a good soldier: you are
a bad priest. Come on.'

A nod of magnanimous resignation to the duties
of his office was the captain's signal of readiness.
He knew exactly the method of fighting which
Angelo must adopt, and he saw that his adversary
was supple, and sinewy, and very keen of eye.
But, what can well compensate for even one
additional inch of steel? A superior weapon
wielded by a trained wrist in perfect coolness
means victory, by every reasonable reckoning.
In the present instance, it meant nothing other
than an execution, as he had said. His contemplation of his own actual share in the performance
was nevertheless unpleasant; and it was but half
willingly that he straightened out his sword and
then doubled his arm. He lessened the odds in
his favour considerably by his too accurate
estimation of them. He was also a little unmanned
by the thought that a woman was to see him

using his advantage; but she stood firm in her distant corner, refusing to be waved out of sight. Weisspriess had again to assure himself that it was not a duel, but the enforced execution of a criminal who would not surrender, and who was in his way. Fronting a creature that would vainly assail him, and temporarily escape impalement by bounding and springing, dodging and backing, now here now there, like a dangling bob-cherry, his military gorge rose with a sickness of disgust. He had to remember as vividly as he could realize it, that this man's life was forfeited, and that the slaughter of him was a worthy service to Countess Anna; also, that there were present reasons for desiring to be quit of him. He gave Angelo two thrusts, and bled him. The skill which warded off the more vicious one aroused his admiration.

'Pardon my blundering,' he said; 'I have never engaged a saltimbanque before.'

They recommenced. Weisspriess began to weigh the sagacity of his opponent's choice of open ground, where he could lengthen the discourse of steel by retreating and retreating, and swinging easily to right or to left. In the narrow track the sword would have transfixed him after a simple feint. He was amused. Much of the cat was in his combative nature. An idea of disabling or dismembering Angelo, and forwarding him to Meran, caused him to trifle further with the edge of the blade. Angelo took a cut, and turned it on his arm; free of the deadly point, he rushed in and delivered a stab; but Weisspriess saved his breast. Quick, they resumed their former positions.

'I am really so unused to this game.' said Weisspriess, apologetically.

He was pale: his unsteady breathing, and a deflection of his dripping sword-wrist, belied his coolness. Angelo plunged full on him, dropped, and again reached his right arm; they hung, getting blood for blood, with blazing interpenetrating eyes;—a ghastly work of dark hands at half lock thrusting, and savage eyes reading the fiery pages of the book of hell. At last the Austrian got loose from the lock and hurled him off.

'That bout was hotter,' he remarked; and kept his sword-point out on the whole length of the arm: he would have scorned another for so miserable a form either of attack or defence.

Vittoria beheld Angelo circling round the point, which met him everywhere; like the minute hand of a clock about to sound his hour, she thought.

He let fall both his arms, as if beaten, which brought on the attack: by sheer evasion he got away from the sword's lunge, and essayed a second trial of the bite of steel at close quarters; but the Austrian backed and kept him to the point, darting short alluring thrusts, thinking to tempt him on, or to wind him, and then to have him. Weisspriess was chilled by a more curious revulsion from this sort of engagement than he at first experienced. He had become nervously incapable of those proper niceties of sword-play which, without any indecent hacking and maiming, should have stretched Angelo, neatly slain, on the mat of green, before he had a chance. Even now the sight of the man was distressing to an honourable duellist. Angelo was scored with blood-marks Feeling that he dared not offer another chance to a fellow so desperately close-dealing, Weisspriess thrust fiercely, but delayed his fatal stroke. Angelo stooped and pulled up a handful of grass and soft earth in his left hand.

'We have been longer about it than I expected', said Weisspriess.

Angelo tightened his fingers about the stringy grass-tuft; he stood like a dreamer, leaning over to the sword; suddenly he sprang on it, received the point right in his side, sprang on it again, and seized it in his hand, and tossed it up, and threw it square out in time to burst within guard and strike his stilet below the Austrian's collar-bone. The blade took a glut of blood, as when the wolf tears quick at dripping flesh. It was at a moment when Weisspriess was courteously bantering him with the question whether he was ready, meaning that the affirmative should open the gates of death to him.

The stilet struck thrice. Weisspriess tottered, and hung his jaw like a man at a spectre: amazement was on his features.

'Remember Broncini and young Branciani!'

Angelo spoke no other words throughout the combat.

Weisspriess threw himself forward on a feeble lunge of his sword, and let the point sink in the ground, as a palsied cripple supports his frame, swayed, and called to Angelo to come on, and try another stroke, another—one more! He fell in a lump: his look of amazement was surmounted by a strong frown.

His enemy was hanging above him, panting out of wide nostrils, like a hunter's horse above the long-tongued quarry, when Vittoria came to them.

She reached her strength to the wounded man to turn his face to heaven.

He moaned, 'Finish me;' and, as he lay with his back to earth, 'Good-evening to the old army.'

A vision of leaping tumbrils, and long marching columns about to deploy, passed before his eyelids: he thought he had fallen on the battle-field, and heard a drum beat furiously in the back of his head; and on streamed the cavalry, wonderfully caught away to such a distance that the figures were all diminutive, and the regimental colours swam in smoke, and the enemy danced a plume here and there out of the sea, while his mother and a forgotten Viennese girl gazed at him with exactly the same unfamiliar countenance, and refused to hear that they were unintelligible in the roaring of guns and floods and hurrahs, and the thumping of the tremendous big drum behind his head—'somewhere in the middle of the earth:' he tried to explain the locality of that terrible drumming noise to them, and Vittoria conceived him to be delirious; but he knew that he was sensible: he knew her and Angelo and the mountain-pass, and that he had a cigar-case in his pocket worked in embroidery of crimson, blue, and gold, by the hands of Countess Anna. He said distinctly that he desired the cigar-case to be delivered to Countess Anna at the Castle of Sonnenberg, and rejoiced on being assured that his wish was comprehended and should be fulfilled; but the marvel was, that his mother should still refuse to give him wine and suppose him to be a boy: and when he was so thirsty and dry-lipped that though Mina was bending over him, just fresh from Mariazell, he

had not the heart to kiss her or lift an arm to
her !—His horse was off with him—whither ?—He
was going down with a company of infantry in
the Gulf of Venice : cards were in his hand,
visible, though he could not feel them, and as the
vessel settled for the black plunge, the cards
flushed all honours, and his mother shook her
head at him : he sank, and heard Mina sighing all
the length of the water to the bottom, which
grated and gave him two horrid shocks of pain :
and he cried for a doctor, and admitted that his
horse had managed to throw him ; but wine was
the cure, brandy was the cure, or water, water !

Water was sprinkled on his forehead and put
to his lips.

He thanked Vittoria by name, and imagined
himself that general, serving under old Würmser,
of whom the tale is told that being shot and
lying grievously wounded on the harsh Rivoli
ground, he obtained the help of a French officer
in as bad case as himself, to moisten his black
tongue and write a short testamentary document
with his blood, and for a way of returning thanks
to the Frenchman, he put down, among others, the
name of his friendly enemy's widow ; whereupon
both resigned their hearts to death; but the Austrian
survived to find the sad widow and espouse her.

His mutterings were full of gratitude, showing
a vividly transient impression to what was about
him, that vanished in a narrow-headed flight
through clouds into lands of memory. It pained
him, he said, that he could not offer her marriage ;
but he requested that when his chin was shaved
his moustache should be brushed up out of the
way of the clippers, for he and all his family were

conspicuous for the immense amount of life which they had in them, and his father had lain six-and-thirty hours bleeding on the field of Wagram, and had yet survived to beget a race as hearty as himself:—'Old Austria! thou grand old Austria!'

The smile was proud, though faint, which accompanied the apostrophe, addressed either to his country or to his father's personification of it; it was inexpressibly pathetic to Vittoria, who understood his 'Oesterreich' and saw the weak and helpless bleeding man, with his eyeballs working under the lids, and the palms of his hands stretched out open—weak as a corpse, but conquering death.

The arrival of Jacopo and Johann furnished help to carry him onward to the nearest place of shelter. Angelo would not quit her side until he had given money and directions to both the trembling fellows, together with his name, that they might declare the author of the deed at once if questioned. He then bowed to Vittoria slightly and fled. They did not speak.

The last sunbeams burned full crimson on the heights of the Adige mountains as Vittoria followed the two pale men who bore the wounded officer between them at a slow pace for the nearest village in the descent of the pass.

Angelo watched them out of sight. The far-off red rocks spun round his eyeballs; the meadow was a whirling thread of green; the brown earth heaved up to him. He felt that he was diving, and had the thought that there was but water enough to moisten his red hands, when his senses left him.

Vittoria. 1867.

(By permission of Messrs. A. Constable & Co., Ltd.)

ROBERT LOUIS STEVENSON

1850–1894

SAMBRE AND OISE CANAL: CANAL BOATS

NEXT day we made a late start in the rain. The Judge politely escorted us to the end of the lock under an umbrella. We had now brought ourselves to a pitch of humility in the matter of weather, not often attained except in the Scotch *Highlands*. A rag of blue sky or a glimpse of sunshine set our hearts singing; and when the rain was not heavy, we counted the day almost fair.

Long lines of barges lay one after another along the canal; many of them looking mighty spruce and ship-shape in their jerkin of *Archangel* tar picked out with white and green. Some carried gay iron railings, and quite a parterre of flower-pots. Children played on the decks, as heedless of the rain as if they had been brought up on *Loch Garron* side; men fished over the gunwale, some of them under umbrellas; women did their washing; and every barge boasted its mongrel cur by way of watch-dog. Each one barked furiously at the canoes, running alongside until he had got to the end of his own ship, and so passing on the word to the dog aboard the next. We must have seen something like a hundred of these embarkations in the course of that day's paddle, ranged one after another like the houses in a street ; and from not one of them were we disappointed of this accompaniment. It was like visiting a menagerie, the *Cigarette* remarked.

These little cities by the canal side had a very odd effect upon the mind. They seemed, with their flowerpots and smoking chimneys, their washings and dinners, a rooted piece of nature in the scene ; and yet if only the canal below were to open, one junk after another would hoist sail or harness horses and swim away into all parts of *France* ; and the impromptu hamlet would separate, house by house, to the four winds. The children who played together to-day by the *Sambre* and *Oise* Canal, each at his own father's threshold, when and where might they next meet ?

For some time past the subject of barges had occupied a great deal of our talk, and we had projected an old age on the canals of *Europe*. It was to be the most leisurely of progresses, now on a swift river at the tail of a steamboat, now waiting horses for days together on some inconsiderable junction. We should be seen pottering on deck in all the dignity of years, our white beards falling into our laps. We were ever to be busied among paintpots ; so that there should be no white fresher, and no green more emerald than ours, in all the navy of the canals. There should be books in the cabin, and tobacco jars, and some old *Burgundy* as red as a *November* sunset and as odorous as a violet in *April*. There should be a flageolet whence the *Cigarette*, with cunning touch, should draw melting music under the stars ; or perhaps, laying that aside, upraise his voice—somewhat thinner than of yore, and

with here and there a quaver, or call it a natural
grace note—in rich and solemn psalmody.

All this simmering in my mind, set me wishing
to go aboard one of these ideal houses of lounging.
I had plenty to choose from, as I coasted one after
another, and the dogs bayed at me for a vagrant.
At last I saw a nice old man and his wife looking
at me with some interest, so I gave them good
day and pulled up alongside. I began with
a remark upon their dog, which had somewhat
the look of a pointer ; thence I slid into a compliment on Madame's flowers, and thence into a word
in praise of their way of life.

If you ventured on such an experiment in
England you would get a slap in the face at once.
The life would be shown to be a vile one, not
without a side-shot at your better fortune. Now,
what I like so much in *France* is the clear unflinch-
ing recognition by everybody of his own luck.
They all know on which side their bread is buttered,
and take a pleasure in showing it to others, which
is surely the better part of religion. And they
scorn to make a poor mouth over their poverty,
which I take to be the better part of manliness.
I have heard a woman in quite a better position
at home, with a good bit of money in hand, refer
to her own child with a horrid whine as ' a poor
man's child '. I would not say such a thing to
the Duke of *Westminster*. And the *French* are
full of this spirit of independence. Perhaps it is
the result of republican institutions, as they call
them. Much more likely it is because there are
so few people really poor, that the whiners are
not enough to keep each other in countenance.

The people on the barge were delighted to hear

that I admired their state. They understood
perfectly well, they told me, how Monsieur envied
them. Without doubt Monsieur was rich; and in
that case he might make a canal-boat as pretty as
a villa—*joli comme un château.* And with that
they invited me on board their own water villa.
They apologized for their cabin; they had not
been rich enough to make it as it ought to be.

'The fire should have been here, at this side,'
explained the husband. 'Then one might have
a writing-table in the middle—books—and'
(comprehensively) 'all. It would be quite
coquettish—*ça serait tout-à-fait coquet.*' And
he looked about him as though the improvements
were already made. It was plainly not the first
time that he had thus beautified his cabin in
imagination; and when next he makes a hit,
I should expect to see the writing-table in the
middle.

Madame had three birds in a cage. They were
no great thing, she explained. Fine birds were
so dear. They had sought to get a *Hollandais*
last winter in *Rouen* (*Rouen?* thought I; and is
this whole mansion, with its dogs and birds and
smoking chimneys, so far a traveller as that? and
as homely an object among the cliffs and orchards
of the *Seine* as on the green plains of *Sambre?*)—
they had sought to get a *Hollandais* last winter
in *Rouen;* but these cost fifteen francs a-piece—
picture it—fifteen francs!

'*Pour un tout petit oiseau*—For quite a little
bird,' added the husband.

As I continued to admire, the apologetics died
away, and the good people began to brag of their
barge, and their happy condition in life, as if they

had been Emperor and Empress of the *Indies*.
It was, in the Scotch phrase, a good hearing, and
put me in good humour with the world. If people
knew what an inspiriting thing it is to hear a man
boasting, so long as he boasts of what he really
has, I believe they would do it more freely and
with a better grace.

They began to ask about our voyage. You
should have seen how they sympathized. They
seemed half ready to give up their barge and
follow us. But these *canaletti* are only gipsies
semi-domesticated. The semi-domestication came
out in rather a pretty form. Suddenly Madame's
brow darkened. '*Cependant*,' she began, and
then stopped ; and then began again by asking
me if I were single ?

'Yes,' said I.

'And your friend who went by just now ?'

He also was unmarried.

O then—all was well. She could not have wives
left alone at home ; but since there were no wives
in the question, we were doing the best we could.

'To see about one in the world,' said the
husband, '*il n'y a que ça*—there is nothing else
worth while. A man, look you, who sticks in his
own village like a bear,' he went on, '—very well,
he sees nothing. And then death is the end of all.
And he has seen nothing.'

Madame reminded her husband of an *Englishman*
who had come up this canal in a steamer.

'Perhaps Mr. *Moens* in the *Ytene*,' I suggested.

'That's it,' assented the husband. 'He had his
wife and family with him, and servants. He came
ashore at all the locks and asked the name of the
villages, whether from boatmen or lock-keepers ;

and then he wrote, wrote them down. O he wrote
enormously! I suppose it was a wager.'

A wager was a common enough explanation for
our own exploits, but it seemed an original reason
for taking notes.

An Inland Voyage. 1878.

(By permission of Messrs. Chatto & Windus.)

EDINBURGH

THE ancient and famous metropolis of the North
sits overlooking a windy estuary from the slope
and summit of three hills. No situation could be
more commanding for the head city of a kingdom ;
none better chosen for noble prospects. From her
tall precipice and terraced gardens she looks far
and wide on the sea and broad champaigns. To
the east you may catch at sunset the spark of the
May lighthouse, where the Firth expands into the
German Ocean ; and away to the west, over all
the carse of Stirling, you can see the first snows
upon Ben Ledi.

But Edinburgh pays cruelly for her high seat in
one of the vilest climates under heaven. She is
liable to be beaten upon by all the winds that
blow, to be drenched with rain, to be buried in
cold sea fogs out of the east, and powdered with
the snow as it comes flying southward from the
Highland hills. The weather is raw and boisterous
in winter, shifty and ungenial in summer, and
a downright meteorological purgatory in the spring.
The delicate die early, and I, as a survivor, among
bleak winds and plumping rain, have been some-

times tempted to envy them their fate. For all who love shelter and the blessings of the sun, who hate dark weather and perpetual tilting against squalls, there could scarcely be found a more unhomely and harassing place of residence. Many such aspire angrily after that Somewhere-else of the imagination, where all troubles are supposed to end. They lean over the great bridge which joins the New Town with the Old—that windiest spot, or high altar, in this northern temple of the winds—and watch the trains smoking out from under them and vanishing into the tunnel on a voyage to brighter skies. Happy the passengers who shake off the dust of Edinburgh, and have heard for the last time the cry of the east wind among her chimney-tops! And yet the place establishes an interest in people's hearts; go where they will, they find no city of the same distinction; go where they will, they take a pride in their old home.

Venice, it has been said, differs from all other cities in the sentiment which she inspires. The rest may have admirers; she only, a famous fair one, counts lovers in her train. And indeed, even by her kindest friends, Edinburgh is not considered in a similar sense. These like her for many reasons, not any one of which is satisfactory in itself. They like her whimsically, if you will, and somewhat as a virtuoso dotes upon his cabinet. Her attraction is romantic in the narrowest meaning of the term. Beautiful as she is, she is not so much beautiful as interesting. She is pre-eminently Gothic, and all the more so since she has set herself off with some Greek airs, and erected classic temples on her crags. In a word, and above all, she is a curiosity. The Palace of Holyrood has been left aside in the growth of Edinburgh, and stands grey and silent in a workman's quarter and among breweries and gas-works. It is a house of many memories. Great people of yore, king's and queens, buffoons and grave ambassadors, played their stately farce for centuries in Holyrood. Wars have been plotted, dancing has lasted deep into the night, murder has been done in its chambers. There Prince Charlie held his phantom levées, and in a very gallant manner represented a fallen dynasty for some hours. Now, all these things of clay are mingled with the dust, the king's crown itself is shown for sixpence to the vulgar; but the stone palace has outlived these changes. For fifty weeks together, it is no more than a show for tourists and a museum of old furniture; but on the fifty-first, behold the palace re-awakened and mimicking its past. The Lord Commissioner, a kind of stage sovereign, sits among stage courtiers; a coach and six and clattering escort come and go before the gate; at night, the windows are lighted up, and its near neighbours, the workmen, may dance in their own houses to the palace music. And in this the palace is typical. There is a spark among the embers; from time to time the old volcano smokes. Edinburgh has but partly abdicated, and still wears, in parody, her metropolitan trappings. Half a capital and half a country town, the whole city leads a double existence; it has long trances of the one and flashes of the other; like the King of the Black Isles, it is half alive and half a monumental marble. There are armed men and cannon in the citadel overhead; you may see the troops marshalled on the high parade; and at night after the early winter even-fall, and in the morning before the laggard winter dawn, the wind carries abroad over Edinburgh the sound of drums and bugles. Grave judges sit be-wigged in what was once the scene of imperial deliberations. Close by in the High Street perhaps the trumpets may sound about the stroke of noon; and you see a troop of citizens in tawdry masquerade; tabard above, heather-mixture trowser below, and the men themselves trudging in the mud among unsympathetic bystanders. The grooms of a well-appointed circus tread the streets with a better presence. And yet these are the Heralds and Pursuivants of Scotland, who are about to proclaim a new law of the United Kingdom before two score boys, and thieves, and hackney-coachmen. Meanwhile every hour the bell of the University rings out over the hum of the streets, and every hour a double tide of students, coming and going, fills the deep archways. And lastly, one night in the spring-time—or say one morning rather, at the peep of day—late folk may hear the voices of many men singing a psalm in unison from a church on one side of the old High Street; and a little after, or perhaps a little before, the sound of many men singing a psalm in unison from another church on the opposite side of the way. There will be something in the words about the dew of Hermon, and how goodly it is to see brethren dwelling together in unity. And the late folk will tell themselves that all this singing denotes the conclusion of two yearly ecclesiastica parliaments—the parliaments of Churches which are brothers in many admirable virtues, but not specially like brothers in this particular of a tolerant and peaceful life.

Again, meditative people will find a charm in a certain consonancy between the aspect of the city and its odd and stirring history. Few places, if any, offer a more barbaric display of contrasts to the eye. In the very midst stands one of the most satisfactory crags in nature—a Bass Rock upon dry land, rooted in a garden shaken by passing trains, carrying a crown of battlements and turrets, and describing its warlike shadow over the liveliest and brightest thoroughfare of the new town. From their smoky beehives, ten stories high, the unwashed look down upon the open squares and gardens of the wealthy; and gay people sunning themselves along Princes Street, with its mile of commercial palaces all beflagged upon some great occasion, see, across a gardened valley set with statues, where the washings of the old town flutter in the breeze at its high windows. And then, upon all sides, what a clashing of architecture! In this one valley, where the life of the town goes most busily forward, there may be seen, shown one above and behind another by the accidents of the ground, buildings in almost every style upon the globe. Egyptian and Greek temples, Venetian palaces and Gothic spires, are huddled one over another in a most admired disorder; while, above all, the brute mass of the Castle and the summit of Arthur's Seat look down upon these imitations with a becoming dignity, as the works of Nature may look down upon the monuments of Art. But Nature is a more indiscriminate patroness than we imagine, and in no way frightened of

a strong effect. The birds roost as willingly among
the Corinthian capitals as in the crannies of the
crag; the same atmosphere and daylight clothe
the eternal rock and yesterday's imitation portico;
and as the soft northern sunshine throws out
everything into a glorified distinctness—or easterly
mists, coming up with the blue evening, fuse all
these incongruous features into one, and the lamps
begin to glitter along the street, and faint lights
to burn in the high windows across the valley—
the feeling grows upon you that this also is a piece
of nature in the most intimate sense; that this
profusion of eccentricities, this dream in masonry
and living rock, is not a drop-scene in a theatre,
but a city in the world of every-day reality,
connected by railway and telegraph-wire with
all the capitals of Europe, and inhabited by
citizens of the familiar type, who keep ledgers,
and attend church, and have sold their immortal
portion to a daily paper. By all the canons of
romance, the place demands to be half deserted
and leaning towards decay; birds we might admit
in profusion, the play of the sun and winds, and
a few gipsies encamped in the chief thoroughfare;
but these citizens, with their cabs and tramways,
their trains and posters, are altogether out of key.
Chartered tourists, they make free with historic
localities, and rear their young among the most
picturesque sites with a grand human indifference.
To see them thronging by, in their neat clothes and
conscious moral rectitude, and with a little air of
possession that verges on the absurd, is not the
least striking feature of the place.

    And the story of the town is as eccentric as its
appearance. For centuries it was a capital thatched

with heather, and more than once, in the evil days of English invasion, it has gone up in flame to heaven, a beacon to ships at sea. It was the jousting-ground of jealous nobles, not only on Greenside, or by the King's Stables, where set tournaments were fought to the sound of trumpets and under the authority of the royal presence, but in every alley where there was room to cross swords, and in the main street, where popular tumult under the Blue Blanket alternated with the brawl of outlandish clansmen and retainers. Down in the palace John Knox reproved his queen in the accents of modern democracy. In the town, in one of those little shops plastered like so many swallows' nests among the buttresses of the old Cathedral, that familiar autocrat, James VI, would gladly share a bottle of wine with George Heriot the goldsmith. Up on the Pentland Hills, that so quietly look down on the Castle with the city lying in waves around it, those mad and dismal fanatics, the Sweet Singers, haggard from long exposure on the moors, sat day and night with 'tearful psalmns' to see Edinburgh consumed with fire from heaven, like another Sodom or Gomorrah. There, in the Grass-market, stiff-necked covenanting heroes, offered up the often unnecessary, but not less honourable, sacrifice of their lives, and bade eloquent farewell to sun, moon, and stars, and earthly friendships, or died silent to the roll of drums. Down by yon outlet rode Grahame of Claverhouse and his thirty dragoons, with the town beating to arms behind their horses' tails—a sorry handful thus riding for their lives, but with a man at the head who was to return in a different temper, make a dash that staggered Scotland to the heart, and die happily in the thick of fight. There Aikenhead was hanged for a piece of boyish incredulity; there, a few years afterwards, David Hume ruined Philosophy and Faith, an undisturbed and well-reputed citizen; and thither, in yet a few years more, Burns came from the plough-tail, as to an academy of gilt unbelief and artificial letters. There, when the great exodus was made across the valley, and the new town began to spread abroad its draughty parallelograms, and rear its long frontage on the opposing hill, there was such a flitting, such a change of domicile and dweller, as was never excelled in the history of cities: the cobbler succeeded the earl; the beggar ensconced himself by the judge's chimney; what had been a palace was used as a pauper refuge; and great mansions were so parcelled out among the least and lowest in society, that the hearth-stone of the old proprietor was thought large enough to be partitioned off into a bedroom by the new.

From R. L. Stevenson's *Edinburgh*.

SET IN
GREAT BRITAIN
AT THE
UNIVERSITY PRESS
OXFORD
AND PRINTED BY
J. W. ARROWSMITH LTD
BRISTOL